About the Author

Susie Murphy is an Irish historical fiction author. She loves historical fiction so much that she often wishes she had been born two hundred years ago. Still, she remains grateful for many aspects of the modern age, including women's suffrage, electric showers and pizza. A Class Inherited is her sixth published novel.

ISBN-13: 978-1-915770-06-6

www.susiemurphywrites.com

Join the Susie Murphy Readers' Club
for updates and free stories:

https://bit.ly/susie-murphy-readers-club

A Class Inherited

A Matter of Class, Book Six

Susie Murphy

Also by Susie Murphy

A Class Apart
A Class Entwined
A Class Forsaken
A Class Coveted
A Class Reunited

For Aaron and Holly,
two of the bravest human beings I know.

CHAPTER 1

'That stubborn, exasperating man!' Cormac burst out.

Startled, Bridget looked at him across the kitchen table. He was staring down at a letter with dismay on his face. She held a letter too, the other of the pair he had just brought home from the post office, but she left it aside as she rounded the table to him in concern. A smell of mince pies pervaded the kitchen. Gus had requested them for his eighth birthday even though the family would have them again in two and a half weeks for Christmas.

'What is it?' she asked Cormac, sliding onto the chair next to him and touching his arm.

'Lord Bewley,' he said, his voice thick.

'Oh no,' she murmured. The elderly gentleman had been long past his prime but that didn't make the news any easier to bear. 'I'm so sorry to hear it.'

'He's...' Cormac swallowed. 'He's left me the Bewley Estate.'

Bridget blinked. 'He's done what?'

Mutely, Cormac handed her the letter, which contained two pages. She read them both in a hurry. The first had been penned by Lord Bewley's lawyer, Mr Carruthers. In it, he communicated the death of the Earl of Bewley that October and informed Cormac that the entire Bewley Estate had been bequeathed to him, adding that the title had become extinct as there was no legitimate heir of Bewley blood left alive to claim it. Mr Carruthers intended to travel to America in the new year to discuss the terms of the bequest with Cormac. He spoke in neutral language, offering no opinion on Cormac's suitability for the role.

The second page consisted of a short, shaky note written by Lord Bewley himself a month before he died, in which he begged Cormac's forgiveness for not abiding by his wishes but that he had felt bound by his conscience to leave the estate in the most capable hands.

Bridget gaped down at the two pieces of paper that held the power to change their whole lives, though she was uncertain whether it might be for the better or for the worse. 'How do you feel about this?' she asked cautiously.

He blew out his breath. 'I'm aghast that he still went ahead with it even after I so strenuously refused his proposal in England. I couldn't have made my view on the matter any clearer at the time.'

'Two and a half years have passed. Perhaps he hoped your view might have altered in the interim.'

Cormac hesitated. 'But he made no mention of it when he was here over the summer. It would have been the perfect opportunity to speak to me about it then, given that he had travelled so far.'

After Lady Bewley had died, Lord Bewley's own health had revived somewhat and he had decided to visit Boston during the past summer, despite his advanced years. He had taken a suite at Tremont House and called upon Cormac at Acorn House a number of times, engaging him in several absorbing conversations about the estate. Now Bridget realised that Lord Bewley had been priming Cormac to succeed him. All things considered, this letter shouldn't have come as a surprise. She suspected that Lord Bewley probably hadn't brought up the

2

question of the inheritance while he was here because he hadn't wanted to risk another rejection. This time, he was beyond the grave when he asked and thus impervious to Cormac's answer.

Cormac shook his head in disbelief. 'What can he have been thinking? The enormity of this obligation...it's unfathomable.'

'But is it unwelcome?' she asked quietly.

He shifted in his seat. 'I don't know,' he admitted. 'What do you think?'

She was glad to be afforded the opportunity to give her opinion this time. When he had come back from England with Emily and Rory and revealed that Lord Bewley had offered his entire estate to him, she had been annoyed that he had decided to refuse it without consulting her first. It had been such a large decision from which to be excluded, even though it was likely that she would have come to the same conclusion as him that he couldn't accept it. Now she perceived the glint in his eye and wondered whether his feelings had changed.

'We need to consider it from all angles,' she said, 'especially how it would affect those around us.'

He chewed the inside of his cheek. 'It would be a significant upheaval for the boys. They haven't known any way of life other than the one we've led here in America. We'd also have to take them out of Hawes School.'

'We would have to do that soon enough anyway,' she pointed out. 'We certainly wouldn't be keeping them enrolled there once they ascended to the older classes and came under the influence of that awful Mr Miller.' Her blood still boiled to think of the schoolmaster taking a leather strap to Emily's delicate hands.

Her heart squeezed. What about Emily? Bridget looked at the self-portrait of their daughter pinned to the kitchen wall, which she had sketched before she left them to go to New York. That city was already distant enough, though supposedly temporary;

3

could they face being continents apart and in a much more abiding way?

Cormac followed the focus of Bridget's gaze. 'I know what you're thinking,' he said sombrely, 'and it would be very difficult for us to cope with the separation. But she'll be eighteen in May. That separation may be coming, no matter what we choose.'

Bridget nodded, thinking of Rory Carey; Emily had her own choices to make too. That put Bridget in mind of the whole Carey family and how she would have to say goodbye to the close friend she had made in Derval Carey. After a decade of friendship, that would not be easy.

Regrettably, they did not have to include Cormac's sisters in any of these considerations because, after two more years of vacillating, they had finally made the decision to head west. Orlaith, Charlie, Tess, Bronagh and little Maggie would depart Boston for Chicago by the spring. So a parting with them was already inevitable, but how they were dreading it.

And then Bridget and Cormac had to think of themselves too. Were they prepared to pull up their lives by the roots and transplant them into a soil that would be foreign to them in so many respects? What would happen to Cormac's carpentry business? And to Acorn House?

She bit the tip of her tongue. 'I suppose it all comes down to one salient point in the end. Do we want this? And if so, do we want it enough to embrace the immense changes that would come with it?'

He nodded gravely. 'I suggest we sit with the idea for a while before we make any decision.' But even as he said it, she sensed the tiny ripple of eagerness that pulsed through his body and she could tell which way he was already leaning.

She was suddenly struck by the financial implications of Lord Bewley's bequest and a giggle leaked out of her. 'Oh, I'm sorry,' she said, covering her mouth. 'There's nothing humorous about this. But I...' Another titter escaped through her fingers.

He raised a quizzical eyebrow at her.

'I've just realised,' she said, her lips quivering as she tried to control them, 'if you accept this, you'll inherit an earl's fortune. Which means you'll become even wealthier than Garrett.'

He emitted a reluctant laugh. 'I don't think even the most optimistic fortune teller would ever have made such a far-fetched prediction.'

'If she had, you would have demanded your money back,' she sputtered, allowing her mirth to spill over. He joined in and their laughter broke through the tension, though it was only fleeting as their sorrow and doubts came crowding back in. Once it had subsided, he jutted his chin towards her own letter, discarded on the other side of the table.

'Who wrote to you?' he asked.

'It's from Oakleigh,' she said, reaching across the table to pick it up. 'I hadn't actually started to read it.'

She did so now, blinking as she registered the words.

'No, that can't be right,' she said, frowning. 'Mr Enright writes as though he hasn't received the letter I sent in the autumn. Good gracious, surely it did not go astray?'

With a sinking heart, she realised that it must have, because this letter's contents did not make sense otherwise. Mr Enright's tone verged on desperate as he implored her to respond to him as soon as she could. He reported the effects of the continuing potato blight and food shortages on the Oakleigh Estate and reiterated his plea for her guidance and her recommendations for help from any source.

She had already been aware that Ireland had fallen into the grip of a calamity due to the failed potato crop these past two summers. She knew this because waves of Irish immigrants had begun arriving in Boston, more than ever before, bringing with them dire accounts of extreme hunger. Although there was an ever-growing dislike of the Irish from some of the American locals, the more philanthropic people in the community had gathered donations and sent aid across the Atlantic.

However, she had not suspected that the blight might spread so badly into fertile Oakleigh as well. Mr Enright had initially written to say that it wasn't too severe and yet, two years into the crisis, it sounded like the conditions there had greatly deteriorated. Back when she had tasked him and John Corbett with reviving Oakleigh, they had given over a lot of the land to the potato plant as it had been an efficient way to both feed the tenants and generate income for the estate, but they had since become too reliant on it and now it was failing them all. He had stated as much in his last correspondence, to which she had reacted swiftly, giving him the order to sell Courcey House on Merrion Square in Dublin which would redirect significant resources to the estate in Carlow. But this crucial instruction had evidently not been received and she wondered how much damage had been caused by the fact that her letter had not reached its destination. How many tenants had continued to go hungry?

In particular, how were Ellen and her family coping? Once a lady's maid, Ellen had married Liam Kirwan, Cormac's old friend and fellow stable hand at Oakleigh Manor, and she, Liam and their three children now occupied the cottage that had previously been the McGoverns' home. The food scarcity that was impacting the Oakleigh tenants would no doubt be having an impact on the Kirwan family too. With a hiccup, it occurred to Bridget that it had been quite some time since she had even received a letter from Ellen. A flood of guilt swept over her and, with it, the conviction that she had neglected her responsibilities at Oakleigh for far too long.

She was in the process of relaying Mr Enright's appalling news to Cormac when Gus came tearing into the kitchen.

'Are my mince pies ready, Ma?' he demanded eagerly, a slight wheeze at the edge of his voice.

Distracted, she gave only a cursory glance towards the stove. 'Not yet, little miracle,' she said, thinking a mince pie would be deemed an absolute extravagance by those currently suffering on Oakleigh land.

'I amn't a miracle,' he chirped, skipping over to plant a kiss on her cheek. He finally understood the meaning of the word and no longer believed it to be a chastisement – instead, it had become an affectionate exchange between them.

As he turned to go, a wet cough erupted out of him, so severe that it sounded like there were marbles rattling around inside his chest. Unperturbed, he ran back out of the room, puffing, 'Jack! The pies aren't ready yet!'

Bridget couldn't bear to hear his cough, knowing that she was entirely to blame for it. The damage to his lungs had come about as a result of his and Jack's kidnapping in New York when they had been forced to climb up sooty chimneys for Malachy Kelly's criminal gang. That would never have happened if she hadn't so foolishly brought the boys with her to the city on her and Orlaith's quest to find Bronagh. His breathing had not been the same since and it always worsened during the winter months, so such fits were an all-too-common occurrence these days.

'I'll be glad for his sake once this cold weather is behind us,' she said morosely, hoping for an early spring.

'The smokiness of the city probably doesn't do much good for him either,' Cormac mused. 'He'd be far better off breathing in fresh country air.'

He and Bridget locked gazes, the ramifications of his statement hanging between them.

And the decision was made.

Chapter 2

Emily hurried along a busy street in New York City, exhausted but optimistic as she contended with the fierce cold after a recent snowfall. She was on her way to meet Mr and Mrs Brubaker at Brubaker Art Academy, where she hoped to hear that her application to the prestigious National Academy of Design had been successful. It would make the toil of the past two years finally worthwhile.

Balancing her maid's duties with her art studies had proved to be a monumental challenge. Every day, she rose earlier than her fellow housemaids and went to bed later, working her fingers to the bone cleaning and dusting and changing linens, while practising her art skills whenever she could and attending classes at Brubaker on Saturdays. She had commenced the classes six months after arriving in the city, once she had saved enough to begin covering the reduced fees for a course of study with fewer hours. Her father had supplemented this a little to help pay for materials but she had been determined to shoulder most of the costs herself. Unfortunately, the other housemaids believed she was getting preferential treatment from their employer by being permitted to attend the art classes and usually lumped the worst of the housework upon her. Her supposed afternoon off each week was used to catch up on all the tasks she had fallen behind on and, of course, to keep practising. She sorely missed the staunch companionship of Matilda from Marlowe House in Boston for she had made no such friend among the staff at the Meeling residence.

Her employer, Miss Amelia Knight, had become Mrs Meeling and often complained about her ugly, tongue-twisting surname and about missing her home city of Philadelphia. She had met Emily and acknowledged her as Samuel Marlowe's artistic discovery of the future, but had dismissed her as insignificant after that. Samuel had visited his cousin just once since she married and had sought Emily out on that occasion to see how she was faring. She had thanked him again for his help in securing this role for her, as living in the servants' quarters at the Meeling residence meant she did not have to pay for accommodation in New York, and she had assured him that she was working hard to make herself worthy of the opportunity while trying not to reveal how tired and lonely she was.

She sidestepped a patch of slushy snow that looked quite lethal and berated herself for her self-pity. She ought to be very grateful for her circumstances; the attendant hardships were merely challenges that would make the ultimate achievement of her ambitions all the more worthwhile. But sometimes she couldn't help acknowledging the reality of her loneliness.

She never had a spare moment or a spare penny and had only managed to go back to Boston once in the past two years. Her parents had come to visit twice, although her mother had refused to bring Jack and Gus; she had been on edge both times but she had met Hester Temple on one of the visits and had found both her and Willie to be well. Of course, Emily understood her mother's anxiety and had always taken care not to go anywhere near the Five Points district herself.

Her single trip home had been short and, to her regret, she had had next to no time alone with Rory, for she had spent most of it with the whole extended family. In a brief exchange on their own, he had kissed her cheek but it had been awkward and fleeting. Upon her departure, their goodbyes had been mumbled and accompanied by red cheeks on both sides.

That hadn't stopped her from thinking about him incessantly. She pictured his green eyes as she opened the shutters in Mrs Meeling's bedchamber, she replayed the passionate kiss they had shared in her father's workshop as she polished the mirror on the dressing table, she yearned for his quiet, steadfast presence as she raked the ashes from the fireplace. Frankly, it was alarming just how much she missed him.

He had written to her but his letters were few and short and, most infuriatingly, lacked any reference to his feelings. He just wrote about inconsequential things like his latest project at the workshop, so by the end of his letter she had a great deal more knowledge about how to fit a drawer into a dresser but not about whether he was missing her. She had to assume that he just didn't know how to articulate himself very well with a pen and so she kept her own missives restrained in that regard too, speaking mainly about her studies. She decided that on her next trip home she would make sure to find time for them to discuss their relationship openly, although she didn't yet know when that would be – the Meeling residence required a full complement of staff over the festive season. She ached with homesickness to be missing another Christmas with her family and to have missed Gus's eighth birthday last week. The result of her meeting with Mr and Mrs Brubaker today would likely mean she would continue to be tied to New York, but Rory had said he would wait for her. What if he came to New York himself? That would be splendid.

She imagined how proud she would be to achieve a place at the National Academy after all her sacrifices. In all honesty, she had to admit that Brubaker had not been an experience of undiluted joy. The stringent study environment had stolen much of the happiness that she usually derived from creating art, though of course it was necessary to increase her proficiency. It was just gruelling to have to work twice as hard to keep up with her fellow students who were studying throughout the week. The Brubakers didn't encourage too much friendliness between the students, but she had developed a tentative friendship with their daughter, Frieda, and had even shared artistic advice with her on watercolours, as Frieda was not quite as advanced in her skills, despite the fact that she was seventeen, the same age as Emily.

For her part, Emily had begun studying oils at last. Throughout her first year at Brubaker, she had only done watercolours as that was considered to be the most suitable area of study for women, but the Brubakers allowed the more talented girls to attempt oils too, once they had proved their potential. She was not permitted to draw nude models, however, which was exasperating because depicting human bodies in a lifelike manner was an essential skill to improve, and she could only do so much by studying her own arm or hand or foot. She didn't have a mirror or enough privacy in the servants' quarters to attempt anything more intimate than that. As she lamented this deficiency in her education, she passed some workmen lifting bricks on a derelict property, some of them labouring in their shirts in spite of the cold. She tried to visualise the muscles moving beneath their clothes and longed to peer under their shirts to sketch them. One of the men whistled lasciviously at her and she hastened onwards.

When she reached Brubaker Art Academy, she knocked the snow off her boots before entering the vestibule. Too full of anticipation to strive for a more dignified pace, she scurried down the hallway towards Mr and Mrs Brubaker's office. She rapped brightly on the door and opened it after a

11

voice responded from within. She found Mrs Brubaker alone, staring pensively over a large table upon which lay an array of artwork exhibiting various levels of accomplishment. At Emily's entrance, she straightened and her frown broke into a smile.

'*Fräulein* McGovern,' she said warmly in her thick German accent. 'You are welcome. I'm very glad you could meet me today.'

'I'm delighted to be here,' Emily replied, effervescent with expectation.

Mrs Brubaker gave her a fond look. 'I can see you are eager so I shall jump straight to the point. My husband and I believe you are one of our very best students. We are both convinced you will go far in this competitive field.' She emitted an exaggerated sigh. 'Which is why it pains me so greatly to have to tell you that you have not secured a place at the National Academy on this occasion.'

Emily blinked in shock. For a moment, she struggled to find breath or words. At last, she gulped and said weakly, 'Was the Academy disappointed in my portfolio?' If so, the news was crushing because she had submitted only the pieces that she had deemed to be most exceptional and she had spent weeks perfecting them.

'No, indeed, they were highly impressed with all of your compositions. But they received multiple applications and only had one open spot for a female, so naturally we were obliged to recommend the most suitable candidate.'

'Who?' Emily asked, perplexed. Though she had no desire to succumb to vanity, she had seen enough of her peers' artwork to recognise that her own abilities at the very least matched theirs and, in many cases, exceeded them.

'Why, Frieda, of course.'

Mrs Brubaker glanced away as she spoke her daughter's name. If she had had the backbone to look Emily in the eye, she would have felt the heavy weight of Emily's reproachful gaze in return.

'I see,' Emily said quietly.

Mrs Brubaker rushed on, 'Do not believe that this is any reflection upon your own remarkable talents. I can say with absolute conviction that the female place next year will undoubtedly be awarded to you. It is just unfortunate timing that it could not happen for you this year.' She beamed. 'I have something else to say that I hope might soften this little blow. Mr Brubaker and I are so encouraged by your progress and your potential that we have a marvellous proposal. How would you like to tutor some of the other girls while you continue your studies here? It would be a splendid opportunity for you and we think you would make an excellent teacher.'

Emily gritted her teeth. Mrs Brubaker made the offer as though it were a reward and not an extra burden on Emily's already limited time.

'That is very kind of you,' she said, her voice tight. 'Could I perhaps take a little while to think on it? I would need to consider how I would manage it along with my other commitments. Unless,' she added, growing hopeful, 'do you suppose that the tutoring might be enough to replace my earnings as a maid?' She would have to seek alternative accommodation as she would no longer be able to stay in the servants' quarters at the Meeling residence, but perhaps she would be able to scrape by if—

'Oh, no, no,' Mrs Brubaker said, her beaming smile becoming rather fixed. 'There would be no financial remuneration. Surely you can see that the prospect of expanding your teaching skills would be compensation enough, given that we would be equipping you with the expertise to pursue another valuable vocation, should your personal ambitions change.'

Emily felt her chin tremble. 'That is very kind of you,' she repeated. 'Thank you for inviting me here today to discuss this.'

She bade Mrs Brubaker a perfunctory farewell and hastened from the office, struggling to hold back hot tears. She couldn't believe she would have to wait another whole year for her next chance to enrol at the National Academy. It was devastating, all the more so because it was so unjust.

She scuttled back along the hallway, desperate to get outside before she bumped into a fellow student who might observe her distress. When she reached the door, she pulled up short as a figure came through it from the street. He crossed the threshold into the vestibule and she gaped in utter astonishment at his dear, familiar face.

'Papa?' she spluttered.

Her father grinned. 'I found you, *a stór.*'

Pure joy swept over her but it vanished in an instant as sudden fear took hold. 'H-has somebody died?' she managed to squeeze out. What other possible reason could there be for him to travel all the way from Boston to New York to make an unexpected appearance like this?

'The family's all fine,' he said quickly. 'I don't come bearing bad news as such. However, it's still news which I'd prefer to deliver in person. I've only just arrived in the city. I went to the Meeling residence first but they told me you had recently left to go to Brubaker, so I followed you here.'

Remembering where she was and still desirous to leave its vicinity at once, she said, 'Let's go for a walk.'

They left the art academy and she led him along two streets to a nearby cemetery, which might have seemed like an odd choice except for the fact that many people frequented it for peace and recreation as there was no decent park in the city. The cemetery was quiet at present on account of the bitter weather, but in the summer its green spaces would be thronged with picnickers.

They began to follow a path among the snow-covered graves, their breath misting in the cold air.

'Tell me your news,' she said.

'Well, there has in fact been a death,' he said cautiously and she peered up at him with alarm. 'Lord Bewley,' he said, his tone sad.

She sucked in her breath in shock.

Voice still grave, he told her about the inheritance Lord Bewley had left him, as well as the terrible troubles at Oakleigh. It was so staggering that she could scarcely fathom it all.

'Your mother and I have weighed it up from every perspective and have come to the conclusion that we must go where we are most needed. I mean to accept the bequest and take over the Bewley Estate, and she is determined to do everything she can to provide support to the Oakleigh tenants. I came to New York because I couldn't put such an enormous revelation in a letter to you, not considering how much disruption it will create in our family.' He hesitated. 'Your mother and I and the two boys are definitely leaving Boston. We plan to travel to England first and to Ireland as soon as possible thereafter. Naturally, we have no desire to be parted so far from you, but we have to acknowledge that you should be able to choose your own path. So I am here to ask what you wish to do.'

Speechless, she looked away from him, her gaze skimming over the gravestones beside the path, noticing the names and dates but absorbing none of them. Disruption didn't even begin to describe what was about to happen to their family. Her parents and brothers were going to relocate their entire lives to another country. And she had to decide whether to stay or to go with them.

She reflected on that day's disappointing news and the consequences of it – she would have to wait at least another year to gain entry to the National Academy of Design and, in this disillusioned moment, a year felt like a lifetime away. Furthermore, her feelings towards Brubaker had soured after the way she had been so unfairly treated; she experienced a fresh wave of resentment that Mr and Mrs Brubaker had influenced the National Academy to take their daughter instead of a candidate with a worthier portfolio. New York, already growing tarnished, had completely lost its shine.

In addition, she did not strictly need to work at the Meeling residence anymore if her family was about to come into a huge fortune that wasn't tied up in a contract like Oakleigh. She had really wanted to earn her own way, which was why she had refused Lord Bewley's offer to pay for her tuition when he was alive, but it seemed a little senseless to scrounge for every penny once that money belonged to her father. In truth, it would be quite absurd for her to carry on working as a maid while the rest of her family lived on an earl's income.

On top of all that, she missed her family so very much, even while they were still living in the same country. Surely it would be more than she could bear to let them sail to Europe and leave her behind. But what about...

'You may be wondering about Rory in the midst of all this?' her father guessed with uncanny accuracy.

She blushed.

He gave her an affectionate wink. 'I propose two choices. I can either offer Rory the opportunity to continue his apprenticeship with me in a fashion by coming to England and gaining the skills of a land agent on the Bewley Estate, or I can pass the workshop in Boston on to him. Either option should suffice, depending on what you both choose to do as a pair.'

At this, she blushed even more but she was indescribably grateful to her father for factoring her fledgling relationship with Rory into the situation.

'I'll leave the decision entirely in your hands,' he said, 'although I do hope you might give earnest thought to coming with us, despite the fact that it would entail getting on a ship again. There are well-respected art institutions in England, and the continent too, if that is a concern that could sway you.'

Setting dreadful visions of her past seasickness aside, she believed that going with her family might very well be her preference. But how open would Rory be to the idea of leaving his life in Boston?

CHAPTER 3

Cormac answered the knock on the front door of Acorn House to find Lord Bewley's lawyer, Mr Carruthers, standing on the doorstep, bundled up in a heavy overcoat and carrying a large pile of documents under his arm. The sight of him stirred up erstwhile emotions of both dread and relief; after Cormac had been caught in London trying to rescue Emily from Garrett's clutches, Mr Carruthers had argued in his defence at the Old Bailey courthouse and secured his acquittal. Swallowing back the memories, Cormac welcomed him into the house.

Mr Carruthers removed his coat and they settled across from each other at the table in the kitchen where the stove gave off a comfortable heat during this freezing January afternoon. Cormac watched the lawyer's gaze rove around the room as he rubbed a fingertip meditatively over the purple birthmark on his cheek.

'These are humble surroundings,' Cormac acknowledged without apology.

'A substantial change is certainly forthcoming,' Mr Carruthers replied.

Cormac didn't need a lawyer to tell him that. 'Before we begin, I'd like to thank you for your efforts that day in court. Your shrewd arguments won me my freedom.'

Mr Carruthers spread his palms wide. 'I merely obeyed Lord Bewley's orders. He showed great faith in you at the time. I hope you will in due course prove that the old gentleman's judgement was sound.'

Before Cormac could respond to this subtle challenge, Jack and Gus came scampering in from the back yard having just fed Beulah; they had only one of Emily's hens left to mind since Delilah and Jemimah had both died during the past year. Gus was wheezing worse than usual after being outside in the cold air.

'Take off your boots,' Cormac told them, 'and please try to be quiet upstairs while I'm having an important meeting.'

The boys goggled at Mr Carruthers and Gus asked, 'Is this the man who's giving you the big house and all the money, Da?'

'Shh,' Jack said, glancing at the lawyer's stern face and nudging his younger brother. 'Come on, let's hurry up.'

As they bent to unlace and remove their boots, Cormac said, 'Rory's due to call by in a while. You can come back downstairs then.'

Jack beamed and Gus let out a whoop. The two boys revered Rory as much as he had revered Cormac when he was a young lad. He was like an older brother to them or, indeed, an additional son in the McGovern family. His visits to Acorn House had become a common enough occurrence that he just let himself into the house now. Gus was so excited as he and Jack ran out of the kitchen that he dropped one of his boots on the threshold, causing the door to remain ajar.

Cormac shook his head ruefully. 'Sometimes I feel like I'm raising a pair of wild dogs instead of boys,' he said to Mr Carruthers. At least Bridget was upstairs sorting through their clothes and possessions to decide what they should bring or leave behind, so she would keep the lads' noise to a minimum.

'Their accents are markedly American,' said Mr Carruthers.

Cormac shrugged. 'That's to be expected. They've spent all their lives in this country.' Noticing the lawyer's pensive expression, he added, 'Do you foresee it as being some kind of impediment?'

'Probably not,' Mr Carruthers replied evasively. 'Besides, their accents will no doubt soften the longer they spend in England.'

Cormac reckoned that the boys were certainly still young enough for their accents to change, but he hoped they would pick up new influences from the voices they would hear in Ireland rather than in England.

After that, he and Mr Carruthers settled down to the matter at hand. The lawyer went through the tedious legal work first, explaining the steps that needed to be taken to make Cormac's inheritance official, discussing the assets that now belonged to him, presenting exact figures on ledgers, getting him to sign documents, and arranging for funds to be made immediately available to the family while they were still in Boston. He informed Cormac that he was only touching briefly on most areas and that the land agent, Mr Sandler, would go over them in much greater detail once he got to the Bewley Estate. Totally absorbed in the proceedings, Cormac found himself overwhelmed by the sheer breadth of it all. Lord Bewley had been even wealthier than he'd realised. And now all that wealth was his.

Then Mr Carruthers set the papers aside and stared hard at Cormac. 'I must put it to you bluntly, Mr McGovern. You and your family will have much difficulty assimilating into any kind of life in England. Your scandalous past is known to many in society's higher circles, given the public nature of Lady Wyndham's desertion and your own criminal trial. You will be shunned because of your Irish, Catholic, lower-class background, and because of her adulterous behaviour and the fact that you cohabitate in an unmarried state. Although the lady herself is English, Anglican and upper class, that won't be your saving grace. She may be a peeress but she is a disgraced one.'

Cormac's throat tightened. He could offer no objection. Every word the lawyer spoke was true.

Mr Carruthers deliberately twisted in his seat to study Emily's self-portrait on the wall. 'I met your daughter briefly outside the Old Bailey so I can say that this is a remarkable likeness. She is a striking beauty.' He turned back to Cormac. Expression serious, he said, 'The best hope you have of being accepted by the upper classes is to ally yourselves with an influential family via a marriage alliance. I strongly counsel you to seek out an impoverished peer of good standing, one who will overlook your daughter's less desirable qualities in favour of her more attractive ones. Turning one important family to your side will likely turn more or, at least, keep the others quiet.'

A surge of disgust rose up in Cormac. 'No,' he said flatly. 'Absolutely not.'

'Think wisely before you reject the idea,' said Mr Carruthers, undeterred. 'It cannot be denied that she has flaws, most of which stem from possessing your own unfavourable attributes in half measures, not to mention the doubt that has been cast over her legitimacy. However, she has extraordinary beauty and now she also has extraordinary wealth. What is more, she is heiress to an estate in Ireland. These are not advantages that any gentleman would dismiss lightly, while an insolvent one simply could not afford to do so. She is your one asset among a host of damning impediments.'

'*No*,' Cormac repeated. 'I categorically refuse to entertain this proposition. My daughter will marry for love and not status.' He was determined that this would be the case, whether the man turned out to be Rory, who had been completely taciturn on the matter while Emily was away, or someone else. He would never put her in the same situation that Bridget endured with Garrett. He crossed his arms and glared at Mr Carruthers. 'Under no circumstances will I even suggest such a thing to Emily.'

'I urge you to reconsider,' said Mr Carruthers. 'Without an unimpeachable connection to improve your reputation, you and your family will become outcasts. Consequently, the Bewley Estate will suffer as nobody will wish to keep company with you or do business with your agent. What would Lord Bewley think of his choice of heir then?' He arched a critical eyebrow.

Cormac clenched his jaw at this guilt-provoking dig. Of course he did not want to fail Lord Bewley, but living up to the earl's expectations could not come at the cost of Emily's happiness. 'It's out of the question,' he said through gritted teeth.

The lawyer changed tack without a flinch. 'If you won't encourage an advantageous match for your own sake or for the sake of the estate, you should at least do it for your daughter's. Should you allow your family to become social pariahs, there will be no coming back from it and she will forever remain a spinster. But if you help her to capitalise on her eligibility, she can hope to find contentment along with a solid foothold in society. I'm convinced you would not wish to deny her the chance to enjoy such a future.'

Cormac said nothing.

Perhaps Mr Carruthers interpreted this as a crack in his resolve for he said hopefully, 'All I ask right now is that you take some time to re-examine your position. Will you do that?'

'Very well, I'll think about it,' Cormac said, just to silence him on the subject. He had no intention of giving it another moment's deliberation.

Looking relieved, Mr Carruthers moved on. 'That was the upper classes. Now for the lower classes.' Once again, he skimmed a fingertip over his birthmark. 'It's hard to predict how they will react. The staff at Bewley Hall will likely be unhappy to serve a man who deceived them the last time he set foot in the house. You ought to expect some resignations from the higher staff who have enough experience to seek positions elsewhere, which will in turn weaken your authority among the lower staff. The tenants, too, might take exception to the idea of working for someone who is as lowborn as themselves.' Mr Carruthers gave a shrug. 'But who knows, perhaps they will find common ground with you. Much will depend on your ability to handle it all.'

Cormac could feel his stress levels rising with every word out of the lawyer's mouth. Before he could frame a reply that would demonstrate confidence rather than trepidation, he heard Bridget speak beyond the kitchen door.

'Rory? What are you doing here?'

Rory's subdued voice replied, 'Mr McGovern asked me to come see him today after I closed the workshop.'

She bustled into the kitchen, picking up Gus's boot along the way. She didn't appear surprised by Cormac's visitor so the boys must have enlightened her that the man giving away the big house and all the money was there.

'Good day, Mr Carruthers,' she said nervously. 'You are welcome. Did you have an agreeable journey from England?'

'Middling. It was my first winter voyage across the Atlantic. I cannot say that it tempted me to plan future itineraries on a similar schedule.'

She gave him a sympathetic grimace. 'I imagine the sea is quite turbulent at this time of year.' She added to Cormac, 'Just to let you know, Rory's waiting for you in the front room.'

He looked at Mr Carruthers, who said, 'I think we've covered enough for today. I plan to stay in Boston for two weeks. We have time to discuss the details further.'

Cormac could guess which particular detail the lawyer wanted to discuss most of all and was glad to bid him goodbye. How he imagined Cormac could ever inflict such a punishment upon his daughter was unfathomable.

Mr Carruthers donned his overcoat and, leaving the documents behind for Cormac's further perusal, departed from the kitchen accompanied by Bridget, who said she would see him to the door. A moment later, Rory entered. Cormac invited him to take the chair where the lawyer had been sitting and, as he sat, his green eyes strayed to Emily's self-portrait on the wall before returning to Cormac.

'All fine at the workshop?' Cormac asked.

'Yes, sir. I've nearly finished the set of nesting tables—should be done with them by the end of tomorrow.'

Cormac gestured towards the papers and ledgers still spread out on the kitchen table. 'You already know what's happening here.' He and Bridget had waited until after Christmas to break the news to their family and friends living on Broad Street. They had been flabbergasted, to say the least. 'I told you at the time that you'd no need to worry, that your job would be safe, one way or another. I now want to talk with you in more depth about your options.'

Rory nodded, his shoulders a little hunched.

'You've been my apprentice for nearly four years and it saddens me that our productive time together is drawing to a close. However, there is a way to continue that relationship if you're interested in doing so. Landlords who own large estates are generally assisted by land agents. The Bewley Estate already has an agent, and a deputy too, but both men are getting older and it makes sense to begin training a younger man to eventually take their place. That is the position I have in mind for you, should you be willing to take it on—another apprenticeship of sorts.'

Privately, Cormac felt that the skills Rory would gain in the role would be an enormous help to Emily when the time came for her to inherit Oakleigh, but he conjectured that such a long-term prediction might scare Rory at this particular juncture, judging by his immobile posture.

Cormac cleared his throat. 'I'm conscious that accepting this position would mean moving to England, which you might not like to do. So my alternative suggestion is to offer you full ownership of the workshop here in Boston instead. You've already proven that you can manage the daily tasks on your own, and before I leave I could guide you through what would be entailed on the administrative side. Perhaps in time the business would expand enough that you would be able to take on your own apprentice.' Rory's twelve-year-old brother, Brian, would be a logical choice, once he grew a bit older.

Cormac laced his fingers together on the table. 'I'm not putting any pressure on you to commit to either path today. Besides, and at the risk of making assumptions, you may wish to discuss the situation with Emily. She's due to come home from New York in a couple of weeks, so that gives you a chance to evaluate your two choices in the meantime.'

Rory lowered his gaze. To Cormac's surprise, he said, 'There's actually a third choice, sir.' He drew in a breath. 'Seeing as everyone's leaving Boston, my ma's decided she wants to go too. She's going to Chicago with Orlaith and Charlie and the others. This city is still a port for the *Integrity* and now that she knows what my da did...' Rory trailed away, his face pinched with the loathing that always emerged whenever his father was mentioned.

Cormac, too, experienced a dart of revulsion. Brian Mór Carey was a despicable fellow of the lowest kind, having deceived his wife and four children in Boston by marrying another woman in Liverpool and fathering three more offspring by her. The news of her husband's bigamy had come as a grievous shock to Derval, even more so once she learned that Brian Mór had previously come back to Boston when the *Integrity* had docked there but that he had not even got off the ship to see her. Yes, indeed, Cormac could easily understand why she would desire to leave her memories behind, especially when all her closest friends were moving away. He and Bridget ought to have seen this coming.

'Ma's taking Una, Sorcha and Brian with her,' Rory mumbled. 'But I'm not far off twenty-one—she said she can't treat me like a child anymore. So she's given me the choice of staying in Boston or going to Chicago.'

And with that, Cormac realised that Rory's decision amounted to choosing between Emily and his mother.

CHAPTER 4

Emily unpacked her valise in her box room at Acorn House, looking around fondly at the small space and even appreciating the banging noises coming from the boys in the next bedroom. She had just arrived back from New York the night before, after serving out her notice at the Meeling residence and withdrawing from Brubaker Art Academy. The fact that she had experienced no sense of regret as she left New York City behind reassured her that she had chosen the right path.

She didn't unpack everything as her time here would likely be short thanks to the imminent move to England, but she took out some artwork she wanted to show her parents later and put a few articles of clothing in the cupboard. She found Mabel lying patiently inside the cupboard and gave the doll's arm an affectionate squeeze. They had had a tumultuous past – and how she resented her old school friend, Emmeline, for having caused that strife – but she decided then and there that Mabel would come with them to England. After all, Emily would doubtless have a daughter of her own to pass her on to in the future.

Remembering her companion Louise and her baby daughter Philippa from the *Integrity*, she found herself longing for the joy of holding a newborn. Gracious, she needed to slow down – she wouldn't be eighteen for another three months and she wasn't sure how Rory felt about such things yet. Then again, he had three siblings, so perhaps he would be happy to have a large family. She gulped as she recollected that he actually had six siblings if he counted the three Brian Mór had fathered by the woman Maud in Liverpool.

A solitary clucking below her window drew her from her reverie and, with a sigh, she mourned the loss of Delilah and Jemimah, which had occurred since her last visit home. Her parents had already told her the news in a letter, but it hit harder when she heard Beulah's forlorn voice.

She supposed it was silly to feel bereaved over a couple of hens. Still, her father had gifted them to her right after the family had moved into this house and it had been a sign of their small step up in the world that he had been able to afford to do so. But now they were on the brink of a much steeper ascent on the social scale.

Shutting her valise, she left the box room to go downstairs. The eighth step from the bottom squeaked as she stepped on it.

'Nice to see you again too, Barnabas,' she said.

She found her mother in the front room below, gathering items from her sewing desk and putting them into a chest. She suffered a stab of the familiar guilt that always accompanied any reminder of her past folly – she had been responsible for her mother's loss of employment as a seamstress with Madame Roche. Her mother had since managed to get some work with another dressmaker, although it had been sporadic and only for ordinary clothes, nothing so beautiful as the blue silk gown that had brought about so much disaster. Not for the first time, Emily wondered how she would ever make it up to her mother and father for all the hurt she had caused them.

The gown made her think of the ball at Marlowe House and of Samuel. She ought to pay him a visit and explain to him her decision not to continue pursuing her artistic career in New

York. She would assuage his disappointment by telling him that she intended to explore tuition options in Europe instead. Just because the Brubakers had impeded her path to the National Academy of Design did not mean she was going to give up on her dream, not after how long and how hard she had worked for it. While she was at Marlowe House, she would also want to bid a fond farewell to Matilda. However, both of those visits could wait for today – she was far more eager to go to Broad Street to see Rory. She tried to conceal the enthusiasm bubbling inside her as she helped her mother pack the last few sewing items into the chest.

As it was a Sunday, her father was at home; he sat on the sofa in front of the cosy hearth, perusing a thick, official-looking document.

'What are you reading, Papa?' she asked him, crossing to the sofa while her mother closed the lid of the chest.

'A report on the income and expenditures of the Bewley Estate for the last five years,' he replied. 'Mr Carruthers is coming by to collect it later. He needs to bring it back to England with him and is due to depart tomorrow.'

'You're under pressure to get it finished in time then,' she said, spotting her opening. 'I'll leave you in peace. In fact, I think I shall pay a visit to Broad Street.'

Her parents exchanged a glance. After a delicate nod from her mother, her father said, 'Before you go, *a stór*, there's something I should tell you.'

She didn't like the note of caution in his voice. 'What is it?'

'The Carey family have some news. They've also decided to move to Chicago.'

The bottom dropped out of her stomach. 'Rory too?' she croaked.

'I don't know. He didn't know himself when last we spoke of it. I just thought it best for you to be prepared before you see him, in case...'

The end of his sentence hung in the air unspoken. She swallowed hard.

'Thank you for telling me, Papa,' she said tremulously.

Her mother came over and put a sympathetic palm on her cheek. 'There might be no cause whatsoever for concern,' she said, her tone encouraging.

Filled with misgiving nonetheless, Emily put on her bonnet, cloak and gloves and left Acorn House in a hurry.

Along the way to Broad Street, she realised that at some point over the last few weeks she had begun making an assumption that she and Rory would go to England, forgetting that there was every possibility that he might not be keen on that prospect at all. Would he really prefer Chicago though? She wasn't sure if she did. She envisaged a compromise where they married immediately so that they could live together in Boston instead of leaving with either of their families. But then they would be so isolated. The only friend still nearby would be Matilda at Marlowe House and, while that would be splendid, would it be enough? Ought Emily to consider the idea of moving to Chicago so that she and Rory could be close to at least some of their family? Although it would break her heart to be parted so far from her parents and brothers, especially after having only just reunited with them following her two long years in New York, it would be the selfless decision to agree to go with Rory's family and not her own, and at least her aunties would be there. Yes, she could be open to that option.

She reached Broad Street with a renewed, if slightly more subdued, sense of enthusiasm. As she drew near the building where her family had first lived when they came to Boston, she noticed two figures approaching from the opposite direction.

She recognised the shaggy head on the taller one and her spirits lifted even more with excitement. Then she realised his arm was draped around the shoulders of the smaller figure who had bushy hair. Could it be one of his sisters? As she got closer, she blinked rapidly, dumbfounded. It was her old classmate from Hawes, Emmeline.

Rory dropped his arm at once when he caught sight of Emily and took a self-conscious step away from his companion. Emmeline grinned widely at Emily as they all stopped at the door to the building.

'So wonderful to see you!' she exclaimed. 'How is your exceptional artist career coming along?'

'Very well,' Emily replied with stiff lips.

'Marvellous,' Emmeline said and sniggered as though she could tell that Emily was lying. She leaned up to kiss Rory on the cheek. 'I won't call into your mother today but I can't wait to see you next Sunday as usual,' she said with a coquettish wink in his direction and a smirk in Emily's. Then she flounced away down the street, bushy hair bouncing around her shoulders.

Rory grimaced. ''Tis cold,' he said awkwardly. 'D'you want to step indoors?'

He held open the door for Emily and she passed through it, mute and dazed. She had no desire to go into the Careys' rooms so she halted in the hallway. She and Rory had argued in this very spot before agreeing to get on the *Integrity* together. That had been the beginning. Was this now the end?

Plucking up her nerve, she asked, 'Is there any possibility that what I saw just there wasn't what it actually looked like?'

'No, it was what it looked like,' he admitted. 'I didn't want you to find out that way though.' He looked down at his feet, embarrassed. 'I know I said I'd wait but...'

'It was too long,' she finished for him, her insides splintering with anguish.

His infrequent, inexpressive letters ought to have warned her. Of course his affection would have waned when she wasn't around. It was probably only their close proximity on their journey to England that had sparked anything to begin with. A fledgling fire was easily snuffed out without any fuel to put on it.

'I'm sorry—' he started to say.

'Don't be,' she interrupted quickly. 'I chose to go to New York. I had no right to expect anything upon my return.'

'Are we going to end up back where we started?' he asked, gesturing vaguely at the hallway.

Even though it would be easier for her to hate him as she had back then, she said, 'Of course not. We'll continue to be friends, if you like.' Somehow, she mustered a smile as she added, 'Friends at a distance though, I suppose.'

She had meant that they probably wouldn't be so close on a personal level anymore but she realised that he had interpreted it geographically when he nodded and said, 'You're going to England.'

It would have mortified her if he had guessed that she had been envisioning an alternative future for them, so she replied, 'Yes, I am,' as if it was always going to be her choice. 'Are you moving to Chicago with your family?'

He hesitated. 'I don't think so.'

She gaped. He hardly planned to accept her father's offer of a role on the Bewley Estate, which meant... 'You intend to take over the workshop?'

'I do. I'm going to tell your da tomorrow. I think I'm ready for the responsibility.'

That stunned her. Practically everyone he knew was leaving the city – it was the most isolating choice he could have made. 'You're going to stay in Boston?' she said in disbelief. 'With no one?'

'Well, Emmeline's here.'

'Oh,' she said in a small voice.

After a pause, he said, 'Will you come in to say hello to my ma?'

'I'm afraid I can't today,' she said. 'But please do give her my best.'

She didn't even want to go upstairs to visit her aunties. She desperately wanted to be alone so she could cry.

'I'm sure I'll see you again before I leave,' she said with a heroic effort at cheery nonchalance. Then she turned and walked calmly out of the building, hoping he wouldn't notice her shoulders beginning to shake.

Out on the street, she tried to hold in her emotions, but her self-restraint cracked apart before she had made it a dozen steps along the footpath. She passed old Mrs Kane at the corner and managed to blubber a greeting.

'Still a quare child,' Mrs Kane said and shuffled on.

On her tear-drenched walk home, Emily berated herself for not having foreseen this. Her selfishness had often caused strife with Rory in the past and now it had happened again with the worst ramification possible: he had become indifferent to her. She recalled their kiss in her father's workshop – soon to be Rory's own workshop, perhaps with 'Carey' on the sign above the door – and wondered whether she should have stayed in Boston. What if she had said to hell with Brubaker and pursued her artistic ambitions at a lesser art academy nearer to home? Would she now be the girl at Rory's side? Or might their flame have sputtered out regardless? She would never know and she couldn't torture herself with 'what ifs'. What was done was done. She could only look forward now, even though the future seemed much bleaker than it had mere hours ago.

She rubbed her gloved palms into her eyes before she got back to Acorn House. She didn't want her parents to witness the extent of her distress. She would make light of it all when she told them what had transpired. If she pretended she didn't mind, perhaps eventually the lie would come true.

Just as she reached the house, she met a man on the footpath outside it. She discerned the birthmark on his cheek and recognised him as Mr Carruthers. He carried the thick document her father had been examining earlier, along with several others, and he looked very pleased to see her.

'Good day, Miss McGovern,' he said. 'This is a happy coincidence. I thought I'd missed the opportunity to speak with you while I was in Boston.'

'Good day, Mr Carruthers,' she said, hoping he would not observe the redness in her eyes. 'How nice to see you. My father said you are departing for England tomorrow?'

'Indeed, and he told me today that he intends to follow by March at the latest.' He surveyed her with a beady gaze. 'Will you be travelling to the Bewley Estate with the rest of your family?'

'I will,' she said with a small wrench of her heart as she remembered who would not be going with them.

He emitted an expressive sigh. 'There are many challenges ahead for you all. The upper classes are not renowned for their tolerance. But I assume you already know how you can best contribute to your family's advancement?'

Startled, she said, 'I-I don't.'

'Of course the most selfless thing you could do for your parents would be to marry well.'

She stared at him, utterly taken aback.

He adopted an apologetic look. 'Forgive me, perhaps you are not at liberty to do so. Do you already harbour an attachment for someone?'

With another wrench of her heart, she shook her head.

'Then, despite your father's protestations about *love*, I would strongly urge you to attract an eminent suitor whose standing will help improve your family's reputation. In the long run, that is what will serve you and them best. Lord knows your parents will need all the aid they can get.'

It was as though the lawyer had drawn back the curtains on a window that revealed a new path for her to tread, clear of any obstacles or doubt. Her parents needed help and she still needed to make amends for her dreadful behaviour when she ran away. Her mother had encountered a distinct lack of success in marrying for status but not every peer could be like Garrett. Emily would find a distinguished gentleman with whom she could get along reasonably well, and no doubt affection, if not love, would come in time. Surely such an arrangement would help heal the wound in her heart left by Rory.

If marrying well would be an advantage for her family, then she would do it gladly.

CHAPTER 5

Bridget climbed the stairs at Broad Street, thinking that it would be the last time she would ever do it. The door upstairs was open and she rapped on it lightly as she walked through. Orlaith stood at the table packing flour, beans and rice into a sack. Her pregnant belly had begun to show more prominently in the past few weeks and she patted it tenderly before she placed the final bag of rice into the sack. She smiled when she saw Bridget, but it was a watery one, as was Bridget's own in return. The imminent parting was going to be gut-wrenching.

'The wagon is ready and waiting below,' Bridget said, masking a weepy sniff by unnecessarily clearing her throat.

Cormac and Rory had helped Charlie to harness the oxen and pack the covered wagon with possessions and provisions. Among these was a set of beautifully carved wooden bowls and spoons which Cormac and Rory had crafted at the workshop as a parting gift for their two families. The gift couldn't be extravagant as it needed to be light and practical for the journey ahead, but it had been received with delight by all the travellers and tears from Orlaith and Derval.

'And that's the last of the food packed,' Orlaith said now, tying the sack.

Bronagh emerged just then from the back bedroom with her two-year-old daughter, Maggie. After coming to Boston, she had chosen to live with her sister rather than her brother even though there was more room at Acorn House, especially once Emily went to New York. But Bronagh seemed more at ease with Orlaith, so Cormac hadn't argued. Tess hadn't been thrilled to share her room with a fractious baby, though, and had started staying in the servants' quarters at Tremont House almost on a full-time basis.

Maggie wandered near Bridget, but Bridget didn't bend down to pick her up for a hug. They had all learned to be careful around the little girl as she invariably shied away from sudden touches or loud noises. Even Bronagh limited her physical contact with her, but Bridget wondered whether that had less to do with her child's preferences and more to do with her own nature. Two and a half years had passed since they had liberated her from her appalling circumstances in New York and yet she still did not interact well with others. Much like her daughter, she flinched whenever people came near her, exuding a constant air of wariness as though she expected this life to crumble around her at any moment and to suddenly find herself back in the warehouse in Five Points under Malachy Kelly's abusive influence. However, when the idea of Chicago had been broached with her, she had eventually agreed to go and had even expressed a tentative desire to become a nurse like Orlaith, showing that she was beginning to believe she could live a normal life again.

'Ready?' Orlaith said brightly to Bronagh, not faltering when Bronagh just gave a nervous shrug.

Bridget continued to be impressed by how much Orlaith had grown over the years. After all she had been through, she had somehow managed to cultivate an unabated outlook of optimism. She had suffered poverty and slavery as a child, which had forced her to build a hardened wall around herself, but cracks in that wall had formed when Cormac found her in

Dublin, and then she had fully opened herself up to love when she found Charlie in Boston.

As if Bridget's thoughts had fetched him, Charlie's voice and footsteps came up the stairs. 'We're all set,' he called out.

He entered the room, throwing them all a jolly smile, even though today was painful for him too – his own reason for leaving Boston was his parents' disapproval of his choice of wife. Crossing over to Orlaith, he kissed her temple and put a gentle hand on her bump.

Orlaith and Charlie had stumbled a little after the events in New York. She had wanted to forgive him, but he hadn't wanted to be forgiven. It had taken a long time for her to convince him that she viewed his entanglement with a young member of the Kelly Greens not as an act of infidelity but as an act of sacrifice to help save Jack and Gus. He had continued to despise himself, but she had patiently reiterated her feelings day after day, month after month, and gradually he had come to accept her absolution like a wilting plant revived with attentive care. And now, with that ordeal behind them, they were finally having a baby.

The baby had accelerated their departure from Boston now, at the end of February, even though they would have preferred to wait for warmer temperatures to travel. The tempting prospect of Chicago could no longer be ignored – the itch had become too strong and they knew they would always regret it if they didn't go – but Orlaith didn't want to travel with a newborn so they had to complete their journey before its arrival.

Her expression full of affection, Orlaith put both of her hands over Charlie's on her bump, the ring finger on her left hand noticeably bare. Her wedding ring had been stolen by the Kelly Greens and never recovered afterwards, but she and Charlie had agreed to wait to replace it, saving their money instead for their move to Chicago. Bridget knew that he intended to buy Orlaith another ring once they were comfortably settled in their new home, and that would be the final step in consigning the rockiest period of their marriage to the past. Bridget hoped there would be nothing but joy in their future.

Letting go of Charlie, Orlaith picked up the sack from the table, but he took it from her and slung it over his shoulder before leading the way downstairs. Bronagh lifted Maggie to carry her down the steps and the child whined until she was released at the bottom. They went out onto the street where Cormac was checking the harnesses on the oxen. The two families were travelling together by wagon instead of stagecoach because there were so many of them and because they were bringing everything they owned with them.

Tess lingered near the front of the wagon, her posture casual but her eyes following Cormac hungrily. Although Bridget had chosen to overlook Tess's past transgressions, thanks to the lengths she had gone to in New York to help save Jack and Gus, part of her was greatly relieved that an ocean would soon separate Tess and the object of her yearning.

Derval stood close to the wagon too, clutching Rory's arm tightly, while Una and Sorcha hovered nearby looking excited – they were old enough now that they would both seek work themselves when they got to Chicago. Little Brian was nowhere to be seen, and neither were Jack and Gus. Although it always gave Bridget a hiccup of anxiety whenever they left her sight, she had only seen them just before she went upstairs so she knew they couldn't be far away. Emily loitered by Cormac's side, pretending to be interested in what he was doing, but her gaze kept flicking covertly to Rory in a manner not unlike Tess's with Cormac.

Bridget suspected that her daughter still liked Rory and couldn't fathom how things had fallen apart between the pair of them. Emily had told her and Cormac very little about what had happened the day she went to Broad Street to see Rory, only that he was keeping company with another girl now but that she didn't mind at all as she had hardly given him a moment's thought while she was in New York. Then, in corroboration of this unexpected development, Cormac had come home from the workshop the next day to say that Rory had requested to take over the carpentry business, rather than assume a role on the Bewley Estate. When Bridget and Cormac had made the decision to uproot their family from Boston, they had devised the perfect pretext for Rory to travel with them to England and develop a proper relationship with Emily if she wanted to go with them. The fact that he had passed it up indicated that he had lost interest in her, but Rory did not strike Bridget as a fickle soul. It was both surprising and disappointing and Bridget ached to see her little girl's heart broken for the first time.

It was surprising, too, that Rory had chosen to stay in Boston rather than go with his family to Chicago but, on balance, much less so. He was a man of nearly twenty-one years of age – of course he would want to step out from under his mother's wing and stand on his own two feet. No doubt his unplanned trip to England with Emily had resulted in a strong sense of independence and a desire to make his own way in the world. While part of Bridget felt a certain reserve towards him for what had transpired between him and Emily, she couldn't deny that she still looked upon him almost as fondly as her own sons, and she hoped he would flourish, even though none of them would be there to witness it.

Jack, Gus and Brian came running out of the building. 'The Sheehans have already started moving into our rooms,' Brian announced.

The Sheehan family of four had taken over Mr Lorenzo's tiny room at the top of the building after he passed away from scarlet fever, but Rory had arranged to swap with them once his mother and siblings had departed; the room on the top floor would be more than sufficient for a single young man living on his own and he could save a little on rent.

He shrugged at the report from his brother and said, 'I'll go grab my things in a minute after...' He motioned awkwardly towards the wagon.

Derval gulped back a sob and embraced her eldest child, which precipitated a series of farewells all around the group. Bridget hugged Orlaith and Charlie in turn and expressed her earnest hope that they would find all the happiness in the world in their new home with their new baby. She was more restrained with Tess and Bronagh but still gave them a brief embrace each and wished them well. She said goodbye to Maggie in a cheery voice, but the child just looked up at her in silence.

As she and Derval clasped each other, she caught Tess's farewell with Cormac out of the corner of her eye. Tess held back self-consciously but Cormac initiated the embrace and she stepped into the circle of his arms, closing her eyes and clinging to him. They didn't speak and the hug lingered until he was the one to break it. Tess inhaled deeply as he let her go. She turned away, her face filled with a look of intense concentration as though she were storing up the experience to return to the memory of it in the future. Bridget transferred her attention from Derval to Una, Sorcha and Brian and pretended that she hadn't noticed anything.

The final pair to say their goodbyes were Cormac and Orlaith. Like Bridget, Cormac's farewell to Bronagh had been moderate, knowing that she would be discomfited to be the recipient of any sort of demonstrative behaviour. But his relationship with his youngest sister went much deeper and their parting was painful to watch. She wept openly and he clearly struggled to contain his own emotion as she nestled against him. He held her as long as they both needed it, right there in the middle of Broad Street. Bridget could see old Mrs Kane's beady eyes riveted on the scene from her doorway further up the street.

Orlaith's shoulders shook and Cormac squeezed her even tighter. 'We've known for a long time that this was coming,' he murmured. 'Our paths diverge here but they'll intertwine again, I promise.'

Although no one could foretell what the future held in either Chicago or England, Bridget was certain that he intended to keep his promise, no matter how many years might pass before he reunited with his sister.

This time it was Cormac who couldn't seem to pull away and Orlaith who finally drew back. 'Thanks for being the best big brother any sister could hope for,' she said, wiping her eyes.

He managed a lopsided grin. 'Goodbye, chicken.'

The travellers climbed into the back of the wagon, where they would ride for now. Once they were gone beyond the city streets, they would escape its jolting confines and walk alongside it instead.

As Charlie settled himself on the seat up front, Cormac said to him, 'This wagon carries the most precious cargo. Look after them all and yourself too.'

Charlie saluted him seriously and then called a command to the oxen. The wagon trundled slowly away, giving the travellers plenty of time to stare out the back for one last look. Derval's gaze was trained upon Rory. The three Carey children waved excitedly at their brother but he seemed too rigid to wave back. A jerky movement of Emily's arm suggested that she wanted to take his hand to comfort him, but she clutched her wrist with her other hand to stop herself.

Tess and Bronagh peered out from the back of the wagon, then retreated into its depths with Maggie. Orlaith remained there looking back at Cormac. Although her cheeks were still wet with tears, she was smiling and her face was ablaze with hope.

Then the wagon turned the corner and the intrepid travellers were lost to view.

CHAPTER 6

Emily stood on the step above Barnabas. This past week had been full of goodbyes and here was another to add to the list. She stepped down and Barnabas emitted a rather forlorn squeak.

There was nothing left to do on this final day in Acorn House. Their possessions had already been packed in trunks and brought to the docks ahead of their ship's departure. They were leaving behind the furniture in the house, most of which had been built by her father, as her parents had decided to gift it to the next owner. Even their magnificent bed, its posts topped with carved acorns and its headboard etched with a beautiful oak tree, would remain, which they said was a way of acknowledging that a special part of them would always belong in Boston. The back yard was empty too – Emily had already brought Beulah next door to Mr and Mrs Hill and she hoped to God that the poor hen wouldn't end up as their dinner as soon as the family were gone.

They were about to head to the docks, which she was dreading with every fibre of her being. She had been nauseous just anticipating the voyage and had come to the conclusion that this would have to be the very final time she ever crossed the ocean, which meant she and Rory would probably never see each other again. The family had said goodbye to him the day before when they gathered at the workshop to witness her father officially hand it over to his apprentice. Her mother had embraced Rory in farewell and her father had shaken his hand, while Jack and Gus had tussled good-naturedly with him. When Emily's turn came, she hadn't known what to say or do and neither had he, judging by the way he shuffled his feet and shifted his gaze away from her. They had ended up exchanging an awkward handshake without making eye contact. As she left the workshop, she had reminded herself that it was for the best – he had found happiness with Emmeline and she would seek something similar with a suitor in England. Her future was full of possibility.

And at least three days of vomiting.

Sighing, she carried on down the stairs. Her parents and brothers were passing through the doorway from the kitchen into the front room. Her mother cast one last wistful glance over her shoulder at the stove and Emily reflected that her mother wouldn't need to cook for the family once they got to Bewley Hall. Their lives were going to change in so many ways. Her naïve fifteen-year-old self would have gladly welcomed the transformation. Now, she felt uneasy. Were any of them ready for it? Jack and Gus had never lived in an upper-class situation at all.

As she reached the bottom step, she was startled by a loud knock on the front door. Before anyone could approach it, it opened and Rory stood on the threshold. His face was ashen.

Her heart leapt. In that instant, she was absolutely certain that he had come for her. He was going to announce that he had been a fool and he would beg her to forgive him. He would say that he wanted to come with them to England or he would ask her to marry him and stay in Boston. She could picture it all so vividly. And she knew she would answer yes to anything he asked.

But his troubled green eyes glanced away from her towards her father. 'Sir, I'm glad I caught you before you left. I need your help.'

He came into the room, pulled a letter from his pocket and held it out. Frowning, her father stepped forwards to take it. Emily stood rooted to the bottom step as she watched him scan the page, his frown deepening.

After he finished reading, he said, 'My condolences, Rory.' He looked at Rory as though asking for permission. When Rory nodded, he told everyone else, 'This letter is from a Mr Martins, who is a solicitor in Liverpool. He writes that Rory's father has passed away.'

Brian Mór was dead? Emily recalled him swinging lithely across the rigging on the *Integrity* and could hardly believe that a man in such vigorous health could have died.

Then her father explained further. 'He suffered a minor injury to his leg while at sea, which festered and poisoned his body. He perished before the ship managed to reach shore.'

Emily's mother expressed her condolences too but Emily stayed silent, wondering how Rory actually felt about his father's death. His last encounter with Brian Mór had been an exchange of angry words, which had ended with him punching his father and storming away. Could he have forgiven him enough in the intervening years to find it within himself to grieve his father's passing?

Emily's father cleared his throat. 'Mr Martins was not merely writing to notify the family of Brian Mór's death.' He read the next part of the letter aloud. '"In the process of registering the death, my firm traced the deceased's origins back to Kerry in Ireland, which is how we discovered that Mr Brian Carey was in fact already married prior to entering into a union with a woman in Liverpool. This woman shall be hereafter referred to as Miss Maud Pratt owing to the recently established illegitimacy of her marriage contract. Mrs Derval Carey has been identified as the lawful widow of the deceased and her eldest son, Mr Rory Carey, as the beneficiary of all of the deceased's property and possessions. This includes an address at Number 5 Penny Close, which the deceased owned outright and at which he had resided with Miss Pratt and their three offspring prior to his death. I must advise you, Mr Carey, that you will be obliged to evict these illegal occupants in the process of taking ownership of your property. My firm will be happy to assist you in this regard upon your arrival in Liverpool."'

In the ensuing stunned silence, Jack, always quiet but perceptive, asked curiously, 'So is Rory coming to England too then?'

'No,' Rory muttered and then looked hesitantly at Emily's father. 'At least, I don't think so. Can you help me decide what to do?'

Emily's father pulled out a pocket watch which she knew had once belonged to her grandfather, Lord Courcey. He winced. 'I wish I could discuss it at length with you but we need to head to the docks very shortly. My advice will have to be brief.'

Emily's mother knitted her brows. 'Would it be feasible for Rory to actually join us on the voyage if we're all going in the same direction?'

Emily was delighted that her mother had raised the question because it was the one foremost in her own mind. Her father, however, was chewing the inside of his cheek.

'Impossible, I think. Not if Rory wants to get his mother's opinion before he makes a decision. Which I'm sure he does?'

He tilted his head towards Rory whose expression cleared.

'Yes, that's the first thing I've got to do,' he said gratefully. 'I'll either have to follow her to Chicago or wait for her to send me a letter with her address so I can write back.'

Neither process would be swift. Emily deflated with silent disappointment.

Her father rubbed his jaw. 'The way I see it, you have four choices to weigh up with your mother. You could ignore the letter entirely which would likely result in the local authorities eventually taking possession of the house on Penny Close and no doubt evicting its current occupants. Or you could take full ownership and occupancy of the house, although I question whether you would want to move to England after your recent decision not to.'

Emily got the impression that Rory was purposely avoiding her gaze when he said, 'Emmeline probably wouldn't like it.'

She withered a little inside – was he serious enough about Emmeline to take her preferences into account in a matter as colossal as this one?

'You could sell the house,' her father continued, 'but it's highly improbable that Maud has the funds to purchase it so she and her children would doubtless be ousted from the house in this scenario too.'

Rory looked uncomfortable.

'Finally, you could make arrangements to keep the house but allow Maud and her family to remain there and pay rent to you.'

A muscle in Rory's neck twitched and Emily wondered how Auntie Derval would feel about that.

Emily's father scrutinised the letter again. 'Mr Martins states here that "given the complicated nature of the deceased's marital status while alive, any and all proceedings will need to be done in person to verify the legatee's identity and entitlements". Therefore all but the first option I mentioned would necessitate a voyage to England at some stage. Only for that stipulation, I would have offered to meet the solicitor in Liverpool on your behalf.'

'I'll talk through it all with my ma before I decide,' said Rory, 'but what do *you* think I should do, sir?'

'I'm afraid I can't answer that for you.'

Rory gnawed on his lip. 'What would you do if you were me?'

Emily's father gave him a wry look. 'I suspect you might have already guessed that. But you mustn't let it influence you. This is your own choice to make and I know you'll consider carefully before you make it.'

Rory bowed his head in resignation. 'I will, sir.' He took the letter back and pocketed it. 'Thank you. I'd better leave so ye can get going.'

Emily's mother stepped forwards and put a compassionate hand on his arm. 'If you do go to Liverpool, make sure you come visit us in Bedfordshire, won't you?'

He gave her a grimacing smile but didn't commit. 'I hope ye have a safe voyage.'

There were no prolonged goodbyes this time. As he headed for the front door, his gaze cut to Emily still standing on the stairs. She discerned the pain in his eyes and desperately wished she could console him over his distressing dilemma. But that privilege belonged to Emmeline now. He disappeared out the door.

Emily's father exhaled. 'That letter must have hit him like a thunderbolt.'

'Poor lad,' her mother said. 'I wish we had more time to be with him. How lonely he will feel bearing this news by himself.' She eyed the pocket where Emily's father had tucked away his watch. 'Ought we to hurry now?'

'Just one moment,' he said and tugged her back to the door leading to the kitchen.

Standing on the threshold, he reached up to the lintel, patted it and murmured something. Her mother smiled and they shared a sweet kiss. Jack waited patiently but Gus was already bouncing on his feet by the front door.

Emily watched her parents in fascination and not a little envy. She hoped she would be lucky enough to find a man in England who would not only bolster her family's reputation but would kindle the same kind of ardour that always filled the air around her mother and father. Would that be too much to ask?

CHAPTER 7

All through the month-long voyage across the Atlantic, Cormac was certain he had made the right decision. On the train journey to Bedfordshire, he reminded himself that he had made the right decision. By the time the carriage pulled up to the front door of Bewley Hall, he doubted whether he had made the right decision at all.

Spring had truly blossomed while they'd been travelling and the evening April air was fresh and fortifying when the door of the carriage opened. Jack and Gus both gawked in bemusement at the footman and jumped down to the gravel. Emily, who was still looking tired and wan after her sickness on the ship, understood the footman's role and took his hand with a grateful smile as she shakily stepped out. Cormac inhaled a deep breath and Bridget squeezed his knee.

'Here we go,' she said and stepped down next.

He emerged last and stared up at Bewley Hall. He could hardly credit the fact that this immense house was actually his. Thoughts of the humble McGovern cottage nestled on Oakleigh land fluttered away as his gaze fell upon two figures coming out the front door. There was no swathe of servants lined up to greet their new master and he was glad of it, happy to begin with just these two: the land agent, Mr Sandler, and his wife and Bewley Hall's housekeeper, Mrs Sandler. Both had aged since he had last seen them more than a decade ago but neither seemed infirm. He could only guess at their ages – late fifties or early sixties, perhaps? Mr Sandler's expression appeared benign, his small eyes, nose and mouth squashed between his large forehead and chin. His wife's face was more neutral but she had always been reserved, even with her own husband. The years had not added any flesh to her bony frame. A set of keys dangled at her waist.

'You're welcome back to Bewley Hall, sir,' Mr Sandler said.

He raised an eyebrow of polite enquiry in Bridget's direction, even though Mr Carruthers would have already informed the household about her, and Cormac commenced the first of what would no doubt be many awkward introductions. While he had no noble title and could only be addressed as 'sir' or 'Mr McGovern', Bridget possessed two titles and, regrettably, neither of them were 'Mrs McGovern'. They had got away with that name in Boston where nobody had known them, but here their reputation preceded them. Though 'Lady Wyndham' was her higher status, there was no question of her going by that title. She would be addressed as 'Lady Courcey' or 'my lady'. After Cormac made this clear, Mr Sandler cordially inclined his head towards Bridget. Mrs Sandler's body quivered before going rigid, like she had considered bobbing a curtsey and then thought better of it.

Mr Sandler called to the coachman and footman to bring the carriage around to the rear of the house and then turned back to Cormac. 'The house is ready for you and your family, Mr McGovern. Your trunks arrived half an hour ago and have already been brought inside.'

The contents of the trunks included clothing for the whole family which Bridget had made for them before they left America, using a finer material and a more fashionable cut than what they had been accustomed to wearing in Boston.

Even their travelling clothes were of a higher quality. It had felt somewhat pretentious to don them, but they couldn't arrive at Bewley Hall in clothing of the lower classes. The fewer opportunities they presented for criticism the better, especially given the muted air of disapproval already drifting from Mrs Sandler.

In contrast to his wife, Mr Sandler waved his arm in an inviting gesture. 'Please come in.'

They climbed the broad front steps and entered the house. It felt simultaneously nerve-wracking and freeing to Cormac to stand there in the entrance hall wholly as himself, having shucked off his cloak of lies as an impostor.

'Shall I show the family around?' Mrs Sandler offered in a strained tone.

Cormac registered the exhaustion in the children's sagging postures. 'I suggest instead that we focus on baths and beds,' he said, finding it hard to give the order, mild though it was.

Her lips tightened. 'As we only lit the fires in the bedchambers after the trunks arrived, those rooms may still be a little cold. But the drawing room fire is in fine fettle so that's where I would advise the tub to be set up.'

'Thank you, that would be perfectly satisfactory,' he said while thinking guiltily of the maids having to carry buckets of hot water up from the kitchens.

'Right this way, Mr Davenport,' Mr Sandler said and then froze in mortification. Flustered, he hurried on, 'I meant Mr McGovern, of course.'

Crimson, he swivelled on his heel and led the family towards the drawing room. Cormac tried to ignore how his guts felt like they had been shredded by a serrated blade.

Mr Sandler escorted them to the drawing room, embarrassment emanating from him in waves. To liberate them both from the discomfiture, Cormac asked if they could meet in the study before breakfast the next morning and Mr Sandler agreed before leaving the room at once, still red-faced.

The family hovered awkwardly as a copper hip bath was brought in and filled with water. While they waited, Cormac spotted a pair of stained wine glasses half hidden behind a vase on the wide mantelpiece; it appeared that someone had been enjoying a comfortable evening in front of the fire before their arrival.

Jack eyed the maids trooping in and out. 'Should we give them a hand, Da?' he whispered.

Cormac shook his head. 'They'd perceive it as a slight, that you think they aren't performing their job as well as they should.'

He had already spent a good deal of time on the ship explaining to the two boys how things would be in this big house, but no doubt they would need regular reminding at first.

Mrs Sandler came in bearing a tray laden with slices of cold meats, wedges of currant pudding and a steaming pot of tea. Jack and Gus rushed over as she laid it on a round table. Once again seeming to wobble on the verge of a curtsey, she stiffened and said primly, 'Is there anything else you require, sir? My lady?'

'Can you tell us which rooms have been designated as our bedchambers?' Cormac asked.

She threw him a look of surprise. 'The master apartment in the west wing is yours, naturally.'

He winced. How could he and Bridget possibly occupy the suite of rooms Lord and Lady Bewley had once shared? But of course it was to be expected.

Mrs Sandler went on, 'Three chambers have been assigned to your children in the east wing, all fine rooms and well appointed. I believe one of them used to be your own, sir.' She paused as though a thought had just occurred to her. 'Unless you would prefer a different arrangement? If you'd like to request a change, we can accommodate—'

'No, no,' he said quickly. 'That's all perfectly satisfactory.'

Why did that phrase keep tripping off his tongue? The last thing he wanted was to come across as condescending to these people who knew his lowly origins.

Emily suppressed a yawn behind her hand. 'If it's convenient, could I please be shown the way to my chamber now?' she asked Mrs Sandler. 'Slumber is more appealing to me at this moment than a warm bath. If there is a wash basin in the room, I'll brave its cold water if it means I can get to bed sooner.'

'As you wish, Miss McGovern.'

Emily bade her parents and brothers goodnight and Mrs Sandler led her out of the drawing room just as two maids entered with towels and clean nightwear for the boys, the latter extracted from their trunks. Cormac appreciated their efficiency and noted that their standards had not dropped during the months that Bewley Hall had been without a master.

Bridget had to drag Jack and Gus away from the tray of food one at a time for their baths. Afterwards, she and Cormac brought the yawning boys up to the bedchambers in the east wing. They had no need for a guide; Cormac remembered the way. It pierced him more than he expected when he saw the door to the room he had once occupied as Oliver Davenport. He recalled the nightmares he had suffered within those walls and the times Lady Bewley had come like an angel in the night to comfort him. All was dark now beneath the door and he surmised that Emily had taken this room as her own. As they passed, he silently wished her sweeter dreams than he had ever had.

There were two more chambers further along the corridor with light gleaming beneath their doors. Upon inspection, they found each one contained a flickering fire, the hearth protected by a fireguard, and a large bed with the covers turned down, ready to welcome its drowsy occupant.

'We have two rooms?' Gus said, his eyes growing round. 'I-I don't think I want to sleep alone.'

His apprehension was understandable. He had shared a room with Jack every day of his eight years. They had never been separated at night, not even when they had been held captive in the warehouse in New York.

Bridget stroked his mop of chestnut curls, still damp from the bath. 'You can sleep in the same bed tonight,' she said, to which Jack didn't demur. 'And Emily is just down the corridor. Go to her in the morning and she'll bring you downstairs for breakfast.'

After tucking the boys in, Cormac and Bridget returned to the drawing room, where they discovered that the two maids had placed another block of wood onto the fire and were adding more hot water to the bath.

'Thank you, that's much appreciated,' Cormac said to them. 'It's getting late so please consider your duties here finished for the night. And thank you again.'

Rather stony-faced, they curtseyed and exited the room. Mr Carruthers had not been wrong in his predictions to Cormac about how the staff would react to him.

He brushed the discouraging thought aside to say teasingly, 'Now that the children have bathed, shouldn't their mother do so next?' His fingers grazed the front of Bridget's dress, just below the curve of her breast.

'Indeed, she should,' she replied, playing along. 'I imagine their father needs to as well. And it would be a shame to waste the maids' efforts to reheat the bath.'

She trailed the fingertips of her left hand in the water and he pointed at her thread ring which was visibly fraying beneath the gold ring. 'That's looking a bit worn, isn't it?'

'I'm minding it,' she promised.

He helped her strip down to her shift, but she didn't get into the tub just yet. They hadn't had the opportunity to be intimate with each other since they had embarked on their journey from America and their bodies were insisting that this deprivation be addressed without delay.

She kissed him passionately and pulled him down to the hearthrug, the heat from the fire matching the feverish excitement swiftly building between them. It would be quick, for neither of them had the patience to dawdle after having been constrained from enjoying this pleasure for over a month. She hitched her shift up to her thighs and straddled him. He didn't lie back, instead keeping his body upright so that their lips and tongues would not be separated. Her hands were grappling at his trousers beneath her exposed flesh when the door opened.

'Sir, I'll remove the tray if you're fin—' Mrs Sandler began to say as she came in, but she snapped her mouth shut when she saw them on the rug, both of them paralysed by her appearance. Without another word, she backed out of the drawing room and closed the door firmly behind her, leaving the tray untouched.

Bridget buried her face in Cormac's neck, trying to stifle her convulsions. He laughed too, but he couldn't help thinking that they could have started off their residency at Bewley Hall with a better impression.

Chapter 8

The next morning, Bridget stood patiently in her dressing room while her new lady's maid, Hawkins, put the finishing touches to her attire. Though she had managed to dress herself for the past ten years without the assistance of a lady's maid, she didn't object to her current situation. It was not vanity that compelled her to remain silent but acuity. Were she to speak up and say she had no need for a lady's maid, then that would put an end to this woman's employment. Bridget's new mantle as lady of the house included sustaining the livelihoods of all those in her and Cormac's employ. It might make them feel uncomfortable to be waited upon like this, but there were expectations that came with this elevated social station and she and Cormac had to meet them.

Hawkins was unaware of Bridget's benevolence as she sullenly adjusted the linen fichu around Bridget's neck and tucked the ends of it into the bodice of her morning dress. She stood back and eyed her up and down.

'Would your ladyship care for some ornamentation?' she asked.

She went over to a cabinet by the dressing table and extracted a jewellery box, revealing several beautiful necklaces and brooches nestled within its compartments. Bridget had brought no jewellery with her, so she comprehended that these must have belonged to Lady Bewley.

'I don't believe I am yet worthy to wear these,' she said simply.

Hawkins said nothing as she shut the box, but Bridget sensed that she had given the right answer.

Knuckles rapped sharply on the door and Hawkins answered it to reveal Mrs Sandler, who stepped inside.

'I seek a few moments of your time, Lady Courcey,' she said.

'I'll leave you be,' said Hawkins. 'Unless you have any further need of me at present, my lady?'

'No, thank you, you may go.'

After Hawkins strode out, Mrs Sandler said, 'Lady Bewley tended to discuss household matters in the comfort of her dressing room. Is this suitable for you, my lady, or do you have another preference?'

'This is perfectly fine,' Bridget said, discomfited to realise that the phrase was rather reminiscent of Cormac's 'entirely satisfactory'. Were they trying to be too accommodating and at risk of losing the staff's respect in the process?

She took a seat at the dressing table for this housekeeping meeting. On its surface sat one of the most precious possessions she had brought from America: the wooden figurine Cormac had carved for her of their family of five. It depicted a man and a woman with their arms around each other, the man's free hand clasping that of a little girl by his hip and two even smaller boys standing at the woman's side. Their three children had grown quite a bit since the carving had been made, but it captured a particular period of their lives and she always experienced a surge of fondness whenever she looked at it. It had been a much simpler time.

Turning her attention away from the carving, she offered a nearby chair to Mrs Sandler but the housekeeper remained standing.

'I desire to acquaint your ladyship with the particulars of how the household is run,' she said, 'though of course you are at liberty to alter anything you wish.'

Bridget's stomach rumbled just then in protest at the delay in going down to breakfast but she pretended that neither of them had noticed. 'Please do proceed.'

Ironically, Mrs Sandler began by advising her of the times when the daily meals would be served to the family. It appeared that Lord and Lady Bewley had been disposed to rise and to dine at later hours than the McGoverns were accustomed to.

'Hmm,' said Bridget, 'I wonder whether these mealtimes could be brought forwards by an hour perhaps?'

Mrs Sandler arched an eyebrow. 'I can certainly raise this request with the cook. I'm sure the kitchen staff would be able to adapt.'

Bridget hastily shook her head. 'Oh, please refrain from doing so for now. We are of course amenable in the first instance to trying this new routine.'

Mrs Sandler's lips pinched together. 'Very well, my lady. In matters of finances, I coordinate with the cook on the housekeeping accounts and these are available for your viewing if you should like to peruse them at any time.' Her tone conveyed her belief that this would not be necessary. 'Given the time of year and the clement weather, the indoor staff are currently engaged in a thorough spring clean of the entire house, including the washing of the heavier bedcovers and the replacing of the winter curtains with the summer ones. This will be accomplished with every effort to minimise disruption to the family. However,' she added with a meaningful clearing of her throat, 'it is hoped that the family will strive to keep out of the staff's way during these endeavours.'

Bridget discerned that Mrs Sandler was referring to the likelihood of Jack and Gus's interference and was all too conscious of the fact that she could not guarantee Gus's obedience without issuing a very strong warning to him. With this thought came the realisation that she didn't feel as fearful about letting the boys out of her sight here. In comparison to the perilous city streets they had left behind, these rural surroundings seemed so much safer. After all, she and Cormac had grown up on an estate not unlike this one and had run wild around it. She wanted Jack and Gus to experience the joy of that freedom too, although not to the extent that they hindered the activities of the staff.

'I'll ensure that the whole family is informed of this,' she promised.

'Lastly,' Mrs Sandler said, 'if your ladyship is unhappy with any aspect of the house's cleanliness or the staff's performance, you must bring your concerns directly to me and I shall deal with them forthwith.'

'I'll be sure to do so. Thank you for imparting all of this information. On another matter, I need to write a pressing letter. Could you arrange for it to be posted?'

'I will get one of the footmen to bring it to Gildham—the village has a postmaster.'

Bridget wanted to write to Oakleigh at once to let them know where they should send their correspondence and to vow that she and Cormac would be coming to Ireland very soon; they just needed a little time for him to establish himself as the new landowner before leaving England. She expected that they would end up travelling quite frequently between the two estates in the future.

'That would be ideal,' she said. 'I'm most grateful.' Then she went on hesitantly, 'I feel I must mention the incident that occurred in the drawing room last night. It was an embarrassing moment for all concerned. I apologise for our indiscretion and assure you that it won't happen again.'

Mrs Sandler only nodded coolly. 'Thank you for your time this morning, my lady.'

***

Cormac entered Lord Bewley's study feeling more like a fraud than he ever had as Oliver Davenport. He supposed it would take a while for him not to think of it as the domain of that dear, departed gentleman. It appeared to have been left untouched since his passing, though Cormac had to assume that Mr Carruthers had been in to retrieve the documents he had brought to Boston. Moreover, he could see in the morning sunlight that no dust coated its surfaces, which meant the housemaids had continued to clean it. Nevertheless, he appreciated their respect in leaving the essence of Lord Bewley intact throughout the room, right down to the elegant inkstand that still sat upon the broad desk.

With not a little nervousness, he approached the desk and rounded it to the far side where Lord Bewley had always sat. There, his breath caught as his gaze alighted upon an object propped up against the chair: Lord Bewley's cane. A lump came to his throat. Reverently, he picked up the cane and skimmed his fingers along the beechwood shaft all the way up to the brass, T-shaped handle, recalling how Lord Bewley would tap it on the floor to emphasise a point or twirl it in his hands when in deep contemplation.

Becoming contemplative himself, he reflected that, at thirty-eight, he was drawing near to middle age, if he was not already in it. Granted, his body was still fit and strong, but Lord Bewley had carried this cane long before he had actually needed to rely upon it. Adopting it himself might be an apt way to honour the gentleman's memory.

Smiling to himself, he leaned the cane against the desk as a light knock came on the door and Mr Sandler appeared on the threshold.

'Come in, Mr Sandler,' Cormac said. 'I appreciate you meeting me at this early hour.'

He waved a hand to invite the agent to take a seat on the other side of the desk and then lowered himself into Lord Bewley's chair, sternly reminding himself that he had every right to sit there.

'Thank you for our welcome last night,' he said.

Mr Sandler dipped his head. 'Don't mention it, Mr Daven—' He choked himself off. 'I beg your pardon. That will not happen again, I assure you.'

'Much obliged,' Cormac said dryly, trying not to betray how much the slip had stung.

'Sir, Lord Sinclair has expressed a desire for a short interview,' Mr Sandler said, moving on in a hurry, but Cormac interjected.

'I requested your presence here today to discuss estate matters, but there is another issue I wish to address first.' He surreptitiously touched the cane next to him, hidden from Mr Sandler's view. 'Because I have no desire to skirt around it, I want to frankly acknowledge the fact that, although Lord Bewley chose me as his inheritor, it cannot be denied that you would also have been a suitable recipient of the honour, given your extensive knowledge and longstanding connection with the estate. It would be understandable if you felt a measure of dissatisfaction with Lord Bewley's choice and that this might prompt you to consider alternatives to remaining in your role here as land agent.'

Mr Sandler's eyes widened. 'Are you dismissing me, sir?'

'On the contrary,' said Cormac, 'I would be very grateful to retain your expertise. But I would like to ensure that you feel it is worth your while to stay.'

A shadow of confusion passed across Mr Sandler's face. 'Worth my while?'

'Tell me, where do you and Mrs Sandler live?' Cormac asked, chagrined that he didn't know this already.

Though this seemed to baffle Mr Sandler further, he replied, 'We have a small lodge on the outermost edge of Bewley Hall's main grounds. It gives us a degree of privacy but enables us to get to the big house with reasonable ease.'

Cormac nodded. 'I intend to provide you with the funds to refurbish the lodge or, if you prefer, to build a new house in the same location or another of your preference.'

Mr Sandler stared at him, stunned. 'Sir, what—'

'I will also increase both of your incomes and guarantee you a substantial pension whenever you choose to cease your services in the future. I hope that this will alleviate any strained relations that may or may not exist between us.'

'Nothing of the sort exists, sir,' Mr Sandler said with great sincerity. 'Thank you for being so forthright and, might I say, gentlemanly in addressing the matter upfront. Your proposal is very generous—far beyond what could be deemed necessary.'

'I'm glad you are willing to accept,' Cormac said, relieved.

They then embarked upon a discussion about estate affairs, during which Cormac demonstrated his knowledge and shrewdness, having closely studied the documents Mr Carruthers had brought him. Though different in scale and particulars, running his own business in Boston had fostered an astuteness in him that he could now apply to estate management, just as Lord Bewley had envisaged. Mr Sandler appeared quite impressed and left afterwards with an air of having considerably revised his opinion of the new landlord at Bewley Hall.

***

Taking the advice of the maid who had waited upon her when she rose that morning, Emily and her brothers made their way downstairs for breakfast at a later hour than they were used to. Jack tugged on the end of his stylish fitted jacket while Gus whined that he was almost on the edge of starvation.

'I thought rich people never went hungry,' he complained. 'Also,' he added, a tinge of worry coming into his tone, 'I heard a ghost inside the walls last night.'

'It was just the servants moving through the house,' Emily told him. 'They have secret staircases to help them get around more quickly.'

How strange it was for all three of them to be wearing fine clothes and to have servants to attend to their needs. This elevated lifestyle had been such an unlikely one to ever befall Jack and Gus, and it had arrived to Emily much sooner than she had expected; after all, becoming baroness of Oakleigh was still very far on the distant horizon and it would entail her mother's death which, needless to say, she had no wish for. She hadn't decided yet how much she liked being thrust back into this world. It was too reminiscent of when she had lost her head and risked everything for Garrett's empty promises. She was no more deserving of an inheritance now than she had been then, but at least this time she had an obligation she could fulfil to make herself worthy.

They reached the breakfast room and Gus's complaints swiftly dispersed when he saw the array of food on the sideboard.

'Look how much there is!' he exclaimed, his expression ecstatic.

A strapping young footman stood in attendance next to the sideboard; Emily detected a quiver at the corner of his mouth and nudged both of her brothers' shoulders.

'You can't eat like feral animals here,' she warned them in a low voice. 'Remember to mind your manners.'

She guided them in how to calmly fill their breakfast plates with a moderate portion of bacon and eggs and they all took their seats at the table.

'I wonder whether the cook might make mince pies sometime,' Gus was saying hopefully when their parents came into the room.

'Breakfast at last,' their mother said. 'My stomach actually rumbled in front of Mrs Sandler a short while ago. It was terribly undignified.'

Jack giggled and she touched an affectionate knuckle to his cheek as she passed the table.

Their father handed her a plate at the sideboard and she reached for the tongs that lay next to a dish of sausages. She smiled at the footman as she did so.

'What is your name?' she asked.

'David, my lady.' He was sandy-haired and, as all footmen were supposed to be, very good-looking.

'And how long have you worked at Bewley Hall, David?'

'Four years, my lady.'

Emily pricked up her ears at that. If he had only joined the household four years ago, that meant he had never known her father as Oliver Davenport. Perhaps it was for that reason that he did not come across as aloof as some of the other servants. He answered her mother readily enough as she enquired whether he had grown up in the local village of Gildham, though he seemed a little nonplussed at the attention.

As her mother and father took their seats, her father said, 'I've had quite a productive meeting with Mr Sandler this morning.'

Her mother grunted. 'Well, my own meeting with Mrs Sandler was' – she glanced at David – 'ah, instructive.' She pointed her fork at the boys. 'Which reminds me, the staff are spring cleaning the whole house at present. Under no circumstances are you to get under their feet, do you both hear me?'

'Yes, Ma,' said Jack.

'That's a lot of people to avoid between all the staff and the ghost,' said Gus, scraping the last bit of egg off his plate. 'May I have a second helping?'

At a subtle shake of Emily's head, her mother said, 'No, little miracle, you've had enough.'

Gus set down his fork in disappointment while their father said, 'I can scarcely believe I'm saying this but Mr Sandler told me that Lord Sinclair has requested to pay a visit to Bewley Hall.'

'Who's Lord Sinclair?' asked Emily.

'Our nearest neighbour and the viscount of Sinclair Manor. His land borders the Bewley Estate on the northern side. This request for a visit is a surprise but a positive one.' Her father grinned. 'Maybe our situation is not as dire as Mr Carruthers originally painted it.'

She wondered whether her father was being too optimistic. 'Does Lord Sinclair have any sons?'

'I don't know,' he replied. 'I never actually met the Sinclair family during my previous time here.'

Casually, she traced her fingertip along the edge of her breakfast plate. Then she said, 'If Lord Sinclair has a son and puts forward a proposal regarding a marriage alliance, you must tell him that I am receptive to the idea.'

Both of her parents stared at her in shock, utterly speechless. Prepared for this reaction, she remained serene.

'I know that Mr Carruthers advised you to secure an advantageous marriage for me in order to bolster our family's reputation. I bumped into him in Boston before he left.'

'We would never even consider—' her father started to say.

'I know you wouldn't,' she interrupted. 'But I am willing to do it.'

After a pregnant pause, her mother cleared her throat. 'Boys, have you both finished your breakfast?'

'Yes, Ma,' Jack said, even though he still had half a slice of bacon in front of him.

'Off you go, then. Remember that the indoor staff are very busy, so perhaps explore the grounds instead. Don't stray too far though—always make sure you can see the house's chimneys from wherever you are.'

Gus scampered from the room and Jack followed, casting an inquisitive glance behind him at Emily.

'David, could we please ask you to leave too?' Emily's father said quietly.

Betraying nothing in his expression, the footman bowed and departed. Emily's parents looked at her in dismayed bewilderment.

'You cannot mean it,' said her mother.

'I do, very much so.'

'You cannot,' her mother repeated, appalled. 'Please think about what you are saying.'

'I have thought about it, and I am perfectly open to the suggestion.' Her heart squeezed a little as a pair of green eyes darted into her mind but she said, 'I have no attachment to anyone else and nothing would make me happier than to help you.'

Her father swallowed. 'We want you to marry for love, not for status.'

'There's no reason I cannot do both. An advantageous match and a love match are not mutually exclusive conditions.'

Her father winced at the validity of this argument while her mother bit the tip of her tongue.

'Do you agree that there is much to be gained from following the advice of Mr Carruthers?' Emily asked.

They sat there dumbly. Eventually, her father gave a reluctant, jerky nod.

'Then in the first instance it would be useful to find out if Lord Sinclair has any sons, would it not?' She smiled. 'Do not fear for me. If I am fortunate enough to receive a proposal at a future stage, I will only accept it in the event that it will bring us all greater ease and happiness.'

CHAPTER 9

Bracing himself for the recoil, Cormac fired his rifle. As the cloud of smoke billowed up, a disapproving voice next to him said, 'You're rusty.'

Mr Sandler's second-in-command, Mr Comerford, glared at Cormac, his mutton chops bristling with reproach as he set the butt of his own rifle on the ground, which was wet after a night of rainfall.

'It's a pity it's not pheasant season,' he said with a grunt. 'The dim-witted bird would be an easier target.'

Cormac decided not to tell him that he had deliberately missed his shot. He'd had no inclination to kill the rabbit now racing away across the field, its white tail disappearing into the roots of a nearby grove of beech trees. Instead, he had aimed at one of the tree trunks and, although he hadn't quite hit his mark, he hadn't been too far off it. Not bad, considering he hadn't discharged a firearm since the last time he had gone shooting on the Bewley Estate, also in the company of the censorious man at his side, who was the proud owner of several rifles and a number of pistols too.

He didn't quite know why he had suggested this as the activity during which he and Mr Comerford could become reacquainted while discussing the latter's continued contribution to the running of the estate. He only knew that after Emily's revelation yesterday morning at the breakfast table, he had developed an urgent need to get outdoors and release some of the tension coiled in his body.

He still couldn't wrap his head around the fact that his daughter had so nonchalantly announced her willingness to throw away her happiness for the sake of society's expectations. Even after witnessing the repercussions of Bridget's marriage to Garrett, even after feeling the impact of those repercussions herself, Emily still somehow judged it wise to tread the same path.

In the privacy of his and Bridget's bedchamber – which was technically the chamber assigned to the lady of the house but he had joined her there for he had no intention of sleeping alone in the adjoining master's chamber – they had shared their consternation. He was furious that Mr Carruthers had sought to ambush Emily when he already knew Cormac's opinion on the matter. He would have a few words to say to the lawyer when next they met.

How were they to convince Emily of the folly of this scheme? It wasn't that a man could only be decent if he were born into the lower classes – take Bridget's father, after all, an honourable man down to his bones, or even her uncle, Lord Walcott, whose enormous bulk had sheltered a very generous heart. But when a marriage was to be carried out like a transaction, how could it not be regarded as a precarious undertaking? Emily's wealth and beauty might attract a gentleman with status and connections, but his affections and even his basic respect would not be deemed a requisite part of such a negotiation. Cormac would far prefer to live as an outcast than to gamble with his daughter's future in such a way.

Distracted by his thoughts, he was scarcely paying attention to his surroundings as he reloaded his rifle and was startled when his companion let out a bellow beside him. Mr Comerford gesticulated with his rifle at the nearby trees and yelled, 'Get out of there, whoever you are! Can't you see you're in range of our guns?' He added in a low mutter, 'Especially the way this fellow's shooting today.'

Cormac peered towards the grove of beech trees and his heart nearly stopped when he caught a flash of fair hair between the trunks, which meant that a mop of chestnut curls wouldn't be far away. 'Christ, I think it's my two lads.'

Swinging his rifle over his shoulder, he dashed across the sodden field to enter the woods and, sure enough, found both Jack and Gus too stricken to move. Relieved to see them unharmed, he wanted to upbraid them and hug them at the same time.

'Do you realise how much trouble you're in?' he demanded.

'We're sorry,' Jack blurted. 'We mostly followed Ma's rule—we'd be able to see the chimneys on the house from here if the trees were shorter.'

Mr Comerford came stumping up behind Cormac. 'They deserve a hiding for such foolhardiness,' he growled, and Jack and Gus looked even more fearful.

'That's true,' said Cormac, 'but an even worse punishment would be depriving them of their dinner.'

They gazed woefully downwards. 'We came outside to be out of the way of the spring cleaning and because I was scared of the ghost,' Gus said plaintively to his feet, his manner all the more pitiful because of the wheeze in his voice.

'Ghost?' Mr Comerford said in a suspicious tone.

Gus peeked up at him eagerly, keen to divert attention from their disgrace. 'There's a ghost at Bewley Hall. I know because I heard it moving inside the walls again—I even heard its chains clanking. I think it's lost and very angry, so I'm scared of it.'

Before Cormac could assert that it must have been the servants carrying dishes and cutlery back down to the kitchens,

Mr Comerford said quite seriously, 'Ghosts don't set out to scare you. They're too fixated on their own troubles to add to yours.'

Surprised by Mr Comerford's superstition, Cormac decided that the conversation had veered wildly off course. 'Back to the house, both of you,' he said, striving for curtness, 'and don't you dare go within fifty feet of the kitchens or the dining room. I'll be informing your mother about this as soon as I return myself.'

They plodded away glumly between the beech trees. Mr Comerford shook his head but Cormac couldn't tell whether his censure was for the boys' recklessness or for Cormac's leniency. He reckoned Mr Comerford would be a tough father.

'Do you have any family, Mr Comerford?' he asked. The man had been a bachelor when Cormac had last known him, but perhaps he had married later in life.

'Just my widowed sister and her daughter, who both live with me,' Mr Comerford said gruffly. 'My niece, Polly, works up at the house as a lady's maid.'

'Oh?' said Cormac. 'Is her surname Hawkins?'

'Yes.'

Bridget had told Cormac of her lady's maid's cool attitude and, discerning that this generally matched Mr Comerford's own, he wondered what conversations had been held privately in their household.

'Do you believe Lord Bewley made a mistake in his bequest to me?' he asked directly.

Mr Comerford made a huffing noise. 'I think it's mighty strange that he could ever forgive you for your deception. And I don't see how you could do a better job than Mr Sandler, who knows this land like the back of his hand.'

Judging by his resentful tone, there was likely a personal sense of betrayal as well.

'Given your view on the situation,' Cormac said, his stomach sinking, 'does that mean you are looking elsewhere for employment?'

'I might be,' Mr Comerford muttered.

It appeared he was a less forgiving man than Mr Sandler. Of course, Cormac had proposed a generous arrangement to help appease the indispensable land agent, but he couldn't exactly offer house refurbishments and increased incomes to every disgruntled employee on the estate.

'I appreciate your honesty, at any rate,' he said, resigned to the prospect of losing his deputy agent, and possibly Bridget's lady's maid, in the not-too-distant future.

This exchange dulled his optimism for his meeting with Lord Sinclair that afternoon. By the time Sheppard, the butler, ushered Lord Sinclair into the study, Cormac felt convinced it was going to go badly and his visitor's expression did not give him any reason to think otherwise. Undisguised disdain shadowed his overhanging brow as he sat opposite Cormac.

'Can I offer you some refreshment, my lord?' Cormac asked.

'No, thank you,' the viscount said tersely. 'I do not intend to stay long.'

Cormac steeled his nerves.

Lord Sinclair sat rigidly in his chair. 'I am a scrupulous man, Mr McGovern, and will always abide by the precepts of society, no matter the distasteful situations they sometimes necessitate. When a newcomer moves into the neighbourhood, it is expected that one will call upon the new arrival out of common courtesy. Hence, I am here to discharge that duty with all possible haste and hope that the memory of it will soon be forgotten.'

Remaining calm, Cormac raised his eyebrows. 'In your haste, I believe you have also forgotten the meaning of the term "courtesy".'

74

Lord Sinclair flushed. 'An individual of your rank can have no presumption of a high level of civility from mine. I am, in effect, speaking to a man no more elevated than a servant.'

'On the contrary,' Cormac said coolly, 'you're speaking to a man who *employs* servants and, more than that, one who possesses self-respect. I may come from a humble background but I am not without my pride and I won't tolerate your disparagement under my own roof. Consider, my lord, what defines a gentleman and then ask yourself if there is even one man in this room who can honestly lay claim to it.'

Lord Sinclair was silent. At length, he shifted uncomfortably. 'Perhaps I was a touch too strong in my accusations. But do you in fact believe yourself entitled to this position you now hold?'

'I do not. I never sought such responsibility. However, Lord Bewley saw something in me that he deemed worthy of the privilege and I will not dishonour his memory by shirking the duty he has passed into my hands.'

Lord Sinclair folded his arms. 'You certainly talk with confidence, I'll grant you that. But what use are words if they are not buttressed by the appropriate actions? How can you suppose yourself to be capable of managing an estate of this size? Do you know the first thing about how to care for the needs of hundreds of tenants?'

'If it's not too audacious of me to say, I fancy myself in a more advantageous position than you to carry out my obligations in that regard. Who better to help improve the lives of those who dwell and work on this land than someone who has already occupied that way of life?'

Lord Sinclair looked taken aback. Recovering his composure, he challenged, 'And you think that insight is sufficient?'

Cormac shrugged. 'My pride does not stretch so far as to render me incapable of asking for help. I trust that my land agent and his deputy will steer me in the right direction when needed. If relations were better between you and me, perhaps I could have relied upon some neighbourly support as well, but I perceive now that it was unrealistic of me to hope for that.'

Lord Sinclair's mouth fell open. He shut it and shook his head. 'I might be in need of that refreshment after all,' he muttered. 'How have you contrived this? You have made me feel no more than two inches tall and, in the process, given me the most emphatic impression that you were born to take up this role. I confess I am quite astounded. Could it be that Lord Bewley had *not* actually descended into senility when he named you as his heir in his will?'

'It was not my intention to criticise you, my lord, but I'm glad my words have encouraged you to reassess your misgivings regarding Lord Bewley. He was one of the best gentlemen I ever had the privilege to know.'

'Indeed, I feel the same.' Lord Sinclair's heavy brow furrowed, possibly as he tried to digest the notion that he could have anything in common with Cormac. 'Then you have not accepted this inheritance purely out of greed?' he finally asked. 'You don't plan to fritter your wealth away and let the estate go to ruin?'

Comprehending Lord Sinclair's personal stake in such an event, Cormac said dryly, 'I wouldn't dream of being so thoughtless to my neighbours.'

Lord Sinclair coloured.

Cormac spread his hands above the desk. 'I am fully conscious that my mere presence has damaged the prestige of the neighbourhood to a regrettable degree. But that, I hope, will be where the damage ends. I assure you that I am determined to do everything in my power to live up to my predecessor's expectations and to make sure that the Bewley Estate continues to thrive. No doubt I shall stumble along the way, but I'll do my utmost to prove that Lord Bewley's faith was not misplaced.'

Lord Sinclair appraised him for a long moment. 'You will not have an easy time of it.'

'My lawyer has impressed that upon me already.'

'You are not upper class, and yet you are no longer lower class either. You fall between the two and therefore you will be shunned by both. It is a thankless endeavour with a lifetime contract. Were you not tempted to refuse such a yoke around your neck, despite its obvious perquisites?'

'I did refuse it when Lord Bewley initially offered it to me,' Cormac confessed. 'But when it came to me again, I strengthened my resolve.'

A protracted pause stretched out between them.

'I believe I have underestimated you,' said Lord Sinclair.

'You are not the first,' said Cormac, 'and I expect you won't be the last.'

A trace of a smile played around Lord Sinclair's mouth. 'I find myself looking forward to seeing how you confront the challenge. And, quite possibly, I might even wish you success with it.'

'How very gracious of you, my lord,' Cormac replied, allowing himself a hint of humour too.

Lord Sinclair chuckled. He didn't apologise outright for his earlier rudeness, but the light-hearted exchange conveyed both contrition and forgiveness.

'You have children?' he asked, his tone nigh on conversational now.

'Three,' Cormac replied. 'A daughter and two sons, aged seventeen, ten and eight.'

Lord Sinclair's brow twitched when he heard Emily's age but he didn't comment. Instead, he said, 'I have one final office to execute on this visit and that is to mention that my wife and I are hosting a small gathering a week from today as she has cousins staying with us at present and she wants to introduce them to our social circle. I was instructed solely under the onus of heeding niceties to extend the invitation to Bewley Hall, on the assumption that you would of course decline.'

'Thank you, my lord, I will accept.'

'I thought you might.'

CHAPTER 10

Emily blessed herself and rose from her knees, checking that her lace mantilla was still secure over her head and shoulders as she followed her parents and brothers out of the pew and down the aisle of the chapel. There was no Catholic place of worship in the local village of Gildham which meant that today, the first Sunday since they had arrived in England, the family had travelled by carriage to the town of Bedford, where the Chapel of St Paul's was tucked away down a quiet side street. Given how difficult it had been to locate this unobtrusive chapel, it was clear that Catholicism was unpopular in this Protestant-dominated country and she realised that practising their minority faith was yet another obstacle to their acceptance in society.

A further black mark in that regard was their association with the bedraggled people filing out of the chapel who had been sitting in its back rows. She overheard their murmurs and could tell by their accents that they were Irish. When they got outside, she smiled down at one little girl who looked back up at her with a haunted expression in her eyes. In fact, a pall of gloom hung over the whole group. Emily saw her mother speak to a gaunt woman in shabby clothing and press some coins into her hand. She compared the quality of her mother's mantilla to the frayed covering on the other woman's head; though she plainly had next to nothing, it was in better condition than anything else she was wearing, as though she had protected it with great care.

When they got into the carriage, Emily's mother said in a distressed voice, 'They have only arrived recently from Ireland. The poor woman said the situation there has grown more desperate by the day. And the port cities in England are now teeming with so many Irish immigrants that these people ventured further inland in search of work with less competition. But the reception towards them in these parts has been, on the whole, unsympathetic. What a wretched plight they are in.' She turned to Emily's father, distraught. 'We need to go to Oakleigh. We cannot delay much longer.'

'I agree,' he said. 'We will begin making arrangements as soon as we get back to the house.'

Gus, who had been pensively swinging his legs on the carriage seat next to his father, now piped up. 'I've decided that the ghost isn't scary anymore. Mr Comerford said that ghosts only care about their own troubles, which means our one must be worried and needs help of some kind.' He puffed out his chest. 'I'm going to begin an investigation to figure out who the ghost was before it died and what it needs to find peace. Jack will help too.' He beamed at his brother and then plucked at his father's elbow. 'Da, do you know whether anyone died under horrible circumstances at Bewley Hall in the past?'

'I don't,' his father replied. 'Perhaps you should put it to the servants—they may be more familiar with the history of the Hall.'

Gus nodded sagely. 'I'll ask the cook,' he said to Jack, 'and you can ask the butler, and I'll ask David, and you can ask—'

'You mustn't be a nuisance to the servants,' said their mother with an annoyed glance at their father for sending them down this path.

'We'll interview them on the night of the party,' Gus replied breezily. 'They won't have as much work to do with you and Da and Emily gone out.'

Emily missed how he used to call her Emmy. He and Jack were growing up so fast, although they weren't old enough yet to attend the upcoming gathering hosted at the Sinclair residence.

Her father's countenance turned contemplative. 'This gathering will be our first test,' he said to Emily and her mother. 'At least we can be grateful that we're in the country and not trying to breach the indomitable bedrock of London society.'

For her part, Emily felt nervous about living up to her promise. Her father had not asked Lord Sinclair about his offspring nor about the other invited guests, and the viscount had not volunteered the information, so she had no idea whether to expect any eligible young men at the party. What if there would be some in attendance but they found nothing appealing in her?

When they returned to Bewley Hall, they were surprised to discover Sheppard and David attending to Mr Carruthers in the entrance hall as though he had only just arrived himself. He turned and offered them a perfunctory bow.

'I hope you are all settling well into your new home,' he said in a preoccupied tone that suggested he wasn't too concerned with their answer.

'Good day, Mr Carruthers,' Emily's father greeted him, his own tone chilly. 'I'm aware that I have no need to introduce Emily to you, given that you already ran into each other back in Boston.'

Emily was struck by guilt that her disclosure had put the lawyer in hot water but he seemed unperturbed.

'Forgive my intrusion on this day of rest,' he said, 'but I am bound for London and have some unwelcome news to impart before I leave.'

Emily's father frowned. 'What news?'

'I'm afraid an objection has been legally filed against your right to inherit the Bewley Estate.'

'Oh, good gracious,' Emily's mother said faintly.

Mr Carruthers went on to say that the disputing party, a Mrs Turnbull, was a distant descendant in a lower branch of the Davenport family tree – her ancestor in a previous generation had married outside of the peerage and spawned an inferior line in the family that had no nobility and little money. However, she still possessed Davenport blood and therefore her husband claimed that they had more entitlement to it than an Irish stranger.

'Is there enough legitimacy in the claim to prove a threat?' Emily's father asked, his voice even.

'I should be able to defeat it,' said Mr Carruthers, 'but we will need to go to court to have it settled.'

Forehead creased with apprehension, Emily's father escorted Mr Carruthers away to his study to discuss it further before the lawyer departed for London. The boys were already running off across the entrance hall, but Emily shared an anxious glance with her mother as Sheppard directed David to take their cloaks.

It would be crushing for her father to lose the estate after so wholly committing himself to it.

CHAPTER 11

Bridget gave Cormac's hand a reassuring squeeze as they approached the front door of Sinclair Manor. He in turn squeezed the handle of Lord Bewley's cane and she guessed that he was invoking that old gentleman's encouragement. Beside them, Emily looked enchanting with cascades of golden curls hanging on either side of her face. A tiny crease sat between her fair brows, but when she noticed Bridget's attention upon her, she lifted her chin with a radiant smile. They were all ready to enter the fray.

A footman ushered them inside and led them to a brightly lit reception room filled with a dozen or so gentlemen and ladies holding drinks and conversing amiably. Bridget discerned a slight hitch in the chatter at their appearance but it resumed almost at once. Lord Sinclair and his wife came forward to greet them. The viscount was quite welcoming and bowed cordially, although Lady Sinclair's curtsey was a little more reserved.

'Welcome to our home and to the district,' she said with some stiffness.

Lord Sinclair leaned towards Cormac. 'I have prepared our guests as well as I could,' he murmured, 'but I fear you are still walking into the lion's den.' His mouth twisted wryly.

'Thank you for the warning,' Cormac replied. He kept his manner casual but Bridget could sense his nervousness beneath.

Lord Sinclair beckoned to a young man and woman in a nearby group and they dutifully came to his side. 'My son, Mr Alfred Bertram,' he announced, 'and my daughter, Miss Harriet Bertram.'

Mr Bertram looked to be in his mid-twenties and had an attractive face. His sister was probably only a couple of years older than Emily and her hair was styled in a similar fashion, though her brunette curls did not bounce in as much abundance. She curtseyed in a half-hearted manner while Mr Bertram bowed and flashed a rather roguish grin. Emily gave him a particularly charming curtsey in response. Lady Sinclair waved to a footman carrying a tray of glasses and managed to furnish them all with drinks while adroitly steering her children away again.

'Allow me to facilitate an introduction or two,' said Lord Sinclair, and Bridget believed he truly was in earnest about helping them. He brought them over to a group of two gentlemen and two ladies, to the palpable consternation of the latter. Pretending not to notice their dismay, Lord Sinclair presented Bridget, Cormac and Emily to them and introduced them in return as Lady Sinclair's first cousin, Lady Meadows, along with Lord and Lady Talbot and their son, Mr Edgar Grover.

'Our neighbours,' he explained. 'Talbot land borders the Sinclair Estate on two sides.'

Mr Grover was not as handsome as Mr Bertram but his gaze lingered for a considerable time on Emily during the introductions. When an awkward lull came after Lord Sinclair finished speaking, Mr Grover was the one to break it.

'How was the voyage from America?' he asked Emily, giving her an engaging smile. 'Did you enjoy being at sea? I've always taken great pleasure in the sound of waves.'

'I feel the very opposite,' she replied. 'Regrettably, I was obliged to endure waves of seasickness for much of the crossing.'

Her humorous rejoinder elicited a ripple of amusement around the group. This diffused the initial tension, and Lady Meadows asked Bridget quite politely if she had any other children while Lord Talbot made a comment to Cormac about how it was a shame it wasn't hunting season. As the pockets of conversation continued, Bridget recognised the truth in Mr Carruthers's assertion that Emily's eligibility could pave the way for their acceptance into society, but she felt miserable about the pressure that it put upon their daughter.

Mr Bertram joined the group just then, leaving his mother and sister looking vexed behind him. He eyed Emily with appreciation before blithely cutting across Mr Grover. 'I must say,' he declared, 'it is my profound regret that we did not plan to have any dancing this evening. Do you like dancing, Miss McGovern?'

'Oh, I do, very much,' she said agreeably, even though Bridget knew for a fact that Emily had no confidence in her steps at all. They would have to hire a dancing tutor for her, preferably one who could teach Jack and Gus too. Bridget wondered how she might convince her boys that they would need to learn to dance before it became time for them to join these social circles.

As she listened to Lady Meadows talk about how much of the countryside she had seen on her journey from Somerset, she observed Mr Bertram and Mr Grover flirting with Emily and speculated on their motivations. Standing in the house that Mr Bertram was due to inherit, there could be little doubt, certainly on the face of it, that his family was not short on wealth. The Talbots, too, were clad in finery that indicated Mr Grover's own inheritance was secure. But then, who was to say that they were not concealing enormous debts behind their lavish facades? Or could it be possible that greed motivated them to seek even more wealth to add to their own? Then again, Bridget hoped with the idealism of a mother who wanted her daughter to have every happiness, perhaps they were simply charmed by Emily's sweet manners and liked her for herself.

At least she appeared to be enjoying the occasion and traded banter with Mr Bertram and Mr Grover with relative ease, although Bridget perceived the slight tremor in her hand that was not holding a glass. Bridget couldn't tell whether Emily was aware that she was also under the scrutiny of Miss Bertram across the room, distracted as she was by the attentions of the two young men. She seemed particularly partial to Mr Bertram and beamed at him when he offered to replenish her drink. He clicked his fingers without even looking around and, when the footman approached, took a glass from his tray without a word of thanks. As he waved dismissively in the footman's direction, Emily's expression soured but she fixed a smile back onto her face and continued to be pleasant.

Lady Talbot, who had so far been quiet within the group, now turned directly to Bridget. 'Bewley Hall is a magnificent residence, is it not? I had the pleasure of dining there many times in the past at Lord and Lady Bewley's kind invitation.'

'Indeed, it is a splendid building,' Bridget replied, 'and its grounds are quite breathtaking.'

Lady Talbot sighed. 'I do lament the fact that I shall never enjoy its charming surroundings again.'

Confused, Bridget said, 'Well, of course we shall extend our invitation too—' She faltered at the ugly expression that came over Lady Talbot's face.

'You may save your notepaper,' the lady said, her voice brittle, 'for you will not receive a response. I shall never give you an ounce of recognition as an equal and I can't fathom how Lady Sinclair has done so this evening.'

Lady Meadows gaped as Bridget's throat went dry. She looked towards Cormac, still engaged in seemingly amiable conversation with Lord Talbot. She so dearly wanted this night to be a success for him so she kept her voice low as she said calmly to Lady Talbot, 'I understand your reservations and do acknowledge that our reputations are not without blemish but—'

Lady Talbot snorted. 'Not without blemish? There is no part of your character that is not stained with shame.' Her eyes glittered. 'The gossip about your adultery spread far beyond London when you absconded, Lady *Wyndham*, and we of good breeding do not forget. Not only are you an adulteress, you cast your lot in with the lowest of the low.' Her own gaze flicked to Cormac, her disgust undisguised. 'An Irishman, a Catholic, and a creature of such inferior birth that him wearing such finery is akin to putting clothes on a dog.'

A savage rage rose in Bridget and it was impossible to contain. 'You shall not speak of him in that way, madam,' she practically snarled. 'He is the worthiest man I have ever met and I will defend that declaration with my dying breath.'

'Worthy?' Lady Talbot sneered as Lady Meadows looked ready to faint. 'I can think of no one less so. He is nothing but a peasant. What is more, he has the effrontery to carry that cane as though he can lay claim to the sophistication of the man who carried it before him. Ludicrous. He is entirely undeserving of the inheritance that has been so improperly bestowed upon him.'

Bridget wanted to slap her. 'Do you hear yourself? He may not be a gentleman by birth but he possesses a great deal more gentility than *you*.' Perhaps to preserve the peace she ought to have held her tongue and placated the woman with meek expressions of contrition and humility, but she could not stand by and allow Cormac to be so unjustly maligned.

Lady Talbot drew herself up haughtily. Instead of throwing another retort at Bridget, however, she took a step away from her towards Lord and Lady Sinclair, who were mingling with the next cluster of guests. Raising her voice so the whole room could hear her, she said, 'Lord Sinclair, Lady Sinclair, thank you for your invitation tonight but I regret that my family and I must take our leave. It is impossible for us to remain here in certain objectionable company.'

Cormac's gaze shot across to Bridget and whatever he read in her face made his own drain of colour. Emily, too, blanched as she glanced around at the assembled guests. Her conversation with Mr Bertram and Mr Grover stuttered to a halt, along with every other conversation in the room; all eyes were fixed upon Lady Talbot.

'While I do not wish to cause offence to our gracious hosts,' she said frostily, 'the presence of these unpalatable people cannot be endured. I'm afraid I shall be obliged to cut all further contact with anyone who continues to socialise with them.'

She beckoned to her husband and son. Lord Talbot shuffled over to her at once. Mr Grover offered Emily an apologetic shrug before he also joined his parents; Miss Bertram looked glad to see him part from Emily's company. The Talbots started to move towards the door.

'No,' said Cormac, his voice controlled. 'We'll leave.'

He stepped forwards and bowed stiffly to the Sinclairs. There was a pained expression on Lord Sinclair's face but his wife seemed relieved.

'Please accept our apologies,' Cormac said to them. 'We have no desire to create a disturbance among your guests. Thank you for the goodwill you have extended towards us this evening.'

He shifted his strained gaze to Bridget and she nodded with remorse. Tucking Lord Bewley's cane under one arm, he offered his other arm to Emily; she deposited her unfinished drink on the footman's tray with a murmur of thanks and hurried to take his elbow. Setting down her own glass, Bridget joined them and together they headed for the door. The only sound to be heard was a stage cough from one of the guests which poorly masked a muttered 'Good riddance'. Bridget caught the look of triumph on Lady Talbot's countenance and loathed the woman for her small-mindedness. As soon as they crossed the threshold, a buzz of feverish chattering rose in their wake.

They were utterly silent during the carriage ride back to Bewley Hall.

CHAPTER 12

'We've found out who the ghost is,' Gus announced eagerly at the breakfast table and Jack bobbed his head enthusiastically. Emily deemed it a good thing that the two boys were in such bright spirits to compensate for how glum she and her parents were. 'Even though you came home early last night, we still had time to talk to quite a few of the servants.'

'I spoke to the butler,' Jack said, pushing his shoulders back with pride at his own bravery.

'And I spoke to the two scowly maids who bring the hot water,' Gus added.

'You mustn't call them that,' their mother berated him. 'Thank goodness we gave leave to David to attend to his other duties. Also, "scowly" isn't a real word.'

'I amn't being mean to them,' he protested. 'I'm just describing the way they are.' She opened her mouth again and, anticipating her, he grumbled, 'I meant to say "I'm not".' Mood bouncing back immediately, he said, 'Don't you want to hear about the ghost?'

'Go on, then,' said their father at the head of the table.

'The ghost is a she and her name is...' Gus paused for dramatic effect before bursting out, 'Lady Dorothea!'

He went on to recount how he and Jack had interrogated the servants the previous evening to find out if there had been any suspicious deaths in the history of Bewley Hall and, in the course of their investigations, they had learned that around one hundred and fifty years ago the Earl of Bewley had had a daughter who died in tragic circumstances.

'She wanted to marry her lover,' Gus said, shovelling bacon into his mouth. Emily smiled at how innocently he parroted this word from one of his interviewees. He chewed rapidly and swallowed. 'Except her family refused because he had black skin, like Mr O'Mali.'

Apparently, they had planned to marry in secret but her family had found them out. On the eve of their clandestine wedding, her father had murdered her lover to prevent them from exchanging vows and rings, and he wouldn't tell Lady Dorothea where he had buried him. Devastated, she had thrown herself off the roof of Bewley Hall wearing her bridal dress, and she still haunted the attic to this day.

'So now we know who the ghost is and what happened to her,' Gus said. 'The next thing is to figure out what exactly she wants to find her peace.'

'Maybe she needs to discover where her da buried her lover,' Jack suggested. 'His ghost could be trapped there on account of being murdered, so they can't reunite in death because she doesn't know where he is.'

'I bet that's it!' Gus exclaimed. 'We've got more investigating to do.' He half leapt from his chair before freezing precariously on the edge of the seat. 'May we be excused?'

It was a testament to the distraction of both their parents that they were granted this request without any warning to behave and not disturb the servants. Gus snatched up a final piece of bacon and the two boys ran out of the breakfast room.

Emily's father prodded his uneaten breakfast around his plate with his fork. It was unusual for him to be wasteful with food, an attitude that was borne, she knew, from the painful knowledge of what it was like to have none.

He sighed and put down his fork. 'I must apologise to you both. I exposed you to an unforgiving set of people last night.'

'It's nothing we haven't experienced before,' Emily's mother said lightly, though her grey pallor suggested that it had affected her more deeply than her words implied.

He shook his head. 'I should have known better. It was naïve of me to hope that they would come round like Lord Sinclair. He represents the exception, not the expectation.' He gave them a wry grimace. 'I suppose we should all prepare ourselves to become recluses.'

'Don't lose heart, Papa,' Emily said encouragingly. 'This was only our first try. I am still determined to do all I can to improve our social standing. There will be other opportunities.'

He shook his head again, more emphatically this time. 'You should cast away that notion, *a stór*. I'm afraid your ambition is unachievable. You yourself are blameless but your mother and I are not. You're tainted by our immoral conduct, which unfortunately has spread too far to keep concealed. Our infamy will precede us into every drawing room in the country. It will be too great an impediment for any suitor to overcome.'

At that moment, David entered the breakfast room carrying a silver tray. 'A gentleman has left his card for you, miss,' he said to Emily.

She and her parents exchanged looks of shock and amusement.

'I stand corrected,' her father said with a surprised laugh.

David presented the tray to her and she picked up the card resting on it. It bore the name Edgar F. Grover.

'The gentleman asked me to pass on a message with his card. He acknowledges that the hour is far earlier than customary for a call but he earnestly wishes to convey his apologies as soon as possible for his mother's behaviour last night.' The footman kept his expression blank, even though he had to be immensely curious about what had happened.

Emily bit her lip. 'Should I meet him?' she asked her parents.

'If you would like to, I will act as chaperone,' said her mother. 'We can go into the drawing room.'

Emily nodded. 'David, please wait five minutes before sending Mr Grover there.'

'Yes, miss.' He bowed and left.

'Did you like Mr Grover when you and he spoke yesterday evening?' Emily's father asked.

'I didn't have much time to form an opinion,' she replied, 'but he seemed very amiable.'

If she were being honest, Mr Bertram had been the better looking of the two young men, but there had been nothing objectionable in Mr Grover's appearance or demeanour. Apart from his connection to the horrible Lady Talbot, he had been pleasant company and his particular attention to her last night and now this morning was quite gratifying.

A strangely wistful expression flitted across her father's face but it disappeared as he smiled. 'I'm going to head to my study next.' He stumbled on the word 'my' as though he was not yet used to calling it his. 'Come see me afterwards, won't you?'

'I will, Papa.'

She got up, went over to him and bent to kiss his cheek. Then she and her mother left the breakfast room.

When Mr Grover was ushered into the drawing room, they both greeted him before her mother took up an unobtrusive position at a table by the window, saying that she had a letter to write, which gave Emily and Mr Grover a semblance of privacy. They sat on the sofa a respectable distance apart.

'Thank you for agreeing to see me,' he said. 'It would have been understandable if you had chosen to refuse.' He offered her a rueful grin. 'I am very sorry for how events transpired last night. I hope you know that my mother did not speak for everyone in the room.'

'I'm so glad to hear that,' she said, and her insides quivered with a stirring of attraction as he held eye contact with her.

They exchanged pleasantries for a brief time – he spoke about having spent some of the current season in London, and she told him about her passion for art.

At length, he lowered his voice and leaned closer so that her mother would not overhear. 'Miss McGovern,' he said intently, 'I must confess that I find you irresistible. I beg you to tell me, when and where can arrangements be made?'

She blinked with confusion. Was he offering marriage already? This felt far too quick. Her suspicions rose – did he have a pressing debt that needed to be paid? Aside from the suddenness of the proposal, she was not keen on the idea of being connected by marriage to Lady Talbot. The lady would have to make a sincere apology to her parents before Emily could entertain the notion of forgiving her for the humiliation she had caused them.

Hedging, she said, 'Might it be more correct to ask my father first?'

Mr Grover frowned in bewilderment and not a little horror. 'Your father?'

'Are you not asking for my hand?'

His face cleared as he snickered. 'Of course I'm not.'

She didn't appreciate his sneering tone one bit. 'Then what are you proposing, sir?' she said tightly, her initial attraction fading fast.

He smirked. 'Not marriage, for certain. I am a viscount's son and you're the daughter of a commoner. I could not marry so far beneath me. At the very least, I've got Harriet Bertram in reserve if I can't find anyone better.' He gave a shrug. 'Still, you are adorably sweet and beautiful, even if' – his gaze dropped to her chest – 'your assets are small. I would very much enjoy your company,' he finished with a meaningful arch of his eyebrow.

She stared at him, appalled. She glanced across the room at her mother whose head was bent over her letter, but she did not call for her aid; she would strive to deal with this situation by herself.

'What makes you think I would agree to such an indecent arrangement?' she asked, her voice icy.

He looked over at her mother too and it was clear that he believed loose morals ran in the family.

She stood abruptly. 'Thank you for coming, sir,' she said stiffly, giving him a mechanical curtsey. 'I assume you are a busy man and that we cannot expect our paths to cross very often.' She hoped her message was clear too.

He rose, an insufferable smirk still curving his mouth. 'There's no point trying to save your purity,' he murmured. 'You must know you have no prospects.'

'On the contrary, I do,' she insisted, shocked by his vulgarity.

He emitted a soft snort. 'Don't pin your hopes on Bertram. He shares my views on your mongrel blood. His interest here is entirely monetary—he laid a wager with me that I wouldn't have the plums to proposition you.' Mr Grover's mouth widened. 'I confess, I'm not one to pass up a challenge so juicy.'

Abandoning civility, she hissed, 'You are no longer welcome in this house.'

He affected a sorrowful sigh. 'I regret that I am denied the opportunity to pluck such a ripe apple from the tree. Still, success was not part of the wager, only to prove that my trousers contained a package bigger than Bertram's. I shall head to Sinclair Manor to collect my winnings, even though I would prefer a prize of a different kind.'

He gave her a lewd wink. She wished she could slap him and mentally did so as he walked out the drawing room door.

When she turned to her mother, she found her looking at Mr Grover's retreating back with a furrowed brow. Then she shifted her gaze to Emily.

'How did it go?' she asked.

***

Cormac sat at the desk in his study – yes, *his* study – with a book open before him while his mind strayed to the drawing room. It hadn't been easy to watch his precious daughter leave him to go meet a potential suitor. He knew she was not a little girl anymore and that a man would someday take her from him, no doubt much sooner than he was prepared for. She would certainly not grow old as a spinster, not with her beauty and her goodness, but, damn, what man could ever be worthy of her?

Rory entered his wandering thoughts and he wondered whether the lad had made a decision yet to travel to Liverpool. If so, he sincerely hoped he would come to visit them while in England. They would all be delighted to see a friendly face, especially after the reception they had received last night.

He eyed Lord Bewley's cane propped up against the desk. Letting out a huff of self-disgust, he got to his feet, seized it and placed it on top of a bookcase out of view. He wasn't worthy of it, not by a long shot – he knew it and the Sinclairs' guests had made it plain too. He truly had a daunting uphill climb ahead of him in this role and he doubted whether it was a summit he would ever be able to reach.

He still felt uneasy about Emily's willingness to undertake a strategic marriage union with an influential family. However, after the previous night's debacle, he couldn't deny how helpful such an alliance would be. Loath though he was to accept it, he supposed he might be able to come around to the idea because Emily was the one embracing it so enthusiastically. Perhaps it would work out, so long as the man was decent and kind to her.

As he speculated on the type of man Mr Grover might be with Lady Talbot for a mother, there was a knock on the door.

'Enter,' he said, sitting down at his desk again.

Mr Sandler came into the room with a ledger under his arm. 'Sir, I have the rent figures you asked for.'

Cormac waved him to the seat in front of his desk. Settling himself into it, Mr Sandler opened the ledger and proceeded to apprise him of the details relating to the latest collection of rents, including the total revenue accumulated and the number of tenants who were in arrears.

'Thank you,' Cormac said when the agent had finished his report. 'Allow a respite of two months to be given to the tenants in arrears. And please begin making arrangements for a third of the overall sum to be set aside for transport.'

'Transport to where? And for what purpose?'

'Ireland, in order to provide aid during the potato blight. I intend to bring it myself when Bridget and I travel there.'

Mr Sandler's eyebrows shot up. 'That's very generous of you, sir,' he said carefully, 'but I'm not sure how the English tenants would feel about their rent money being used to help strangers in another country.'

'The Irish would do the same if the roles were reversed,' said Cormac. He could easily picture John Corbett and Laurence Enright leading the Oakleigh denizens to offer whatever help they could.

Mr Sandler nodded deferentially, closed the ledger and got up to leave.

'By the way, have you and Mrs Sandler made any decision yet on the refurbishing of your house?' Cormac asked.

Mr Sandler grinned. 'The missus is still thinking about what she wants.'

After he departed, Cormac returned his attention to the book on his desk. It was a hefty tome about inheritance law and he was combing it for any information he could glean that would help quash the claim that had been made by Mr and Mrs Turnbull. As he turned the page, he found two leaves stuck together and rummaged in the drawers of the desk for a paper knife to separate them. Instead, he discovered Lord Bewley's old penknife for sharpening quills. He unfolded it; though it was long out of use for its original purpose, it could serve a different one today. Its blade was sharper than the rounded edge of a paper knife, so he took extra care as he slit the pages of the book apart and then dropped the penknife onto the desk.

The door opened again and this time Bridget and Emily came into the study. He could tell by their appalled expressions that the encounter with Mr Grover had not gone well and he rose from his chair with misgiving.

'What happened?' he demanded.

'Please do not overreact when we tell you,' Bridget said in preface. 'Emily handled the situation admirably.' With revulsion in her tone, she then summarised what had been said between Emily and Mr Grover.

Cormac listened with burgeoning outrage. How dared that young scoundrel have the gall to speak to his daughter in such a way – it was beyond despicable. His fists ached for violence. He wanted to storm up to the front door of the Talbots' residence and call Mr Grover outside and knock him into the middle of next week for disrespecting Emily. He wanted to do so much damage that the bastard wouldn't be able to stand, let alone set his sights upon another unsuspecting young woman. He wanted to make a public announcement to society that this contemptible man could not be trusted with their daughters.

He forced himself to pause. He was not at liberty to do any of those things. Were he to rough up the cad, all that would achieve would be to validate his critics' assumptions that he was no better than an animal in a stable. Moreover, there was no evidence to prove what Mr Grover had said, which was likely why he had been insolent enough to say it. If Cormac levelled accusations, it would be Mr Grover's word against Emily's and it went without saying who would be believed.

Much as he hated to even think of letting Mr Grover away with this, they would have to endure the insult.

He gritted his teeth. 'At least Lady Talbot did us a favour last night when she cut off all contact with us. It saves us the bother of having to do the same now. I assure you both that we will never have dealings with that family again.' He crossed the room to Emily and gave her a sidelong hug. 'I'm so sorry for the way he treated you.'

'I admit I am rather shaken by his behaviour,' she said weakly. 'It's sobering to comprehend just how negatively these people perceive us.'

'Stepping outside the boundaries set by society will always bring such condemnation,' said Bridget. 'If your father and I had shied away from taking that risk, then you would have been raised your whole life under Garrett's roof.'

Emily shuddered at the notion. 'I learned the hard way that it's far better to have been raised in a loving home.' Her pallid cheeks flushed as they all remembered her ill-advised flight to London. She lowered her gaze. 'However, I fear that Mr Carruthers grossly overstated my ability to attract a well-connected suitor.'

Cormac banished the morsel of disappointment he felt after having so recently begun to come round to that idea; his relief was far greater. 'I hope you will now divest yourself of that obligation he put upon you,' he said, giving her another comforting squeeze.

Before she had a chance to respond, there was a sharp rap on the door and Mr Comerford strode in, prodding a pair of shamefaced figures ahead of him.

'Oh, what have they done now?' Bridget said in dismay.

Jack's and Gus's shoulders drooped with guilt. Gus was clutching what appeared to be an old-fashioned tricorne in his chubby fingers.

'I found them poking around in one of the sheds full of gardening tools hanging on the walls,' said Mr Comerford tersely. 'They weren't taking care. They could've lost an eye if a rake or a fork fell on them.'

'We were looking for a shovel,' Jack mumbled. 'So we could go digging for Lady Dorothea's lover's bones.'

'And while we were looking, we found this!' Gus said, holding up the three-cornered hat. 'It's dusty but I want to wear it. Please, may I?'

'Angus McGovern, that hat does not belong to you,' Bridget remonstrated. 'You will return it to Mr Comerford right this instant.'

Mr Comerford waved his hand. 'He can keep it, so long as they promise not to go digging up the grounds. Leastways, not until they've identified the actual burial place, which isn't possible because no one knows where it is.'

'We're going to find out,' Gus declared, setting the tricorne on his head with resolve. It proved to be too large for him and slipped down over his forehead. Pushing it back up, he said, 'When I'm wearing this hat, I'm a detective. It's what I want to do for my whole life and this is my first case!'

He was so earnest that even gruff Mr Comerford didn't seem inclined to gainsay him.

Cormac marvelled at the stark difference between his daughter's new life in England and that of his sons. Emily had confronted the brutal reality of their position in limbo between the upper classes and lower classes, but the boys were still cocooned in childhood innocence. How shocking would it be for them when they became old enough to face the world that would censure them so harshly? It was going to take a heavy toll on all of them. Had Cormac given that enough consideration before deciding to toss his family into this maelstrom?

CHAPTER 13

A month later, Bridget felt that they had finally made some progress, not with the upper classes but with the lower classes.

The weather was remarkably warm for May, so she decided to go for a ride and combine it with a visit to the postmaster in Gildham to relieve the servants of the duty that day. She was eager to get out of the house following a somewhat prickly conversation with Mrs Sandler, who had looked disapproving when Bridget had mentioned the idea of having a small Independence Day celebration in July. It disappointed her that the housekeeper was so resistant to change, but she supposed her suggestion seemed rather outlandish from the perspective of someone who didn't understand how great an impression their years in America had made on them as a family.

As none of her children could yet ride and Cormac was closeted in his study with Mr Carruthers about their upcoming court case, she solicited the company of Mr Comerford who said he had business with the local blacksmith in the village. Recalling the day she had been ambushed by aggrieved tenants at The Pikeman that summer at Oakleigh, she was not foolish enough to go out by herself in a district where she might be just as equally reviled, and she was grateful for his solid, if dour, presence.

They had just reached the outskirts of the village when she espied an elderly woman taking advantage of the balmy weather by working at the open window of her cottage. Bridget saw her bending over a lacemaking pillow and couldn't resist stopping. She'd had no occasion to do any kind of needlework since they had arrived at Bewley Hall and she found that her fingers itched to be thus occupied again.

She dismounted from her mare, aptly named Nutmeg after the colour of her coat, and Mr Comerford made a grumbling noise in his throat.

'You can go on to the blacksmith's,' she said, deciding that she could not possibly have anything to fear from the old woman. 'I'll meet you in the centre of the village after we have both completed our business.'

He grumbled again and urged his mount onwards.

She led Nutmeg closer to the window. The old woman glanced briefly out at her but didn't say anything, her attention focused on her work. Bridget watched in fascination as the wrinkled fingers deftly moved the bobbins over the pillow, sticking pins into it at intervals.

'What a marvellous skill,' she said. 'I am quite in awe.'

'Thank you, m'lady,' the woman replied. She kept working but after a minute she said, 'You the new lady up at the Hall?'

'I am.'

'We've heard some rumours.'

'No doubt you have, and no doubt some of them are true.'

The woman looked up with a squinting eye and barked out a chuckle. Bridget smiled back. The woman returned her gaze to her lacemaking.

'The Bewleys were good people,' she said.

'Indeed, they were. I was honoured to be acquainted with them many years ago.'

The old woman's hands flashed over and back across the pillow. 'Lady Bewley was a kind soul. I can remember when she ran the soup kitchen hereabouts during some of our harshest winters.'

The challenge hung in the air.

'Lady Bewley's kindness was unparalleled,' said Bridget. 'Though I may only ever be a shadow of her exceptional character, I will strive to emulate her generosity as best I can.'

The woman gave a grunt that conveyed her scepticism and Bridget longed to prove her worth somehow.

'What is your name?' she asked.

'Ethel Cobb.'

'This is remarkably painstaking work. Are there many lacemakers in Gildham?'

'A few, but we're getting fewer. Ever since they invented them machines, handmade lace is becoming less and less sought after. We can't work as fast as machines.'

'That is a shame,' Bridget said with feeling. 'What can be done to preserve your livelihoods?'

'I think the end is certain to come no matter what.'

Bridget was dismayed by the resignation in the woman's tone. 'What if you were trained to use the machines? Would that help you all to adapt to the modern way of lacemaking?'

Ethel gave her an appraising look. 'I'm a bit long in the tooth but some of the younger ones might like to learn.'

'Then may I have your permission to investigate this further to see how I might be able to assist?'

After a lengthy pause, Ethel said, 'You may.'

Bridget departed from the cottage shortly after that with optimism in her heart. This felt like progress indeed to have a tangible opportunity to improve the lives of some of the working-class folk on the estate.

She walked with Nutmeg further into the village where she located the postmaster's house and, after tying the mare to a post in front of the building, went inside. The postmaster was taken aback that the lady of Bewley Hall had come to collect her own correspondence but he duly fetched it for her. There was only one letter and it was postmarked from America. That puzzled her as it was addressed solely to her. If Orlaith had written, she would surely have addressed it to her brother or perhaps the family.

Too intrigued to wait until she returned to the house, she opened the envelope at once and found that it contained a note from Rory, of all people, on top of another letter. How very extraordinary. All became clear when she read his message, however. Following the family's departure from Boston, Rory had checked the post office on their behalf and discovered that the enclosed letter had subsequently arrived for Bridget. Perhaps he could have brought it at a later date himself but, not knowing the urgency of its contents, he thought it best to send it on to her right away. Without going into any detail, he said he expected to follow in due course.

Her delight at this confirmation that he intended to travel to England was eclipsed by profound curiosity and she unfolded the letter. Her spirits rose even further when she realised it was from Ellen Kirwan, but all of her happiness drained away as she proceeded to read it.

Dear Bridget,

I'm sorry for not writing in so long but I haven't had the heart to pick up a pen when I can hardly find the energy to lift my head. This potato blight has brought a misery the likes of which I have never seen before, not even when we all struggled and suffered as a result of the tithes and excessive rents.

The first year of the blight was bad but the second was even worse and, with so few seeds sown, I fear this coming year will test us beyond our endurance. John Corbett and Laurence Enright are doing what they can to keep the tenants out of the ghastly, disease-ridden workhouses: they are ensuring that no one is evicted on Oakleigh land and they are trying to keep every man employed, but the estate is in such a dire way that it cannot support us all. Many, including Liam and I and our children, have flocked to the new wing of Oakleigh Manor in the hope of succour. But if fever breaks out there while it is so overcrowded it will be a disaster.

I implore you to help in whatever capacity you can. You must not be above the idea of beseeching Lord Wyndham for assistance if needs be. Pride is beyond us all at this stage. All we have left are prayers and hunger.

Ellen

Bridget's guts clenched so violently that she almost vomited on the postmaster's floor. She was gripped by horror, anguish and, above all, guilt. Because she heard the unspoken accusation beneath Ellen's words: *why have you not already come to our aid*? Moreover, this letter had crossed the ocean twice since Ellen had penned it. How much worse had the situation grown in the meantime?

Bridget left the postmaster's house and found Mr Comerford waiting for her outside, his horse standing next to Nutmeg.

'Are you quite well, my lady?' he asked, startled.

'No,' she replied. 'We must make haste back to the house.'

He helped her mount and they rode swiftly back to Bewley Hall, her mind and her stomach churning. How she wished her letter to Oakleigh last autumn had not gone astray. She hoped they had at least received the one she had sent since arriving in Bedfordshire so they would know that she had not wholly abandoned them.

As soon as they reached the stables at the house, they passed both sets of reins to a stable hand and hurried indoors. They went directly to Cormac's study where they found that Mr Sandler had joined him and Mr Carruthers. All three glanced up in surprise when Bridget burst in.

'I apologise for interrupting,' she said hastily, 'but I have a pressing matter that cannot wait.' She thrust Ellen's letter into Cormac's hand and allowed him just enough time to skim it before she declared, 'We must go at once. This very night. This very hour! I cannot dally a second longer.'

He looked torn. 'I agree that this is extremely urgent. But the court case is still a week away and I must be in attendance.'

'A week's delay is impossible,' she asserted. 'I shall travel on ahead, and you and the children may follow after.'

Mr Carruthers frowned. 'What is going on?'

'Grave tidings from Ireland,' said Cormac, gesturing with the letter. 'Bridget must attend to the needs of her estate which is in the grip of blight.'

'I will go to Webb & Brereton in Dublin first of all,' she said, 'and instruct them to initiate the sale of Courcey House on

Merrion Square at once. Whatever funds they can release to me immediately, I shall use to bring provisions down to Oakleigh.'

'But you can't travel alone,' Cormac said, his expression troubled.

'Hawkins will come with me, of course,' she replied. 'And maybe...' She eyed Mr Comerford, thinking how his company had been a reassurance today despite his curt manner and wondering whether his niece's presence might soften him a little on such a journey.

But it was Mr Sandler who spoke up. 'I can accompany Lady Courcey to Ireland and, in doing so, serve more than one purpose. I have gathered the rent money you requested, sir, and it can be made ready for immediate transport. If the situation is so desperate that the lady cannot wait a week, then surely the money cannot either. And perhaps, in my capacity as land agent, I may be able to lend my experience to the salvaging of the estate.'

Relief and gratitude coursed through Bridget. 'Thank you, Mr Sandler, I accept your kind offer.'

Though he still looked worried, Cormac nodded his assent.

'I must find Emily and tell her what's happening,' said Bridget. 'I will leave you to discuss the travel arrangements.'

She touched Mr Comerford's arm on her way out in thanks for escorting her to the village and back. His brows were drawn together and he said nothing, hardly seeming to register the gesture. How similar he was to his aloof, laconic niece.

She found Emily in a sunny parlour at the back of the house which she had informally adopted as a space for her painting owing to its abundance of light, even on dull days. The windows looked out over Bewley Hall's wide lawn and a sofa had been pushed to the side to make room for a tall stool and an easel, both new acquisitions since the family's arrival in England, although the watercolour box sitting on a table next to them was the same familiar one that Cormac had made for Emily when she was only six years old. However, her brush lay abandoned in a jar of water and instead she held a piece of paper, perusing it with a perplexed crease on her forehead. She glanced up at Bridget's entrance.

'Oh, Mama, I'm glad it's you. Look at what was just delivered. I have received an invitation from Harriet Bertram.'

Momentarily sidetracked by this unanticipated news, Bridget took the proffered page. They'd had no dealings with any of the other families in the neighbourhood since the disastrous party at Sinclair Manor, but the note from Miss Bertram delicately sidestepped that detail as she invited Emily to spend a week at the Hutchville Estate, which was situated on the far side of Bedford. Miss Hutchville was hosting a country house party for the younger people in the locality – the unseasonable warmth in the city having driven them temporarily away from the social season – and had permitted Miss Bertram to extend an invitation to her new neighbour. There would be entertainments throughout the week, including outdoor games, picnics and at least two separate nights of music and dancing.

'How unexpected,' said Bridget. 'Do you wish to go?'

Emily hesitated. 'I think so. I would be nervous, but it would be a good opportunity.'

Bridget hoped that this invitation hadn't revived Emily's intention to seek a marriage match for the sake of the family. She was about to say so when Emily carried on, 'You look rather pale, Mama. Are you feeling ill?'

Struck afresh by the desolate contents of Ellen's letter, Bridget divulged her plans to travel as soon as possible to Oakleigh.

'Ought I to go with you seeing as Papa cannot?' Emily asked anxiously.

'I'll be fine,' Bridget assured her. 'I'll have both Hawkins and Mr Sandler with me. You wait and travel with your father and brothers.' Suddenly, she remembered Rory's note. 'In fact, you may need to wait longer. Rory might be on his way from America as we speak. He was the one who redirected the letter from Ellen after it arrived in Boston, and he said he expected to follow it thereafter. That must mean he is going to meet the solicitors in Liverpool. It would be a shame if he then came to Bewley Hall and none of us were here to greet him.'

Emily's features shifted at this news but she got her expression quickly under control. 'It would be nice to see him,' she said neutrally. 'Perhaps he will have news from the rest of the family if they wrote to him on the road to Chicago.'

Bridget needed to speak to Hawkins about packing for their journey but she paused a moment longer. 'Two more things, my gooseberry. Firstly, I met an old villager by the name of Ethel Cobb today. She and some of the other women in Gildham are lacemakers but she says their skill is being threatened by the new machines. Could you investigate this further? I want us to help them if we can.'

'Of course I will.'

'Secondly, I'm very sorry but all of this means I shall miss your birthday next week.'

'Don't be sorry, Mama. Judging by the date on the invitation, I will actually be at the Hutchville Estate for the occasion. So it will go by unnoticed in the midst of the entertainments and that will be perfectly fine.'

'It won't go unnoticed by me,' Bridget promised and pulled Emily into a hug. 'My little girl, eighteen years old.'

She thought of Ellen Kirwan's children who were possibly in the throes of starvation and squeezed Emily even tighter.

Chapter 14

Although Emily's mother had wished to leave that very day, it was the following morning before everything could be organised for her departure. Emily and her brothers lined up at the front of the house to bid her farewell. The lady's maid, Hawkins, looked rather disgruntled as she accompanied her mistress outside to the waiting carriage, which had already been loaded with their baggage and a wooden chest containing the rent money. Emily's father emerged from the house too, along with Mr Sandler. They shook hands at the door to the carriage.

'May you all travel safely,' her father said. The agent gave him a solemn nod in response.

Gus fidgeted next to Emily and she nudged him to be still. A month of dining on rich foods had already added more flesh to his pudgy cheeks and his expanding middle; she suspected he paid regular clandestine visits to the kitchens in between meals and that the cook fulfilled his request for mince pies more often than was advisable. He was wearing his tricorne which he had hardly removed over the past month apart from mealtimes and bedtime, but he took it off now as their mother approached for final hugs with all three of her children.

'Happy birthday in advance,' she whispered to Emily as they embraced.

She kissed Emily's father and then she, Hawkins and Mr Sandler climbed into the carriage and it rolled away from the house. Emily noticed the slump in her father's shoulders.

'We will follow her before long,' she said consolingly.

He gave her a lopsided smile. 'As soon as humanly possible.'

Four days after Emily's mother left and a day before Emily was due to go to the Hutchville Estate, she took up her pen to write some letters. With Mrs Sandler's somewhat reluctant help, she had learned of the existence of a lacemakers' society in Nottingham, as well as a number of lacemaking factories there. She composed several letters to the society's leader and the factory owners, enquiring about the current environment of the lacemaking industry and their predictions for its future. As she sealed them, she fervently hoped that their responses would bring positive news for Ethel Cobb and her fellow lacemakers.

After that, she wrote a letter to Matilda in Boston, asking how she was faring as head housemaid at Marlowe House. She longed to confide in her friend about Mr Grover's improper advances but she couldn't include the more salacious details as Matilda wasn't literate and would have to get someone else to read the letter to her. Instead, she dropped some subtle references and trusted that Matilda would detect the real meaning behind them. She imagined her saying 'By golly!' with scandalised fascination.

Next, she began a letter to Samuel but, after staring for a long time at the blank space beneath 'Dear Mr Marlowe', she eventually put it aside. She couldn't justify writing to him until she had gained a place at another art academy, which she had been putting off since she had come to Bedfordshire, ostensibly due to indecision over whether to study in England or Ireland or the continent. In truth, her motivation had languished thanks to her failed attempts at courting. Tuition fees were no object now that her father was so wealthy, but how could she accept his money when she in turn had not succeeded in helping him as Mr Carruthers had so strongly advised? Perhaps she would have more success when she went to the Hutchville Estate. She would remain patient for now and hope that would be the case.

She had passed her letters to Mrs Sandler for posting and had retreated to her parlour to paint when she heard a soft knock on the door. It opened and Jack slipped into the room.

'Um, Emily?' he said. 'I came to tell you that Rory has just arrived.' His gentle manner in revealing this news suggested that he perceived an awful lot more around him than anyone gave him credit for.

Her heart thumped painfully in shock. She hadn't been prepared for Rory to turn up so soon; he must have left Boston barely a week after forwarding Ellen's letter. Swallowing hard, she set down her paintbrush and followed her brother from the parlour.

They made their way to the entrance hall, where they found their father and Gus welcoming Rory, Sheppard and David waiting unobtrusively in the background. Rory's clothes were rumpled and stained from travel, his tall figure hunched with tiredness. As she absorbed the sight of his familiar face, her pulse pounded and her body twitched, as though it might run full tilt towards him of its own volition and throw itself into his arms. She restrained herself with an effort and offered him a small smile instead. He didn't quite smile back but there was a warmth in his green eyes, despite the weariness evident in his posture.

'Come to the drawing room,' Emily's father said. 'You look like you need to take the weight off your feet. Sheppard, please inform the household that there will be a guest staying with us for' – he glanced at Rory, who shrugged – 'an indeterminate length of time.'

'Yes, sir,' said the butler. 'We'll prepare a guest bedchamber at once.'

David took Rory's baggage which, Emily realised with a pang of nostalgia, was the very same canvas bag he had brought on his last trip to England. They then headed towards the drawing room, Rory gaping around at the opulence of the house, Gus chattering at top speed, and Emily striving for equilibrium as she tried to repress her emotions.

By the time they reached the drawing room, Gus had put Rory wise to the presence of the ghost of Lady Dorothea and informed him of his and Jack's quest to help the lady find her peace.

'This shows I'm busy with detective business,' he said, flicking the edge of his ever-present tricorne. His features took on an air of theatrical sombreness as everyone sat down. 'We've actually learned some more about the lady's tragic past. David says he heard that her lover didn't have enough money for a gold ring so he made one out of iron to give to her on their wedding day, but obviously he never got the chance. I bet she's looking for the iron ring and that finding it at last will be what'll allow her to finally rest. It's probably with his bones. We haven't figured out where those are yet though,' he added morosely.

'Enough talk about the ghost for now,' his father chided lightly. 'We have a guest.'

'It's just Rory,' Gus said with a frown.

'Whom we haven't seen for some months. And whom I expect has a lot of news to tell.'

Their father turned to Rory, who nodded.

'I've covered a few miles since I saw ye last,' he admitted.

'West as well as east, I would hazard a guess?' Emily's father said.

'You're right,' said Rory. 'I decided to follow the family on their route to Chicago 'cause there was no way I could tell my ma in a letter that her husband had died, even if she wasn't on good terms with him anymore. I figured I'd be able to catch up with them as I could take a fast stagecoach whereas their wagon would be going a lot slower.'

He recounted how it had taken around a week of keeping a vigilant eye out on the road and asking about the travellers at all the stagecoach stops, but eventually his coach had passed them plodding along with two other wagons and he had convinced the driver to stop and let him off. The family had been flabbergasted to see him and couldn't decide whether to be delighted or alarmed. When he had divulged the news of his father's death, his mother had become upset and then angry at herself for being upset. He had decided to join them on their travels for a while as they needed to keep going so that they would reach Chicago before Orlaith gave birth, but they were moving slowly enough that it wouldn't add too much onto his return journey – and besides, he had wanted to spend time with them. He and his mother had discussed at length the choices he had before him, and Charlie, Orlaith and Tess had contributed their thoughts too. Bronagh never said much, although she had seemed more at peace than she ever had in Boston, as had little Maggie.

'That's very good to hear,' Emily's father said, relief lifting his expression. 'Do you think they preferred the open spaces of the country to the more cramped conditions in the city?'

'That, and the steady rhythm of the days, I think,' said Rory. 'I got used to it too—there was something comforting in the routine. And I liked being with my brother and sisters again as well. To be honest, part of me seriously considered carrying on with them and not going back to Boston.'

'But what about Emmeline?' Emily asked, taken aback.

He looked down at his knees. 'Right,' he said awkwardly. 'Sure, I wanted to go back for her.'

She was dismayed by his lukewarm response – had he given up on her in favour of Emmeline for what had turned out to be not even much of a passionate feeling? That hurt nearly worse than if he had fallen madly in love with the other girl.

He hurried on to say that his mother had encouraged him to go to Liverpool and to choose the honourable path. Much as she had been devastated by the existence of Maud, she had to acknowledge that the other woman was blameless as she hadn't been aware of Brian Mór's deceit either. And if the roles had been reversed, Rory's mother knew how she would feel if she were to be turned out of her home with her children. Rory neither needed nor wanted the house on Penny Close so he could act nobly by allowing the family to stay there and return to America in the knowledge that he had done the decent thing.

Emily quelled her disappointment that he would not be remaining in England. 'At least the rent will bring you some extra money which could help you expand the workshop in time.'

He cleared his throat. 'Well, speaking of the workshop, I had to close it up to make the trip along the Chicago road and I left it shut once I decided I was definitely going to travel to Liverpool. Considering that's twice now in the space of three years that the workshop has closed for an indefinite period, I think its reputation is in trouble and that customers might be hard to come by on my return.' He grimaced. 'If I can't manage to revive it, I should be able to get work as a joiner with Donie Kane.'

'Sometimes these things can't be helped,' Emily's father said, and Emily felt a dart of guilt for being the reason the workshop had been shut the first time. 'Family always has to come first. You were right to go to your mother in person, even though it must have been difficult to subsequently part again.'

Rory just chewed on his lip, imparting no details of his second farewell with his family, but Emily briefly read the pain in his countenance until he masked it again and continued with his story.

'It was only after I got back to Boston that I realised a letter was sitting in the post office for Mrs McGov—I mean, uh, Lady Bri—uh, Emily's ma.' Flustered, he rushed on, 'I didn't know how long it had been there, which was why I sent it on straight away. After that, I made arrangements with the landlord of the workshop premises to extend the lease, but I let my room at Broad Street go. It would've been a waste to keep both. I can always sleep at the workshop when I get back until I find somewhere else to stay.'

Emily noted that he didn't mention Emmeline in any of these plans.

'Then I booked passage on a ship and crossed back over the Atlantic again. We hit a storm on the journey but it wasn't nearly as bad as the one on the *Integrity*.'

His gaze flitted towards Emily for an almost imperceptible instant before he described his arrival in Liverpool and his meeting with the solicitor Mr Martins to verify his identity and sign various documents. He had even paid a visit to Number 5 Penny Close where he had found Maud Pratt still in mourning. She had thought at first that he was there to force them out, but when she realised he was letting them stay she had hugged him in gratitude, although her three children had shied away from him. Following that discomfiting encounter, he had made his way to Bedfordshire.

'And you'll stay here for a little while?' Emily's father said encouragingly.

Rory hesitated but then nodded. Emily guessed that fatigue had dictated his decision – he seemed exhausted down to his very bones.

'You're welcome as long as you wish,' Emily's father said. 'You can write to Emmeline to inform her of your delay in returning to America.'

'Thanks. I will.' Rory glanced around at their luxurious surroundings. 'So how are ye all settling in here?'

Emily's father winced. 'There have been a few bumps in the road unfortunately. Some of our new acquaintances haven't been very welcoming.'

'Even towards Emily?' Rory said, startled.

'She is the exception. In fact, she is departing tomorrow for a week-long sojourn at another estate.'

Rory looked relieved at that. Emily felt stung that he was glad she was going away, but she supposed some awkwardness still remained between them.

'Yes,' she said gaily, putting on a brave front. 'I am looking forward to it tremendously.'

CHAPTER 15

'Will you make sure everything is packed and ready to go by the time I get back?' Bridget asked Hawkins as she pulled on her gloves. 'I want us to be able to depart immediately.'

'Yes, my lady,' Hawkins replied with her usual surly undertone and started moving about the chamber at once, gathering up the items that had spread around it over the past three days.

They had taken rooms in an inn after their arrival by ship to Dublin as the townhouse on Merrion Square was still currently occupied by tenants. Not for much longer, Bridget thought grimly, having already paid a visit to Webb & Brereton Solicitors to discuss serving notice to the occupants and putting it up for sale as quickly as possible. She and Mr Sandler were returning this morning to the solicitors' office on Baggot Street for one final meeting before they boarded the afternoon train on the newly built railway line down to Carlow.

She descended the stairs in the inn to find that Mr Sandler was not waiting in the dining room as they had arranged. However, glancing out the window, she spotted him on the street outside, a leather satchel in his hand. She went out to meet him and saw him passing a coin to a rather shabbily dressed fellow who, she noticed with appalled pity, was missing three fingers on his left hand. She held back as Mr Sandler bade the man farewell with a grin and a smack on the shoulder.

Then he caught sight of Bridget and turned to her with a fleeting bow. 'Good day, my lady. I hope you'll be pleased to hear that I've arranged for that fellow to bring our baggage to the railway station later at a better price than what the inn was offering for the same service.'

Privately respecting the shabby fellow's resourcefulness in overcoming his physical impairment, she said, 'Indeed, I have no objection to such thriftiness. Every penny saved is a penny that can be used to help the tenants at Oakleigh.'

Mr Sandler nodded gravely in response.

They walked together from the inn to Baggot Street. Her brief stay in Dublin had demonstrated to her that the city had been less affected by the hardships occurring outside it. The streets bustled with carriages and carts, the footpaths were thronged with pedestrians, the shops flaunted their wares and teemed with customers. It was not entirely untouched, however – famished-looking beggars huddled on corners in greater numbers than she had ever seen, their rustic accents and peasant clothing indicative of their influx from the countryside. It was cruel to witness the gulf between the thriving city denizens and the rural needy who were so desperately suffering.

When they reached Webb & Brereton Solicitors, they were admitted by a young apprentice, a different man to the suspicious Mr Croft who had been working there the day Cormac had impersonated Garrett for the sake of securing Bridget's guardianship of Oakleigh. Presumably, Mr Croft had since completed his apprenticeship and begun his own firm. Mr Brereton, on the other hand, still presided there, his bulbous nose even larger and redder than before. He greeted Bridget and Mr Sandler with more equanimity than he had upon their unannounced arrival two days previously when Bridget had sprung her demands upon him.

'We took immediate action as per your stipulation,' he said, sitting behind his desk and folding his hands on its polished surface. 'Mr Webb himself paid a visit to the occupants of Courcey House to inform them that the owner wishes to sell the property. They have expressed an interest in purchasing it themselves and asked Mr Webb to relay the price they are willing to pay.'

Mr Brereton imparted the figure in a glum tone and Bridget bit the tip of her tongue in disappointment. She glanced at Mr Sandler for his reaction.

'It sounds like they are underbidding you,' he said regretfully, confirming her suspicion.

She pursed her lips in resignation. 'Still, it would make for a swifter sale than seeking another buyer elsewhere. Mr Brereton, please tell Mr Webb that I authorise him to go back to the occupants and attempt to negotiate a higher price in the first instance, but if that fails, to accept the lower price.'

They discussed the timeframe in which she could expect the completion of the sale and the release of the funds and she once again impressed upon him the urgency of the matter, given the dire circumstances at Oakleigh.

'We will give it our full attention,' he assured her. 'And may I express my deep sympathy that the land and the people are suffering so greatly. I have heard reports that the government's attitude has been far too lax in dealing with this crisis—their work schemes are proving ineffective and the workhouses around the country are flooded with starving wretches. And then there are the landlords, some of whom are taking ruthless advantage of the situation by evicting their tenants, and others who are bankrupting themselves in their efforts to help the poor.'

Bridget registered the warning in his words and blocked her ears to it.

At the end of their meeting, Mr Brereton passed them some papers to bring to Laurence Enright and John Corbett, and Mr Sandler slid them into his satchel. Then Bridget and Mr Sandler left the solicitors' office and returned to the inn where they found Hawkins in an even worse mood.

'A fellow came by to say there's no point in him bringing our baggage to the railway station because two locomotives have crashed on the tracks. The railway line down to Carlow has been closed.'

'For how long?' Bridget demanded.

Hawkins huffed. 'The man reckoned it might be several days before the damage is fixed.'

This was extremely frustrating as the train would have enabled them to reach Carlow that evening, whereas a stagecoach would necessitate an overnight stay along the route. Their business in Dublin was done, however, and movement would be preferable to idleness.

'We'll have to take a stagecoach,' Bridget said, even though the very idea brought back horrendous memories of the fateful stagecoach trip to New York with the diabolical Mr Henson.

'What about hiring a private carriage instead?' Mr Sandler suggested. 'That way, we can dictate our speed to the driver and avoid the delays that the presence of other passengers would incur.'

Although this costlier option was at odds with his earlier economical attitude, she was both glad to avoid the stagecoach and desperate to get to Oakleigh as soon as she could. 'Yes, that is a better plan.'

'Then I'll make the arrangements with all due haste,' said Mr Sandler. 'It shouldn't take above an hour or two.'

With this unforeseen spare time on her hands, Bridget decided on impulse to visit O'Hara's Tobacconist and Lodgings on Meath Street to see how Henrietta Brennan was faring. Though she had no particular yearning to meet the adolescent girl whom she had once feared was Cormac's child, she knew that he would have felt obliged to check on her if he had travelled too.

This time Hawkins came with her, a glower still darkening her face. Weary of her unremittingly frosty company, Bridget seized the opportunity to address the problem as they walked along Dublin's busy streets.

'I can tell that you are unhappy, Hawkins,' she said, her words blunt but not antagonistic, 'and I believe I am the source of your discontent. This situation is not tenable for either of us, so I beg you to be honest with me about your feelings.'

Caught off guard, Hawkins's eyes widened and her cheeks flushed with self-consciousness. But then her jaw tightened. 'Very well, my lady, I shall reciprocate your candour. I was honoured to serve Lady Bewley, but working for you has made a mockery of my role. I'm aware that you lived, and thus dressed yourself, in a lower-class situation for years and that you're only tolerating the presence of a lady's maid now. I don't feel needed anymore,' she finished in a mutter.

With clarity came Bridget's heartfelt regret that the woman beside her had been struggling with such a sense of redundancy.

'Being a lady's maid constitutes far more than simply dressing me,' she said earnestly. 'In my former life, my mother had a lady's maid who was one of the most important people in my world for a long time. It is my enduring personal connection to this woman, and a desire to repay the support that she provided for so many years, that is driving me so frantically towards Oakleigh right now. I yearn to rely on you in the same way, to have you as a confidante, to gain your insight, to seek your guidance on the challenges I face at Bewley Hall. Your advice might help me become a better mistress. For example, do you know much about the local lacemakers in Gildham?'

'I know that their livelihoods are disappearing,' said Hawkins.

'You see?' Bridget said, so animated that she gesticulated with both hands. 'That is precisely what I mean. I had no knowledge of their lamentable situation until just a few days ago, but you are plainly more informed than I was. You could be indispensable to me, and I would trust you implicitly with my confidences if you chose to have faith in me in return.'

Hawkins fell quiet after that, but her demeanour was more pensive than surly.

At length, they reached O'Hara's and, taking a deep breath, Bridget led the way inside the building. She braced herself to meet the fourteen-year-old girl whom she expected to look like a younger version of Thomasina, but Henrietta wasn't there. Instead, Mrs O'Hara was visible behind the counter, her back turned as she balanced on a stool and placed a pipe onto one of the dusty shelves above her head. When she heard Bridget and Hawkins enter, she glanced over her shoulder with a gap-toothed grin.

'Be right with you,' she said and descended precariously from the stool, her short figure almost disappearing behind the high counter. She hurried out from behind it and her grin widened as she recognised Bridget. 'Oh, I remember you,' she said. 'You're his woman.'

'Good day, Mrs O'Hara,' Bridget said, resolved to be polite. 'Yes, I am Lady Courcey and this is Miss Hawkins.'

Mrs O'Hara ignored Hawkins. 'Himself got my letter then? This is a mighty quick response and I appreciate that,' she said in an oily tone.

Bridget frowned. 'He received no letter. We're just here to visit Henrietta.'

Mrs O'Hara's eyes narrowed with confusion and disappointment. She appraised Bridget and a glint returned to her eye. 'Have you brought money for her?'

'No,' Bridget said firmly. 'We are only here to enquire after her wellbeing.'

Mrs O'Hara's expression curdled. 'Well, you might as well be off then. She's not here.'

'Do you know when she will be back? We are planning to leave the city shortly but can wait an hour or two if she—'

'She's not coming back. She's gone.'

'Gone?' Bridget repeated, shocked.

'Ran away, about two months ago. Haven't seen hide nor hair of her since, the ungrateful brat. I raised her for eleven years, I did, and what was the thanks I got? Not even a word of warning before she upped and scarpered and left me doing all her chores.' Mrs O'Hara clicked her tongue. 'I wrote to himself asking for help in finding Henny so I thought that was why you were here. But clearly that's not the case.'

'No, I'm afraid not,' said Bridget. Mrs O'Hara's letter must have reached Boston after Rory had left. 'We recently moved and no longer live at that address.'

'And was himself planning to tell me that or was he just going to quietly forget about the girl altogether? Will he even bother to try and find her now?'

'You know he has no obligation towards her,' Bridget said curtly. 'However, I will tell him what you have told me. The decision after that is his and not mine to make.'

She knew Cormac would be upset to hear that Henrietta had run away because he had been the one to place her in her grandaunt's care. Would he feel compelled to search for her?

Where would he even begin? Bridget had believed their days of searching for lost family had ended when they found Bronagh.

She started when she realised that she had just thought of Henrietta as family. Well, perhaps they would have been a better family for her than Mrs O'Hara had turned out to be. Bridget recalled Hester Temple in New York who would have moved heaven and earth to find her missing son, Willie; in contrast, Mrs O'Hara exhibited no distress over the disappearance of her grandniece, only lamenting the loss of her as a skivvy.

Quashing her dislike, Bridget bade Mrs O'Hara a civil farewell and she and Hawkins left; the old woman's disgruntled mutterings followed them to the door.

As they made their way back to the inn, Bridget said to Hawkins, 'I invite you to satisfy your curiosity. You must have questions.'

Hawkins cocked her head. 'Is this Henrietta a natural child of Mr McGovern's?'

'No. He was the inadvertent cause of her mother's death and so he feels a responsibility for her.'

'But he could have easily walked away.'

'He's not that type of man.'

'You could have insisted that he have nothing to do with her.'

'I suppose I am not that type of woman.'

'I see,' Hawkins said, her face inscrutable.

'His actual children are illegitimate,' Bridget carried on soberly. 'You have deduced that, I'm sure. Emily's birth has a legitimate status because she was born within a legal marriage but Jack and Gus do not have that protection. I bore them after I separated from my lawful husband. I tell you this because I desire your trust but cannot ask for it without complete honesty on my part. It's important for you to understand that you work in a household tainted by much scandal.'

Hawkins didn't say anything for quite a while. 'And yet Bewley Hall does not strike me as an unhappy place under its new owners,' she said at last.

Bridget smiled. 'That is true. We have found our joy outside of society's normal parameters.'

'I suppose there's a lot to be said for that,' Hawkins conceded.

Chapter 16

Bridget and Hawkins got back to the inn where they found Mr Sandler waiting for them by the private carriage he had arranged. Their baggage was already secured on the roof and, when Bridget peered inside, she observed that the chest of rent money was tucked under one of the seats. The interior was rather threadbare, so it appeared that Mr Sandler had employed some economy after all.

'It's a basic conveyance, but the driver has promised to make it a swift journey,' he assured her, adding with some embarrassment, 'He has gone off for a moment to, ahem, relieve himself. Why don't you both climb in while I go into the inn to settle the payment for our accommodation? By the time that's done, the fellow ought to be ready to depart.'

A few minutes later, Mr Sandler joined them inside the carriage, placing his satchel on the empty seat beside him as they heard a male voice upfront bark at the horses. The carriage moved off and Bridget allowed herself a tiny breath of relief, glad to be on the next stage of her journey and another step closer to Oakleigh. She wished Cormac were with her, but she caressed her two rings, gold and thread, for comfort in his absence.

As soon as they got out of the city, they witnessed first-hand the devastation that the ongoing crisis had inflicted upon the countryside. Though the blight had not yet struck this year, many fields lay pitifully bare, the smallholders having been left without enough tubers to plant from last year's decimated crop. As the carriage rolled by, Bridget espied a farmer staring out desolately across his empty land. People in varying degrees of emaciation sat aimlessly outside their hovels or shambled along the side of the road, perhaps trying to muster the energy or the courage to enter one of the overcrowded workhouses. They were scenes of unspeakable misery and Bridget's heart broke at the sight. Ellen's letter had not been enough to prepare her.

The road grew quieter the further they travelled from Dublin. Eventually, any sightings of other carriages vanished altogether; only a sluggish donkey and cart had passed them over the last half a mile. Dusk was no more than a couple of hours away and she wondered how much further they could get before they had to stop at an inn for the night.

Just at that moment, she heard a shout outside and the carriage lurched to a sudden halt. There were more shouts, at least one of which came from the driver's box, and then the carriage door was flung open and they found themselves staring at a man pointing a knife straight at Mr Sandler.

Hawkins let out a faint scream. Mr Sandler gawked wide-eyed at the sharp tip of the knife and said in a rather high-pitched voice, 'Good grief.'

Bridget stared at the man in speechless shock. A highway robbery? In broad daylight? Surely this sort of thing belonged only to the previous century or in novels. Then she perceived the man's haunted eyes and scrawny figure and realised that hunger would drive a wretched soul to take the most desperate of chances. She recalled the money chest below the seat and thought of how many other desperate people needed it too. Forcing herself not to let her gaze drop in its direction, she prayed that another carriage or cart would come along to disturb the robbery.

Evidently conscious of that risk, the highwayman growled at Mr Sandler, 'We need to get off the road. Tell your driver to go where I tell him or I'll kill you.'

Mr Sandler blanched and looked helplessly at Bridget.

Distressed, she said, 'You must do as he says. There's no other choice.'

He nodded and, raising his arms to indicate surrender, moved forwards on his seat. The highwayman waved his knife warningly. Keeping a wary eye on it, Mr Sandler leaned towards the open door and called, 'Mr Duffy, for the sake of our lives, kindly follow this fellow's directions.'

After a pause, the driver shouted back, 'Understood, sir.'

Mr Sandler regarded the highwayman with caution. 'Will you at least let the ladies go free?'

'They're coming too,' the man said briefly before slamming the door shut in his face.

In a matter of seconds, the carriage moved onwards again and presently turned left off the main road onto a narrower track. The three passengers were bounced around as the carriage's wheels rolled over the uneven ground. Barren fields stretched out on one side of the track while sparse woodland lined the other side.

'We need to figure out what we should do,' Bridget said, striving to keep a level head. Her underclothes were sticking to her skin with sweat. 'We can't jump out of a moving carriage.'

Mr Sandler's mouth tightened with resolve. 'When we stop and the highwayman comes to the door again, I'll lunge at him and knock the knife from his hand before he has a chance to use it.'

'You could get badly injured,' Hawkins said, a tremble in her voice.

'I'll do my utmost to avoid harm. Remember, I only need to hold the man off long enough for the driver to come to my aid.

Then we shall be two against one and we'll certainly be able to overpower him.'

Bridget and Hawkins were both encouraged by this likely scenario, although it couldn't eradicate their alarm.

The carriage rattled along the track until it reached a dilapidated farmstead, the woodland encircling it like a ragged halo. It rolled to a stop in the farmyard. Bridget glimpsed a house and a barn from the carriage window, a broad sycamore tree standing tall in the space between them. She raised her eyebrows at Mr Sandler and he nodded back to confirm his readiness.

However, when the man with the knife wrenched open the carriage door, Mr Sandler didn't act. Bridget wasn't sure whether he froze with fear but he just looked dumbly at the man as he ordered them to get out. Bridget and Hawkins both stared at Mr Sandler with disappointment and panic – they had now lost the element of surprise. He evaded their gazes and meekly obeyed the highwayman's order, climbing out of the carriage first and rather absurdly bringing his satchel with him. Bridget and Hawkins followed in silence; dread clutched at Bridget's throat while Hawkins's face was the colour of whey.

The highwayman gesticulated at Mr Sandler with his knife and then pointed to the barn. 'Will this do?'

Mr Sandler's anxious face broke into a wide grin. 'Indeed, it will. Very well done.'

Before Bridget could register this incomprehensible exchange, there was a scuffling sound from the front of the carriage as the driver, Duffy, got down from his box and came to join them. Bridget gaped; he looked entirely relaxed about the whole affair. And he was missing three fingers on his left hand.

'You were supposed to bring our baggage to the railway station,' she said, confused.

'Yes, he's the one who told me about the crash on the tracks,' Hawkins said, seeming equally baffled.

The driver smirked. 'They haven't cottoned on yet?' he said to Mr Sandler. 'You must be a cracking actor.'

'I'm not the only one who deserves plaudits,' Mr Sandler responded. 'Mr Sullivan here was extremely formidable with his knife.'

'What is going on here?' Bridget demanded.

Mr Sandler ignored her, turning instead to survey the farmstead. 'The barn is ideal,' he said and nodded at the two men.

The supposed highwayman, Sullivan, grabbed Bridget by her upper arm and the driver did the same to Hawkins.

'Ow, let go of me,' Hawkins protested.

Bridget tried to shake Sullivan off but he pinched harder and yanked her forwards. When she dug her heels in, he swung his other hand around and suddenly his knife was under her chin. He didn't have to say anything; she stopped resisting. Hawkins saw the knife and went still too. Stunned, they allowed the men to steer them across the farmyard towards the barn, which sat in the shadow of the enormous sycamore tree.

As they approached the barn, the door of the nearby farmhouse opened. Bridget peered over her shoulder to see a grizzled older man staring out at them.

'Help us!' she cried.

But then she perceived the dead look in his eyes and his utter lack of surprise. Their arrival was not unexpected. Horrified, she wondered what on earth was happening as she and Hawkins were dragged inside the barn's partially open double doors.

The barn smelled of hay and manure, although it was empty of livestock. A three-legged stool lay on its side on the ground floor and a wooden ladder led up to a hayloft in its centre, while a bundle of netting had been left abandoned next to a narrow door at the far end of the barn. Mr Sandler glanced around in appraisal.

'It's perfect,' he said, an ugly expression on his squashed features.

'Are you going to explain yourself, sir?' Bridget said coldly.

He gave a mean chuckle. 'You didn't have an inkling, did you? And I'm certain neither did he, since he consented to my accompanying you on this journey. The pair of you really are too trusting for your own good.'

A chill ran over her sweaty skin, raising gooseflesh. Hawkins blinked at Mr Sandler as though he were an utter stranger.

He sneered. 'That Mr McGovern believed we would be content with our lot is laughable. How could my wife and I stomach serving him when Bewley Hall should have been *ours*?' His jaw clenched. 'We spent decades licking Lord Bewley's boots and waiting for him to die, and in the end he threw his estate away on an undeserving Irish upstart. All of our hard work and patience had been for nothing. As if we would stay and endure such an insult.'

'Why didn't you both leave then?' Bridget snapped. 'You had ample opportunity to serve your notice.'

Mr Sandler scoffed at that. 'We had no intention of leaving empty-handed, nor of starting from scratch in some other household. We needed to figure out a way to line our pockets enough to live out the rest of our days in comfort. We'd waited thirty years—we could wait a little longer. So we bit our tongues and continued to play the humble servants.'

Bridget deemed Mr Sandler to have played his part far better than his wife. Mrs Sandler had barely concealed her distaste for the whole family.

'We thought about siphoning off small amounts of the estate's income at a time, in portions negligible enough that they would go unnoticed on the accounts, but that would have taken too long to generate a substantial sum. Then Mr McGovern handed me a gift, an order to gather rent money for this wretched country. It could have been sufficient. We seriously considered absconding with that.' Mr Sandler's eyes glittered. 'And then you handed me a greater gift. Yourself.'

Bridget tensed and Sullivan's grip on her tightened further. 'You mean to ransom me,' she stated in a low voice.

'I do. I'm confident that there's no sum Mr McGovern would not pay for your safe return.' He turned to Sullivan. 'Where's the rope I requested?'

The man motioned at the barn's double doors with his knife without loosening his hold on Bridget. 'Hanging there.'

Dismayed, Bridget twisted towards the doors to discern a length of rope looped over a long nail on the back of one of them. 'You intend to tie me up?' she said disbelievingly.

'Both of you,' Mr Sandler replied.

Hawkins uttered an exclamation of indignation. 'Why me as well? There's no need to involve me in this.'

'I'm sorry, Polly. Your uncle has been my right-hand man for many years, but you're caught up in this now. It can't be helped.' He crossed to the door and lifted down the rope, handing it to Duffy.

'How exactly do you plan to carry out this scheme?' Bridget asked, hoping none of the men could detect the terror swelling inside her.

'I'll continue to utilise my talents as a thespian in this gripping play,' said Mr Sandler, his whole demeanour radiating smugness. 'When I go back to Bewley Hall, I shall be distraught to tell Mr McGovern that we were waylaid on our noble errand to Oakleigh and that his precious lady and her maid have been seized by desperate Irish savages who refuse to release them until a ransom has been paid.'

'What makes you think he'll believe what you say? His suspicions will be raised at once if you have been let go free by my alleged abductors. He entrusted me to your care and therefore he will lay the blame at your feet for any harm that befalls me. How do you hope to convince him of your innocence in the affair?'

'Oh, I probably wouldn't be able to convince him. But I'm certain that you can.' With a flourish, Mr Sandler opened his satchel and drew out a pen, a bottle of ink and a blank sheet of paper. 'He is going to hear from your own hand that the dastardly creatures who accosted us are forcing me to act on their behalf, that I have been sent to collect the ransom and that I will ensure your safety upon my return. You will assure him that he can trust me absolutely.'

She shot him a look of incredulity. 'And if I refuse?'

Leaning offensively close to her, Sullivan brought the knife up to her cheek. She felt his hot breath at her ear. 'Your pretty face won't be so pretty anymore,' he crooned.

'It strikes me as counterproductive to spoil the thing you wish to ransom,' she said coolly. 'A rather hollow warning, if you ask me.'

He snarled and aimed the knife in Hawkins's direction. 'Then we'll spoil *her* instead.'

Hawkins's eyes bulged with fear.

'Don't touch her,' Bridget said, gritting her teeth. 'I will cooperate.'

Mr Sandler picked up the nearby fallen stool and placed it in front of her. 'Your writing desk, my lady.'

She knelt on the hay-strewn floor, her skirts billowing around her. Sullivan crouched beside her, his knife still threatening. Mr Sandler put the sheet of paper and the bottle of ink on top of the stool and handed her the pen.

'Address him as you customarily would and after that write what I say. You may paraphrase to a degree to make sure it sounds like your voice.'

She bowed her head, dipped her pen and pressed its tip to the top of the page. Following Mr Sandler's instructions, she used persuasive language throughout the letter to reassure Cormac of the truth of its contents. She swore that she had not been harmed and that Mr Sandler was blameless, and she included the explicit warning that the brigands would deal with the agent and no one else. After she signed it, he took it from her and scrutinised it.

'This will do nicely,' he said, satisfied. He tucked the letter, pen and ink back into his satchel and then eyed the rope in Duffy's hand. 'Wrists and feet,' he said succinctly.

'Wait,' Bridget objected. 'You cannot tie us up like animals. It's inhumane. We are women, for heaven's sake.'

Mr Sandler contemplated her first and then the interior of the barn. 'The hayloft,' he said. 'If you climb up there, you may remain unbound. We'll remove the ladder afterwards, of course, so you won't be able to get back down unless you wish to break your legs in the process.'

Bridget judged the distance from the loft to the floor and despondently had to agree that it was too far to jump. She began to wonder whether she and Hawkins might have a better chance of escaping by staying below – perhaps they could contrive to remove their binds if they were left unattended for a period of time – but Duffy had already put the rope back on the nail and he and Sullivan were now shoving them towards the ladder. At a disadvantage in both numbers and strength, they were compelled to climb up. The loft above was empty apart from a few mounds of musty hay.

'We'll throw ye up a bucket,' Sullivan said with a rough laugh as Duffy pulled the ladder down and laid it on the floor.

Bridget leaned out over the edge of the loft. 'Your plan isn't going to work,' she said defiantly to Mr Sandler. 'You may have that letter, but Cormac will see through your lies.'

He smirked. 'I have one more manoeuvre to augment the credibility of my mission.' He put down his satchel and squared up to Sullivan and Duffy. 'As we agreed, fellows.'

Features contorted with a repulsive sort of glee, they stepped forwards and rained several blows upon his face and body, hard enough to crack skin and draw blood. He flinched at their concerted assault but did not raise his arms to defend himself. As they beat him, Bridget perceived the grizzled old man peering in through the gap in the barn doors. His expression was still lifeless as he watched the scene within.

After Sullivan and Duffy had finished, Mr Sandler sported a swelling eye socket and a bloody nose and he was doubled over, his arms clutching his midriff. Nonetheless, he managed to grin at the men as he straightened.

'Thanks for that. I reckon the bruises will be quite impressive by the time I return to Bewley Hall. They will truly aid my performance.' He looked up at the hayloft. 'I trust the Sullivans will make your stay at their farm quite comfortable,' he said mockingly. 'Duffy and I shall depart in the carriage now. It's too late to make it back to Dublin this evening but at least we have ample funds to pay for excellent overnight accommodation.' He bent to pick up his satchel, a small groan escaping him.

'What about our payment?' Sullivan asked, his voice sharp.

'I have a chest of money in the carriage,' Mr Sandler replied. 'I'll give you and your father a portion now and you'll receive the remainder of what you're owed once the ransom has been secured.'

The men left the barn without another upwards glance, and no wonder – Bridget and Hawkins were utterly stranded where they were.

Chapter 17

As the Sinclair carriage came to a stop in front of Bewley Hall, Emily harboured strong reservations over whether this was a good idea at all. She had told her mother that she was willing to accept Harriet Bertram's invitation to the Hutchville Estate, and she had done so in the hope that she might still have some slim prospect of fulfilling her duty to marry well, but she couldn't help the doubt that persisted in the back of her mind. Why had Harriet even invited her in the first place?

The answer soon became clear. When the footman handed Emily into the carriage, she took a seat opposite Harriet, who gave her a thin smile and said, 'I'm so glad you are able to join us for the week, Miss McGovern. My father, too, was most pleased to hear that you were free to attend—it was he who had suggested you might like to come.'

So it was obligation and not goodwill that had motivated her. In a way, knowing that Lord Sinclair had been the source of the gesture made Emily feel a little better. She appreciated his kind effort to give her, and thus her family, another chance at gaining a foothold in the neighbourhood. And at least there was no sense of hostility from Harriet, just an air of mild politeness. Perhaps Emily's week at the Hutchville Estate would be more successful than the horrendous party at Sinclair Manor, given that her disreputable parents – how it shamed her to even think of them like that – would not be in attendance.

After the footman had loaded her trunk onto the carriage, they set out for the Hutchville Estate. Along the way, Harriet informed her that, once all the guests arrived, they would number a party of eighteen, to be augmented by a further dozen on both nights of music and dancing, the first of which was scheduled for two days hence.

'My brother and Mr Grover will join us for that occasion,' Harriet said. 'They consider themselves far too busy to sojourn for the full week.'

Beneath Harriet's undisguised exasperation at their self-importance, Emily thought she detected a distinct note of affection. Could it be accorded to Harriet's fondness for her brother or was it perhaps a deeper attachment towards Mr Grover? Knowing the kind of man Mr Grover had revealed himself to be and recalling his dismissive comment about Harriet herself, Emily worried that any attachment on Harriet's part might be gravely misplaced.

'Forgive me for prying, but do you and Mr Grover have a partiality for one another?' she asked tentatively.

The corners of Harriet's mouth turned upwards in a sly curve. 'I know why you are asking. He told me he called upon you at Bewley Hall.'

'He did?' Emily said, disconcerted.

'Yes, he said he went to convey his apologies for his mother's behaviour at the party but that you read rather more into it and he had to gently rebuff you. Do forgive him for his loose tongue but, as you have already guessed, he and I do share a particular affinity. I trust you are now accepting of this?'

'Oh, of course,' Emily said, for there was no other response she could give, even though the memory of her encounter with Mr Grover made her flesh creep.

'I'm glad you have become cognisant of the circumstances so that you and I may now be comfortable acquaintances without any awkwardness in relation to Edgar.'

Harriet's familiar use of Mr Grover's first name was indication enough of her depth of feeling for him. How could Emily warn her against him? They were practically strangers, not to mention the fact that she would look like she was speaking out of jealousy instead of concern. Though it pained her, she refrained from saying anything further and hoped that Mr Grover would somehow make a blunder in the future that would alert Harriet to his unscrupulous character.

A jolly atmosphere greeted them when they arrived at the Hutchville Estate and the first day proved to be quite enjoyable as, after settling into their bedchambers, the guests mingled on a sunny terrace. Now that Harriet no longer viewed Emily as a rival for Mr Grover's affections, she became substantially more congenial and was kind enough to introduce her to several of the other guests, which meant that Emily wasn't left neglected on the edge of the proceedings. She even provided Emily with titbits of insight into some of these new acquaintances, usually murmured behind her hand after the person in question had gone out of earshot.

'Miss Hutchville speaks so prettily now. She had a terrible stammer when she was a younger girl...That's Lord Dartry. He's far and away the oldest man in the group, he's past *thirty*...Rumour has it that Miss Yates over there turned down a proposal this season in London but she will not reveal who the spurned gentleman was. We shall have to try to coax it out of her during the week.'

To her pleasant surprise, Emily found herself having fun and that feeling only increased when Miss Hutchville presented the first entertainment for her guests: a drawing game where a nominated person was obliged to sketch an image using chalk on a slate and the others had to guess what it was. Emily, of course, excelled at the game and swiftly became the most popular participant. After a sketch of such detail that the guests were able to identify it not only as a bird but as a pheasant, Miss Yates exclaimed, 'My goodness, I am stunned with admiration! You have an exceptional talent, Miss McGovern. Is it a natural gift or have you been tutored?'

'It is a lifelong passion of mine, though I confess I have engaged in formal studies over the past two years,' Emily said, her cheeks growing hot. 'I hope to continue to develop my skills and maybe even to sell my artwork in the future.'

Miss Hutchville squinted at her. 'I ought to have researched my guests' pasts before handing one of them such a significant advantage in my game.'

Emily momentarily froze, expecting some sort of snide remark about her questionable origins, but everyone just laughed.

'I suggest we blindfold one of Miss McGovern's eyes to reduce her advantage,' Miss Yates quipped, prompting further laughter, and Emily relaxed.

At the end of the game, they dispersed to get ready for dinner. As they left the terrace, Harriet sidled close to Emily and said in a teasing undertone, 'Lord Dartry hasn't taken his eyes off you all afternoon.'

Emily coloured. 'I'm sure you are mistaken.'

But as it transpired, Harriet was not mistaken. Now alert for his scrutiny, Emily noticed out of the corner of her eye that Lord Dartry's attention landed upon her numerous times during dinner, even when she was not contributing to the conversation. Once, she looked straight over at him and caught him staring. Blushing, he shifted his gaze away at once. She had wondered whether his attention stemmed from a disapproval of her presence, but his blush told her it might be something else.

A coil of pleasure unfurled inside her and her self-esteem rose a notch further.

When the gentlemen joined the ladies in the drawing room later that evening, they splintered into small groups and she and Lord Dartry ended up mingling in the same circle, but they did not converse directly with each other. It wasn't until the following day that he requested to speak with her privately.

The guests had just completed a spirited game of pall mall on the estate's vast lawn, from which Miss Hutchville had emerged the victor, after knocking the ball with perfect precision through the final arch. As the guests clapped at her triumphant win, Lord Dartry stepped up rather diffidently to Emily.

'Miss McGovern, would you honour me with your company for a short walk before we return to the house? If we take a turn across the lawn, we shall remain in full view of the party and thus all will be proper but we won't be overheard.'

She hesitated for just a moment before consenting. They set their mallets down and casually retreated from the group. As they strolled away, Emily saw Harriet glancing over at them with a knowing glint in her eye before returning her attention to Miss Hutchville's glowing countenance.

Lord Dartry spoke first of the fine May weather, and then of the asparagus at the previous evening's dinner which had been 'most palatable', and then of the weight of his mallet which he thought was very well balanced. Emily sensed his nervousness, so she gave him an encouraging smile and let him ramble. Once they reached the far end of the lawn, he halted in front of a row of blossoming rose bushes and turned to face her. He was not as fresh-faced as most of the other young men in attendance but his expression was warm, if a little bashful.

'I will speak frankly,' he began, 'and hope that you will appreciate my candour. I am from an old family in

Bedfordshire. The Earl of Dartry title goes back centuries and commands great respect. Regrettably, the estate fell into debt during my father's generation and so I have inherited both its esteemed reputation and its financial liabilities. I want to revive it to its former glory. I also wish to sire the next generation in my family tree, so I am seeking a lady who will be a suitable companion at my side. For these reasons, I would like to ask for your hand in marriage.'

Her insides somersaulted.

'I'm not unaware of your family's scandalous past, but I can see that you yourself are as unblemished as the first roses blooming beside us. Yes, I am being pragmatic because you are an heiress who can expect to receive a handsome dowry upon your marriage, and you will additionally inherit a large estate in Ireland, though the attraction of that is somewhat diminished in light of the current state of the country. However, you are also beautiful and charming and, although this arrangement would commence upon a practical foundation, I can envision a deep attachment forming between us, given enough time to allow it to grow.'

Emily's heart beat very fast. This was it, the very situation Mr Carruthers had described. Now that the opportunity had presented itself, was she prepared to take it? The unimpeachable Dartry title was precisely the sort of connection her parents needed to cultivate a better standing in polite circles. She would finally be able to make amends for all the grief she had caused them when she ran away.

But what of her own happiness? Lord Dartry made it clear that his proposal was based on a union where she would benefit from his title and he from her fortune. And yet he was open to the idea that affection could develop over time. True, he was closer in age to her father than to herself, but what did that matter if they had an equal meeting of minds? He certainly seemed like a kind man, and he desired children, which she did too.

Her answer was on the tip of her tongue, but he had carried on speaking.

'I am confident that you will be comfortable at Dartry Abbey, especially after we employ some funds to attend to its upkeep. Any redecoration will be to your own tastes, of course. Your enthusiasm for art is evident, so we can ensure that you have a suitable space to indulge in your hobby, though naturally you will cease any commercial endeavours in that area. Furthermore, the fact that my estate is in Bedfordshire means that you will not live very far from your family, which I'm sure will please you greatly.'

That gave her pause. 'What do you mean about ceasing my commercial endeavours?'

He bestowed a gentle smile on her. 'You must confine your artistic pursuits to a private situation only. It would not be seemly for a countess to act in a mercenary way, nor for any woman to intrude in a man's sphere like that.' He said it so easily, as though he were commenting on an assumption as basic as breathing.

Her own breath faltered, catching in her throat as the answer she was going to give him still hovered on her tongue. Could she agree to such a constriction? He was not forbidding her to continue the pursuit, only insisting that she could not seek external recognition for it. Ought not that to be sufficient? Was she vain to desire anything beyond the simple pleasure of creating art for her own satisfaction? After all, nothing might come of it even if she did attempt to bring her art to a wider audience. But to have that possibility categorically removed from her future...

For whom would she be accepting Lord Dartry's proposal? Her parents. And how would they feel if they learned that she had cut off this potential avenue of fulfilment to accept it? Disappointed, she was certain. She would be helping them in one way but letting them down in another and, given all their protestations, she knew which alternative was more important to them. She would be doing herself a disservice too, by curbing her artistic prospects in such a way. She would never know how high she might soar if she didn't try. And sadly, for all his positive attributes, this man before her wouldn't support that aspiration.

At last, her answer moved from her tongue to her lips. 'Thank you, my lord, for your very kind offer. But I'm afraid I shall have to decline.'

His face fell. 'Was I too hasty in my approach? I had assumed that you would prefer me to be honest. You understand I cannot make false claims to love.'

'Indeed, you cannot and you ought not. I am grateful for your honesty and I do acknowledge that a union between us would provide mutual advantages. However, while I'm flattered that you deem me worthy of becoming your countess, I cannot accept the honour.'

He had enough pride not to plead. They walked back across the lawn in silence and he returned her to Harriet's side before disappearing indoors. Another game of pall mall had struck up but Harriet turned her back on it.

'Well?' she said excitedly. 'Did he propose a marriage of convenience?'

'He did.'

'I guessed he might! He is known to be in colossal debt after his father's spendthrift ways. How fortunate for you. No doubt you never dreamed you would attain the rank of an earl's wife!'

'I refused him,' Emily admitted.

Harriet gawked at her. 'Why would you do such a silly thing? Surely you must know you are unlikely to receive many offers, considering the objectionable circumstances of your—' She clamped her mouth shut to stop any more of her insult from flowing out.

'I do not feel that Lord Dartry and I are well matched,' Emily said, her shoulders slumping.

Harriet's eyes narrowed. 'I hope you don't still have designs on Edgar. You are aware that his affections are already engaged.'

Emily bit her lip. If she had enough respect for herself, then Harriet ought to as well. 'I feel obliged to tell you that Mr Grover has not been forthright with you. It was he who made an improper advance towards me. And when he spoke of you, it was in quite a dismissive tone. I fear he views you as a last resort, not as the first and only place where he will bestow his regard. I tell you this out of an earnest wish that, when the time comes, you will give your heart to a man who truly values you.'

Doubt flashed across Harriet's countenance but she quickly replaced it with anger. 'Well, now you have shown your common blood. No woman of good breeding would tell such a lie just to divert from her own shortcomings. I do regret being persuaded by my father to extend a hand of friendship to you. You will oblige me by keeping your distance for the remainder of our sojourn here. And do not expect an invitation such as this again.'

She stalked away as a cheer went up from the pall mall players; Miss Hutchville appeared to be conquering all around her again. Emily plastered an artificial smile upon her face as she comprehended just how much damage she had incurred in the past ten minutes.

CHAPTER 18

Cormac tapped his fingertips agitatedly against each other as he and Mr Carruthers sat on a bench at the Shire Hall in Bedford, waiting for their case to be called. It was uncomfortably reminiscent of his trial in London nearly three years ago but at least this was a civil court, not a criminal one. As Mr Carruthers shuffled through some papers next to him, Cormac's fingers continued to tap and, with a jolt of nostalgia, he realised that he was emulating Orlaith's familiar nervous habit. How he missed his sister. Were she and the family settling well in Chicago? Had she given birth yet? With a conscious effort, he let his fidgeting fingers rest.

The clerk called, 'Turnbull versus McGovern.' Cormac and Mr Carruthers stood, as did three people on another nearby bench: a pinched-looking couple who had to be Mr and Mrs Turnbull, accompanied by their lawyer who was wearing a wig and a determined expression. He scarcely waited for the clerk to finish reading out the details of the dispute before he bustled forwards and slapped a sheaf of papers onto a table with a water glass.

'Your Honour,' he said stridently to the judge, 'the Bewley Estate has always been in the ownership of the Davenport family. My client, Mrs Turnbull, may not be a direct descendant of the late earl but she is the last living member of the Davenport line. It cannot be denied that she has more right to the estate than any other.'

He continued in this vein for fifteen minutes or more, repeating the same assertion in different words: 'sanctity of blood' and 'noble family lineage' and 'rightful inheritor'. Mr Carruthers listened patiently, his expression serene. When the other lawyer's voice cracked and he finally stopped to take a sip of water, Mr Carruthers inclined his head towards the judge.

'Your Honour, Lord Bewley acted with full regard to the law. Witnesses were present when he amended his will in September of last year to name Mr McGovern as his heir. There are no legal grounds for Mr and Mrs Turnbull's declaration that they have an entitlement to any part of the estate.'

He ended there, seeming content with his succinct rebuttal. His counterpart jumped back in at once.

'On the contrary,' he said, a gleam in his eye, 'there is evidence to refute the legality of Mr McGovern's claim.'

Cormac shot Mr Carruthers a sideways glance. The lawyer didn't even blink. 'What evidence do you speak of?' he asked smoothly.

Mr and Mrs Turnbull both smirked as their lawyer produced a piece of paper with a triumphant flourish. 'I have here in my possession a letter which Lord Bewley wrote to Mrs Turnbull a mere three days before his death. In it, he states his regret for not having named her as his lawful heir from the outset. This letter is written in the earl's own hand and stamped with his own seal.' He waved the page about, looking smug. 'Your Honour, I must once again impress upon the court the sanctity of blood. Lord Bewley himself believed in it, belatedly realising so after he had amended his will and taking steps at the eleventh hour to remedy the error prior to his passing. The date of this letter, the twenty-third of October, supersedes the September date on his will, which means it expresses his very final wishes. When that is taken into consideration, there can be but one outcome to the proceedings here today.'

Mr Carruthers rubbed the tip of his finger over the birthmark on his cheek. 'May I see this document?'

The other lawyer held it out with an air of haughtiness. 'You may examine it as closely as you wish.'

Cormac watched uneasily as Mr Carruthers perused the letter. He inspected it at his leisure, his gaze raking up and down the page several times before he returned his attention to the court around him.

He sighed. 'I must admit, Your Honour, that this document has the power to dramatically alter the Turnbulls' circumstances.'

Cormac's stomach dropped.

'It is quite a remarkable piece of evidence,' Mr Carruthers glided on. 'The writing is undoubtedly in the exact same style as Lord Bewley's and the seal is a flawless rendition of the Bewley crest. Of course, samples of his lordship's handwriting could be found in historical records at the House of Lords, while the Bewley seal may be identified in any reputable book on the peerage of Bedfordshire. An agent of even average intelligence would be able to source both without too great an effort. I therefore must conclude that this document is a most impressive forgery indeed.'

The other lawyer emitted a squawk of indignation. 'That is an outrageous accusation, sir.'

Mr Carruthers shrugged. 'I stand by it nevertheless. This alleged letter is nothing but a fabrication. Lord Bewley didn't write it.'

'But you said yourself that the style of handwriting is exactly his!'

'Allow me to rephrase—Lord Bewley *could not* have written it.' Totally composed, Mr Carruthers extracted a document of

149

his own from the papers he had brought to the courthouse. Stepping forwards into the centre of the room, he cleared his throat and announced, 'This is an affidavit from Lord Bewley's personal physician, stating that his lordship had lost all use of his limbs by the fifth of October, 1846. He was unable to feed himself, much less hold a pen, a full three weeks before he passed from this life.'

A squeak of horror leaked from Mrs Turnbull before she was able to stifle it. Next to her, Mr Turnbull's eyes bulged. Their lawyer's mouth hung open in disbelief.

Mr Carruthers turned to the judge. 'Your Honour, I trust you perceive the truth of this situation, which is that the plaintiffs falsified this evidence in a hungry grab for wealth and property. It is a grave offence, one which could have had a detrimental effect on my client's rights, had the deception not been exposed. They came here seeking a fictitious justice, but true justice must now be exacted upon them.'

The judge glowered down at the Turnbulls from his elevated bench. 'Indeed,' he said coldly and beckoned to a bailiff standing at the edge of the courtroom. 'Take them away. They will be obliged to face a criminal trial.'

Mr Turnbull looked ill and his wife appeared close to fainting as the bailiff led them out of the courtroom. Mr Carruthers handed the false letter back to his defeated adversary with a bow and returned to Cormac's side.

'Your inheritance remains safe,' he said.

'Thank you,' Cormac said. 'That was exceptional work.'

Mr Carruthers offered him a wry smile. 'They made my job easy in the end. Such a simple blunder that undid the marvellous handiwork of a highly skilled forger. Thankfully, we can now put the whole affair behind us.'

Glad that the court case had come to a reasonably swift conclusion, Cormac was nonetheless frustrated that it had caused such unnecessary inconvenience and prevented him from travelling with Bridget to Ireland. And now with Emily away at the Hutchville Estate, he would have to wait until after she returned before he and the children could follow Bridget. Would Rory stay around long enough to journey with them or would he want to make his way back to America? Cormac wondered how much of a pull the Emmeline girl really exerted on him. Come to think of it, had Rory even written to her as Cormac had suggested?

He thanked Mr Carruthers once more for his services and they parted outside the Shire Hall. The lawyer was bound for London yet again, while Cormac set off on horseback to return to Bewley Hall. As he rode out of the town on his new mount, Orion, he decided that when he got back to the house he would take Jack and Gus, and Rory too if he wanted, out to the paddock for a lesson in horse riding. He and Bridget would soon have to hire a tutor for the boys to continue their academic studies, so now was the opportunity to take advantage of their unencumbered time.

On the far side of Gildham, he passed a dilapidated cottage at the side of the road that was fronted by a low stone wall covered in moss. A ladder was propped up against the cottage wall and two figures were perched on its thatched roof; they appeared to be trying to repair the thatch. To his shock, he realised that one of the figures was a woman and that she was quite heavily pregnant. He reined in his horse.

'Can I be of assistance?' he called up to them.

They both peered over the edge of the roof, nonplussed. 'Who are you?' the man asked.

'I was just riding by,' Cormac replied, evading the answer, 'and noticed that you might be in need of some help. Perhaps I could lend a hand while your wife takes a rest?'

151

Without giving them time to refuse, he dismounted, led Orion through a gap in the low stone wall and stood at the bottom of the ladder in expectation. Still looking bewildered, the man helped the woman manoeuvre her unwieldy body onto the top rung of the ladder and she descended slowly; as soon as she was within reach, Cormac grasped her arms and assisted her safely to the ground. Then he climbed up himself and joined the man on the roof.

'Thanks, this is mighty kind of you,' said the man.

'It's no trouble,' said Cormac. 'What's your name?'

'Harry Barnes,' the man replied. 'And my wife's Jill.'

Cormac surveyed the roof; it was patched in many places and had holes in several others. He noted the shoddy nature of the handiwork – Harry was clearly not a thatcher. To be fair, neither was Cormac and, now that he could see the extent of the disrepair, he thought the job might be beyond his ability to provide aid. Realistically, only a skilled craftsman could tackle it.

He tilted his head at Harry. 'Why not get a thatcher to do this? And why put your wife to such toil, especially in her condition?'

The man lowered his gaze, ashamed. 'Lord knows I didn't want to. But we badly need to fix this roof. We've been threatened with eviction if we don't see to the upkeep of our home and we can't afford to pay a thatcher, so we've been up here every day for the past week doing our best to patch it up ourselves. We can't risk losing our home with the arrival of our first baby so near.'

'Who threatened you?' Cormac asked, frowning.

'The land agent, Mr Sandler.'

Cormac felt a stab of displeasure at Mr Sandler's lack of sympathy towards the struggling couple, particularly after the order he had given to allow a two-month respite for tenants in arrears. 'I will cover the cost of the thatcher for you,' he said, 'and it will not be taken from your rent.'

Harry gaped. 'Who are you?' he said again, baffled. Then realisation dawned. 'Wait, are you the new lord up at the Hall?'

'I'm not a lord,' said Cormac, 'but I am the landlord. Come to Bewley Hall as soon as it is convenient for you and ask for Mr Comerford. I will apprise him of the circumstances here and he will make arrangements for a thatcher to pay you a visit to carry out the necessary repairs.'

He hardly waited for the man to stammer his gratitude before he climbed back down the ladder and left on his horse.

When he reached Bewley Hall, he brought Orion around to the stables. A stable hand came out to meet him but he released him from his duty with a friendly wave of his hand, wanting to brush down the horse himself. He led the animal into a stall and proceeded to groom it, relishing the familiar actions that had once been so much a part of his life as a stable hand back at Oakleigh. He needed this to keep himself grounded. He might have the power to generously throw money around and save a family from eviction but he must also remember that his origins were just as humble as Harry Barnes's.

'You know you have servants to do that sort of thing for you now, don't you?'

Cormac's hackles rose at the sardonic English voice, horribly familiar and unwelcome. He pivoted towards the half door of the stall and could scarcely believe his eyes. Garrett, of all people, faced him wearing a smart riding coat and carrying a whip.

A spear of loathing shot up through Cormac. What in God's name was this blackguard doing here?

His knuckles clenched on the brush. 'I thought I was quite clear the last time we met. You were to end all contact with this family, categorically and without exception, or suffer the repercussions.'

Garrett tucked his whip under his arm and raised his hands. 'I come in peace, I swear. And I do not come alone.'

He stepped aside and another figure appeared beyond the half door, also clad in stylish riding gear. The figure shared Garrett's height and good looks, with striking hazel eyes and a head of thick black hair beneath his hat. But his mouth...that petulant curve was all Mary.

'Patrick,' Cormac said in shock.

Emily had told him of her dealings with her cousin three years earlier, and how the boy raised as Edward Whitmore under the supercilious influence of Lord and Lady Anner had finally agreed to acknowledge his true parentage and be known as Patrick Lambourne. But Cormac had not had the opportunity to meet his nephew himself while he was in London. Now he stood before him, and it felt like his sister Mary was nearer to him than she had been in years. He could almost imagine her peering over his shoulder and saying smugly, 'You see that handsome lad? He's my sweet baby. I made him.'

Patrick offered no greeting, only looked around him with a bored expression.

Garrett grimaced at Cormac. 'I understand that my own presence is highly unpalatable but perhaps you would tolerate me in order to make a better acquaintance with your nephew? We have taken rooms at an inn in Bedford so we won't be a burden on your hospitality...although your accommodations are evidently vast, greater even than those at Swifton Hall, I'd wager.' His lip curled as he made the comparison to his own country seat.

Cormac contemplated him with dislike. What could be his purpose in coming here? There was some underhanded scheme in motion, no doubt. Part of him wanted to throw Garrett off his property without a second's hesitation, and yet he couldn't do that to his nephew. Apart from his own curiosity about the boy, he knew that if Mary was indeed watching these proceedings, she would be livid were he to turn her son away.

'You rode here?' he asked in a clipped tone.

Garrett nodded. Cormac called for the stable hand he had dismissed earlier and requested him to finish grooming Orion and to see to the two gentlemen's horses as well. Then he said to Garrett and Patrick, 'Come inside so.'

CHAPTER 19

Had he been on his own, Cormac would likely have used a back entrance to enter the house but, given his present company, he brought Garrett and Patrick around to the front door where David admitted them with a bow, before taking their hats and whips.

'Should additional places be set for the evening meal, sir?'

Cormac hesitated and Garrett intervened.

'No,' he said smoothly. 'We shall not intrude any further than necessary.'

Wondering what had motivated Garrett to intrude at all, Cormac asked for coffee to be brought to his study and the footman hurried away.

As they crossed the entrance hall, they were accosted by Jack and Gus, the latter sporting his tricorne as usual.

'Da, we've made a giant discovery!' Gus blurted. 'You've got to come to the library!'

'Have you noticed that we have guests, Angus?' Cormac said, hoping his use of Gus's full name would impress upon him the gravity of the situation.

Gus blinked while Jack looked at Garrett and Patrick with polite inquisitiveness. Garrett's face was impassive, and Cormac felt thankful that he refrained from exhibiting any outward revulsion in front of them, which would have been no more than could be expected, considering that these two children were the flagrant products of his wife's adultery.

'Boys,' Cormac said, 'this is Lord Wyndham and your cousin, Patrick Lambourne. They live in London.'

Jack and Gus goggled at Patrick.

'We didn't know we had another cousin!' Gus exclaimed. 'We just thought there was Maggie and whatever baby Auntie Orlaith has in Chicago.'

A glimmer of curiosity flickered across Patrick's face but he tamped it down, reverting to his previous expression of boredom. Cormac wondered whether Orlaith's name had jogged Patrick's memory of the servant girl who had once worked at Anner House.

'We wanted to show you something important, Da,' Jack said in a softer voice. 'But it can wait if you've got to look after the guests...'

His quiet, earnest hopefulness was too endearing to deny. 'Just for a minute, then,' Cormac said.

Gus whooped and grabbed his arm, dragging him in the direction of the library. Jack, Garrett and Patrick followed.

'Rory's there too,' Gus said. 'After we showed him what we found, he started reading some book.'

Gus sounded mystified and Cormac couldn't help feeling the same; Rory had never struck him as the bookish type.

However, when they entered the library, they did indeed find Rory standing by a bookcase, his shaggy head bent over an open book in his grasp. He glanced up and his features hardened. Snapping the book closed, he strode forwards.

'What the bloody hell is *he* doing here?' he demanded to Cormac, throwing Garrett a glare of deep hatred.

Cormac noted that the volume in Rory's hand was the very one Cormac had read years before to familiarise himself with his role as Oliver Davenport; it contained a comprehensive account of the peerage of the United Kingdom. Returning his attention to the matter at hand, he said, 'I don't actually know yet, though he assures me that he "comes in peace".'

Rory's scowl conveyed his unequivocal distrust.

'Da, look!' Gus said, impatient at this distraction. He pointed dramatically at the fireplace, or rather at the painting hanging above it. It was a portrait of a young lady wearing an elbow-length cape and sitting on a bench in a grove of beech trees. Cormac had seen the painting many times before but had never paid much heed to it. He gave Gus a questioning look.

'It's Lady Dorothea!' Gus announced. 'One of the scowly maids told me she spotted the lady's name written on the back when the frame was taken down for cleaning. Please, Da, can we check the back to see if there are any other clues?'

At Garrett's perplexed countenance, Cormac felt obliged to explain, 'Gus is trying to solve the mystery of a restless ghost on the estate.'

He sharpened his gaze, daring the gentleman to scoff. Garrett said nothing but, strangely, a rather rueful expression shaded his eyes.

'Please, Da?' Gus begged again.

'Not right now,' Cormac replied. 'We have company. Furthermore, the frame is old so it needs to be handled carefully. We can do it later or tomorrow perhaps.'

Gus drooped and then perked up in the space of an instant. 'Maybe Mr Comerford will give us a hand as well. He's a bit frightening but I think he wants to help the ghost as much as we do.'

'That sounds like a good idea.' Cormac ruffled Gus's mop of curls. 'I have to go now, lads, and have a meeting with our guests.'

'Actually,' Garrett said, 'could Patrick remain here? I would appreciate it if you and I could converse in private.'

This situation was growing odder by the second. Cormac asked Rory and the boys to keep Patrick company and then he and Garrett left the library to go to his study. When they reached it, they found David setting a tray on the desk. He glanced from Cormac and Garrett to the three coffee cups.

'Thanks, David, it's just the two of us,' Cormac said. 'Might I suggest stopping by the library to check if any refreshments are required there? At the very least, Gus will give you an enthusiastic response.'

'Very good, sir.' David grinned and exited the study.

Cormac seated himself behind his desk and Garrett sat opposite him, his brows drawn together in appraisal. 'Your new role appears to fit you like a glove.'

Cormac passed one of the cups to his unwelcome guest and took another for himself, waiting for the follow-up insult.

'I can't imagine that just any stable hand could be placed in such a position and succeed. Against my better judgement, I am impressed.'

In the face of the backhanded compliment, Cormac grew even more wary. Why did Garrett want to butter him up? 'I ask you to speak plainly,' he said. 'For what reason are you here?'

Garrett took a sip of his coffee. 'To appeal to you for help,' he replied. Cormac assumed that it was his words and not the coffee that brought a sour twist to his lips.

'Why would I wish to help you?' he asked coolly.

'Oh no, not me. Your nephew.'

That startled Cormac. 'What's wrong with him?'

'Nothing at all in physical terms. He is the picture of perfect health, as you have seen for yourself.' Garrett sighed. 'Apart from that, however, he is a very troubled young man. And it has reached the stage where I'm not sure if I can save him.' He looked directly at Cormac. 'But I believe you can.'

Incredulous, Cormac was stunned into silence.

'Will you hear me out?' Garrett asked.

After a pause, Cormac motioned for him to continue.

Garrett swallowed. 'My son has been in my custody for nearly three years and, while I dearly wish I could say that they have been the happiest of my existence, I regret that I cannot. I must admit that I envy what you are experiencing right now with your two boys. I can see that they are at a delightfully innocent stage and trust me when I say that, for your sake, I hope that reality may continue as long as it can. Patrick was already sixteen when he came under my roof, which meant that any trace of that innocence was utterly gone, while his troubles were only beginning. It would take too long to list all of his failings, but suffice to say that he has disappointed me on many fronts.'

Garrett shook his head. Cormac observed that any lingering black strands in his hair had fled since they had last met, leaving it entirely silver.

'Those wounds have been bad enough, but then several of my acquaintances have rubbed salt in them by commenting on how alike Patrick is to me. I presume they intend such remarks as flattery, but the fact is I can't help but acknowledge that my son is a spoilt, arrogant brat. What does that in turn say about me? Needless to say, it has brought about a marked increase in my own self-awareness.' He snorted. 'No doubt you will say that this sense of maturity is long overdue.'

Cormac wondered whether Garrett had enough self-awareness to notice that, even though he professed that this conversation was about Patrick, he was talking more about himself.

What he said didn't come as a great surprise, for Emily had told Cormac about her interactions with Patrick when he was still going by the name of Edward. By her account, his conceit had already been well established at the age of sixteen. Indeed, when Cormac himself had met him as a seven-year-old child on the doorstep of Anner House in Dublin, he had flaunted his superiority even then. But these qualities were generally valued by the upper classes. What could the boy have done to disappoint Garrett to such a degree?

'Tell me of his failings that you've alluded to,' he said. 'Unless you'd prefer him to tell me himself in an effort to draw out his shame?'

Garrett let out a huff. 'He would feel no shame, for he views them as accomplishments.' He gulped down some more coffee and then confessed, 'He dropped out of Eton. He left at the end of the Michaelmas Half and refused to return after Christmas, even though he only had two terms to go to graduate. Nothing I say will convince him to go back. He says his education is redundant, that he wants to live his life unfettered and no longer continue as a shivering inmate in that prison.' Garrett raised an eyebrow at Cormac. 'Perhaps in the course of your conversation with him you might inform him that you yourself have occupied a prison cell and that a school dormitory cannot realistically compare.'

Cormac picked up his cup, willing himself not to clench it as hard as he was clenching his jaw.

'Unfortunately, that is not the worst of it. Have you heard of the Duke of Northrop? I won't ask if you are acquainted with him as he moves in circles well above me, let alone you, either now or in your guise as Lord Bewley's nephew.'

Cormac gritted his teeth. 'No, I have not heard of the duke.'

'Then you haven't heard of the Duchess of Northrop either. The duke and duchess are very well respected in London. Both come from impeccable stock. The duke has an enormous fortune and I believe the duchess was once considered a match for one of the Prussian princes. That was back in the 1820s. They have been married more than twenty years now and have four or five children.' Garrett cleared his throat. 'The reason I mention them is that, at not even nineteen years old, Patrick took it upon himself to make a conquest of the duchess. And he succeeded.'

Cormac's mouth dropped open.

'Not only is she married and a quarter of a century his senior, but they have flaunted their affair around the city, attending plays together and riding along Rotten Row in full view of the ton. Naturally, the duke is not best pleased. Even he has the sense to carry out his liaisons behind closed doors. He feels that Patrick has made him the laughing stock of London. And he lays the responsibility for my son's poor conduct squarely at my feet. He paid a visit to Berkeley Square where he commanded me in no uncertain terms to get the boy's actions under control. I had a very stiff drink after that interview, I can tell you.'

Even now, Garrett looked like he wished there was something stronger in his coffee cup.

'I know I'm no paragon of morality myself,' he went on wryly. 'But I understand how to be discreet. Patrick's behaviour is reckless beyond belief. To publicly insult a man of such high standing! The duke is but a step below royalty.' He clicked his tongue. 'At least I can be grateful that he pursued a married woman instead of destroying a chaste young girl's reputation.'

Cormac slammed his cup onto the desk and the coffee sloshed over the sides.

Garrett glanced at him in surprise before he grasped the direction of Cormac's thoughts. 'I didn't ruin Bridget's reputation,' he said defensively. 'She did that herself.'

'And my sister?' Cormac ground out.

A shadow of guilt swept over Garrett's features. 'That was different. She wasn't a member of the upper classes.'

'So her reputation wasn't important?' Cormac snapped. 'You cur. I'm dangerously close to throwing you out. You're doing more to harm your plea than to help it.'

162

Garrett winced. 'Once again, I bid you to separate me from your nephew. It is on his behalf that I'm here. Let's set aside our personal grievances for his sake. Believe me, if I had someone else to turn to, I would go to them over you without hesitation.'

Cormac choked back his impulse to show Garrett the door. He would endure his unpalatable presence until they had drilled down to the crux of the matter. 'Why me? I have no dealings with dukes or the like. How could I possibly ameliorate the situation?'

'Oh, there's nothing you can do to appease Northrop. My first and only action there was to get Patrick out of London and physically away from the duchess. I trust that distance and time will operate together to dampen both the scandalised gossip and an eighteen-year-old boy's lust.' Garrett shrugged. 'No, I am seeking your intervention for a more abiding purpose. To help my son perceive the error of his ways and amend them.'

'And you as his father are not in a position to do that?' Cormac demanded in exasperation. 'You went to extreme lengths to assume that responsibility. Now you wish to pass it to somebody else?'

'I do not possess the insight that you do. You see, I am of the opinion that Patrick is struggling with a crisis of identity. He knows now that his mother's origins were humble and that his life in Anner House was a lie. He has finally acknowledged that I am his father and that the Wyndham title is his birthright, and yet that truth does not appear to sit well with him, which leads him to these acts of imprudence. It's as though he doesn't believe he belongs where he is and therefore he doesn't care about the consequences of stepping outside the parameters of acceptable conduct. I suspect that he considers himself to be an impostor and I know of no one else who has experienced that unique condition but you.'

Cormac sat back to digest this. At length, he said, 'What makes you think I would have the capacity to influence him? It sounds like he is not easily swayed.'

'I do worry that he is already too far gone to be redeemed. Certainly, I have failed to make any impression on him whatsoever. However, much as it galls me to admit it, you appear to be quite competent in matters of fatherhood. I could tell as much when Emily came to London in response to my letter. From the way she defended you and attempted to defy my machinations, it was plain that you inspired her respect and that you had raised her to have a profound sense of integrity. I understand that these traits are more easily sown at a young age, but perhaps you are skilled enough to work wonders even on an eighteen-year-old libertine?' Though Garrett's tongue spoke with acerbity, his eyes were eloquent with hope.

When Cormac didn't respond, Garrett's mouth screwed up with displeasure. 'Having addressed the matter of whether you are able to help Patrick, I suppose we should now confront the question of whether you would wish to do so. Your reluctance would be understandable, given that he is my flesh and blood, but might you consider it, given that he is also your family's flesh and blood?'

These words struck Cormac with the force of a physical blow as they dredged up a long-buried memory. He had said almost the exact same thing to Bridget's mother when she met Emily for the first time. *It speaks volumes that you are willing to forego an opportunity to meet this wonderful little girl solely on account of her blood connection to me. She also has a blood connection to you, if you cared enough to recognise that.*

As he reeled from this realisation, Garrett continued, 'I'm sure Mary would want her brother to do everything he could for her son. Moreover, rumours have begun to circulate in polite society that Patrick's objectionable exploits must stem from his lower-class mother's vulgar background, so I expect you would strongly wish to remove that tarnish from her name. But just in case you are not motivated to help out of a sense of family honour, allow me to offer a further incentive. If you assist me in this matter, I will divorce Bridget.'

Cormac's whole body went taut. 'I don't believe you for a single instant.'

Garrett spread his palms. 'I am willing to put my pledge in writing if you deem that to be necessary. I suppose you would be forgiven for not trusting me on my word alone.'

Cormac let out a short, harsh laugh. 'You suppose?' He narrowed his eyes. 'Why would you even suggest it? The way things stand, you retain absolute legal power over Bridget and Oakleigh. Why give that up?'

'Because I don't want it. Or, at least, I don't want it as much as I want my son to be happy. And I'm prepared to go to any lengths to achieve that. After all, I showed up on your doorstep, didn't I?'

There was an undeniable truth in that. It must have taken Garrett a lot of effort to suffer such a humiliation, which certainly indicated that he would sacrifice a great deal for the sake of his son's welfare. But would he really agree to divorce Bridget after all these years of keeping that noose tight around her neck?

'Why did you ever marry Bridget in the first place?' Cormac asked bluntly.

'Pride,' Garrett replied. 'And vindictiveness. And, if you'll believe it, a touch of shame. I had already destroyed one woman's life and thought to at least save Bridget from a ruined reputation. But of course, as we all know, marrying her did far more harm than good. I was a poor husband, although there were worse things I could have done. I could have been violent, or thrown her and Emily out onto the street. I confess

I contemplated it on several occasions, given that she clung to her memories of you with such provoking obstinacy. You shared our house in London throughout all the years of our marriage. We were never rid of you.' His tone was bitter.

While he had no inclination to feel sympathy for Garrett, Cormac wondered how he might have felt were their positions reversed and he had resided with a woman who pined for another man. Resentment must have built up on both sides of their marriage bed. Without doubt, Wyndham House was an unlucky place – it once contained a doomed marriage and now it housed an alarmingly wayward child.

Purposely leaving their exchange about Bridget and the divorce unfinished, Cormac asked, 'Is Patrick aware of your reason for coming here?'

'I only told him that I felt it was time for him to become acquainted with his mother's family. I didn't think it wise to divulge any more than that. If he suspects he is being steered towards rehabilitation, no doubt he will resist.' Garrett blew out his breath. 'I truly am out of ideas. I had half considered dropping an enormous responsibility on him, such as overseeing the management of Swifton Hall, or even banishing him to Ireland to the property my father and I purchased long ago in Kildare. I wondered whether a period of exile might bring him to his senses. But I feared that letting him too far out of my sight would allow his misbehaviour to deteriorate into total delinquency. And I don't believe that either option would address the root of the problem. So, though it nauseates me to say it, I am placing my hope in you.'

What an extraordinary situation. Neither of them could have predicted this the day they had first met, when Garrett had handed the reins of his horse to Cormac without even sparing him a glance.

'I'd like to go back to the library to speak with Patrick,' Cormac said, adding at Garrett's heartened expression, 'I'm not making any promises though.'

While he privately knew there was no possibility he would refuse to help his sister's child, he didn't want to give Garrett any outward guarantees just yet. With a resigned nod, Garrett put down his coffee cup and followed Cormac from the study.

When they returned to the library, they found that Jack and Gus had disappeared, probably on a fresh ghost-related mission. Patrick was lounging in an armchair near the fireplace while Rory sat at a table in the centre of the room, his back rigid and his face bright red. At Cormac and Garrett's entrance, Rory's blush spread down his neck and his eyes widened in embarrassment. What had the two lads been talking about? Rory jumped to his feet but Patrick retained his languid posture.

Already irritated by the boy's nonchalance, Cormac addressed him in an even voice. 'Your father tells me he would like you to become better acquainted with us, your family on your mother's side. Is that something you are amenable to?'

Patrick shrugged. 'I don't really care.'

Garrett stiffened. Cormac surveyed Patrick for a long moment.

'I can tell you much about your mother, your grandparents, and your uncle after whom you are named. I'm willing to answer any questions you may have. I won't expect amiability but I do demand civility. You are welcome to return here tomorrow, but only if you are prepared to adopt a basic level of courtesy for the duration of your visit. If that seems like too great a hurdle to surmount, don't trouble yourself to come.'

Patrick's face whitened in stark contrast to Rory's flushed features.

Cormac nodded at Rory. 'I must speak briefly with Mr Comerford about expecting a visit from one of the tenants, and I was thinking of giving the boys a horse-riding lesson after that. Would you like to join us?'

Rory's mouth hung open before he clapped it shut. 'Yes, sir.'

'I'll send David to you,' Cormac said to Garrett. 'He'll direct you back to the stables at your own convenience.'

He thought he read genuine gratitude in the gentleman's countenance. However, proud to a fault, Garrett merely responded with a cool inclination of his head. 'Thank you for your hospitality.'

Cormac departed from the library with Rory at his side and apprehension in his gut. What had he let himself in for?

CHAPTER 20

Bridget woke on the third morning of her incarceration, her body stiff and frozen to the bone, her feet like ice. It might have been May but the barn had grown cold each night, and she and Hawkins could only rely on their layers of petticoats to stave off the chill. They had not been provided with blankets, nor did they have any extra clothing as their belongings had been carried away when Mr Sandler and Duffy had made off in the carriage. Perhaps they could have huddled together for warmth, but Hawkins occupied a mound of hay on the opposite side of the loft, refusing to speak to Bridget. No wonder. If it wasn't for Bridget, Hawkins wouldn't even be in Ireland, let alone trapped in a hayloft with nothing but a slop bucket.

They had been given no food at all. On the first morning, when Sullivan had righted the ladder and climbed it to give them a cup of water, Bridget had asked about getting something to eat. 'We've got nothing to feed you,' he had spat at her. 'See how *you* like starvation.' The hunger pains were dreadful now and she curled her freezing limbs up tight against the ache. Hawkins moaned weakly at the other side of the loft.

Bridget shivered. It was impossible not to draw a parallel between this awful situation and her ill-fated journey to New York three years ago with Orlaith, Jack and Gus when they had been accosted in a dark alleyway and the two boys had been kidnapped by the Kelly Greens gang. However, that had been the result of happenstance – had they boarded a different stagecoach with a more principled driver, none of it might have happened – whereas this ambush on the road to Carlow had been deliberately intended for Bridget herself and orchestrated by someone she and Cormac had trusted. Thank God her children were not involved this time. She would suffer this ordeal in the knowledge that all three of them were safe, but she felt guilty that Hawkins had become unwillingly embroiled in it.

Sullivan had told them nothing, so she had no idea how he and Duffy had become involved in Mr Sandler's scheming. He only visited them in the barn at sporadic intervals, waving his knife threateningly and telling them to stay far away from the edge of the loft as he pushed a fresh cup of water towards them over the top of the ladder and took away the previous one. He had warned them that if they tried to attack him while he was on the ladder, then that would be the end of their water and they could die of thirst for all he cared. His grizzled father had not made an appearance in the barn since Mr Sandler and Duffy had departed.

She wondered whether Mr Sandler had reached Bewley Hall yet. How would Cormac react to her letter? Would he believe Mr Sandler? The agent's bruises would be very convincing. The sum he planned to extort from Cormac was exorbitant, and that was on top of the chest of rent money. She lamented the loss of it when it could have done so much to help the tenants of Oakleigh.

The barn doors opened below with a grating sound and she peered out from the loft to recognise the elder Mr Sullivan on the threshold. He glanced over his shoulder before coming through, carrying a cup and a small cloth bag. Expressionless, he looked up at the loft.

'You need to move well back,' he said, his voice deeper than his son's, 'or I won't give you anything.'

Bridget scuffled backwards across the hay, her stiff body slow and clumsy. Hawkins didn't even stir except to tremble with the cold. Bridget heard a scrape of wood and then the top rung of the ladder came into view as Mr Sullivan propped it up against the edge of the loft.

'Stay back,' he warned again.

'I am,' she replied.

The ladder creaked and his head appeared. He held onto the ladder's side rail with one hand and used the other to put the cup and bag on the loft floor in front of him. He jerked his chin at the bag.

'Something to eat,' he said brusquely and descended out of sight in such a rush that he forgot to take away their empty cup.

She crawled over to the bag and peeked inside; it contained a few crusts of bread. Rising up on her knees, she leaned over the edge of the loft again. He was setting the ladder down flat with a grunt.

'Where did you get this?' she asked, holding up the bag.

He hesitated, blinking up at her. 'I went to the nearest town. For the first time in months, I was actually able to buy food and even liquor thanks to the money that English fella gave us. Myself and Johnny ate two loaves between us so fast we nearly choked.'

'Does your son know you've brought us some?'

He glanced away furtively. 'He doesn't need to know. And ye don't need to starve. There'll be no ransom paid if ye waste away to nothing.'

'And you purchased liquor too?' she said, her mind racing ahead to various scenarios. What if one of the men attempted to climb the ladder while intoxicated – might she be able to best him? Or what if they both got so blind drunk that they forgot about their captives altogether?

Mr Sullivan narrowed his gaze. 'Johnny wanted it. He plans to drown himself in it once we're done with the two of ye. He's impatient though—I've had to rein him in already.' He added in a low mutter, 'The sooner this is all behind us, the better.'

He turned and she said hurriedly, 'Wait, please don't go.'

He faltered.

'Stay a moment. I am clearly no danger to you. I beg to know why you have chosen to throw your lot in with Mr Sandler?'

'The money,' he mumbled.

'And the money is worth the torment you are putting two women through?'

His dead eyes flashed, the first time she had seen a trace of strong emotion in them. 'You're only a bit cold and hungry. 'Tisn't so bad a thing for you to experience once in your life. And soon you'll be back in your fancy house again.'

'But Mr Sandler has turned you into criminals.'

'If he's looking to swindle a rotten English landowner, that's fine by us.'

She emitted an incredulous laugh. 'The man you are swindling is Irish through and through. He sent that money to this country to help starving Irish tenants.'

Mr Sullivan looked ashamed, but then he drew himself up. 'Well, aren't we starving Irish tenants too? We deserve it as much as anyone else.'

'Yes, but not in this underhand manner,' she said gently, willing her growling stomach to ignore the bread crusts just a little longer. 'Tell me, how did Mr Sandler contrive to establish your farm as the site for our captivity? We were scarcely in Dublin for three days. It was remarkably quick manoeuvring on his part to devise such an intricate scheme in so limited a time frame.'

Even more so given that he had spent much of that time in Bridget's company, although of course she couldn't account for his whereabouts during every single minute. He must have slipped away from the inn when she was with Hawkins in her room, or perhaps even after nightfall when they had gone to sleep.

Mr Sullivan squinted up at her. Evidently deciding that the information could do no harm, he said, 'He found Johnny and Duffy begging on a corner and told them what he needed and how much he'd pay. They couldn't say yes fast enough.'

Bridget gaped in disbelief. 'You mean he just happened upon them by chance? What are the odds of him finding two men in desperate enough circumstances to go along with his plan?'

Mr Sullivan snorted. 'Lady, every beggar in both the city and the countryside has a story the same as ours. There would've been no shortage of willing men. We're just lucky that he happened upon the two of them first.'

That gave her pause. 'What is your story?' she asked quietly.

The dead look returned to his countenance. 'Like I said, same as everyone else's. Blight, hunger, sickness.' His voice dropped to a whisper. 'Death.'

'I'm so sorry,' she said, her sympathy temporarily conquering her fear. 'Who did you lose?'

He looked down at his feet and said nothing. She waited. At last, he slumped onto the stool she had used as a writing desk and let his head fall into his hands.

'My mother,' he said. She opened her mouth to sympathise but he went on, 'And my wife. And my four daughters—Johnny's sisters. One of them was engaged to our neighbour, Duffy. And Johnny lost his wife and his two small girls. Too hungry to even cry, poor things, by the time the fever took them.'

Bridget stared down at him, aghast. 'That's horrific,' she breathed. 'I have no words.'

His shoulders lifted as he heaved a deep sigh. 'Sycamore Farm is only a place of ghosts now, full of painful reminders of their unfinished lives.' Raising his head, he pointed at the pile of abandoned netting at the far end of the barn. 'That was what the women were working on before they died. They were making nets to try to protect the coming year's crop from pests and birds. But they perished before they could complete them, and there weren't enough tubers to plant anyway. Everyone and everything's gone.'

Bridget's teeth clamped down on the tip of her tongue as the discarded netting took on a whole new significance.

''Tis only a matter of time before myself and Johnny go next. We don't want to emigrate. We want to die right here in Kildare, where all our women are buried. That means we need to hold onto the farm, but the landlord has threatened us twice with eviction. So Johnny went up to Dublin with Duffy to see if he could beg, or maybe steal, enough money for the rent. And then they met the English fella who promised even more than what we needed if they'd help him kidnap a lady. It was Duffy who came up with the idea for the sham highway robbery. He used to handle horses on his own farm so he was able to drive the hired carriage. The English fella gave money to Johnny to come down on the train ahead of time. He told me what was happening and then he picked a quiet stretch on the road to stop ye.'

She shuddered at the nefarious actions of all the men involved. 'Mr Sullivan, it doesn't have to be this way. I can get you the money you need without you having to resort to this ransom. I promise I will if you let us go.'

He wavered but then shook his head. 'I can't. We're too deep in it now.'

Desperation climbed her throat. 'But what you're doing is barbaric—your conscience cannot rest easy. Mr Sullivan, if Sycamore Farm is full of ghosts, that means they can see what's happening. What would your mother think of you? Your wife? Your daughters? How could you bear to meet them again in the next life after doing this monstrous thing?'

The hollowness in his eyes disappeared as remorse and fear rushed in. 'You shut your mouth!' he shouted up at her before leaping from the stool and dashing out of the barn, glancing wildly around him as though the ghosts were pulling at his elbows. She cringed as her vain hope of an ally vanished with him.

The shout was enough to stir Hawkins from her restless slumber. She sat up, groggy and shivering.

Bridget showed her the cloth bag. 'They gave us some bread.'

She divided it up between them and they swallowed the dry, hard crusts. A gritty lump stuck in Bridget's throat and she coughed, unable to clear it. For an instant, she panicked as her breathing stuttered. Then Hawkins thumped her back, dislodging the obstruction, and she gulped it down weakly with a mouthful of water from the cup.

'Thank you,' she rasped.

'We can't have you choking before the ransom is paid, now can we?' Hawkins said tartly.

Bridget lowered her gaze. 'I'm truly sorry that you have been dragged into this.'

'You and me both, my lady.'

'Given the situation in which we find ourselves, formalities seem rather redundant. Your addressing me as "my lady" can certainly be dispensed with. And might I perhaps call you Polly?' She looked up hopefully.

'No, my lady,' Hawkins said, turning away to curl up on her mound of hay.

CHAPTER 21

The day after the game of pall mall was Emily's birthday but, not in any sort of celebratory mood, she confided that fact in no one. Most of the guests had planned to sleep especially late that morning anyway as the first night of music and dancing was ahead of them and they all wanted to stay up enjoying themselves until the dawn. However, Emily was unable to sleep with so many wretched thoughts flying around her head – whether she ought to have accepted Lord Dartry's proposal, whether she could make amends for offending Harriet, whether it would be best to feign an illness and return early to Bewley Hall – so she rose and, after the maid assigned to her helped her to dress, she wandered down through the house, unsure whether she sought company or solitude.

She considered making her way to the breakfast room, but the late May sunshine pulled her outdoors to the terrace where they had played the drawing game on the first afternoon. Emerging onto it, she drew a deep breath of the balmy air into her lungs. As she let it out, she was startled to hear a pair of male voices issuing from below the terrace where a flight of steps led down into the gardens. At first, she wondered if they were servants but, as she listened, she realised from their polished accents that they must be guests, though she couldn't distinguish who they were from among the ones she had met.

A thin plume of smoke drifted up past the terrace's balustrade and the pungent smell of a cigar floated towards her.

'I hope I get to snatch a dance with Miss Yates this evening,' one man said lazily.

'And perhaps a little more?' the other teased.

'Unlikely. She has high standards, that one. Especially if she's confident enough to turn down a marriage proposal.'

'I wonder who the gentleman was. He must be licking his wounds after the rebuff.' The second man chuckled.

'Do you have your own sights set on any pretty miss tonight?'

'Maybe.'

'Go on, who?'

'That Miss McGovern is a peach, isn't she?'

Emily coloured. She knew she ought to retreat but she stayed where she was.

'You'd be willing to set aside all the scandalous baggage that comes with her?'

'Certainly, for a dance or two.'

'And perhaps a little more?'

'We'll see. She might be more pliable than the tight-laced Miss Yates.'

The source of Emily's blush changed from flattered pleasure to deep mortification. How had she given that impression?

'Dartry might have something to say about it.'

'Doubt it. Did you see them together yesterday on the lawn? I bet he showed his hand too soon and frightened her off.'

There was a pause, during which she heard one of them sucking on his cigar. The smoke wafted upwards and dissipated. 'She's only a wisp of a thing. Not a lot to grasp.'

'I hope she would be the one doing the grasping.'

They shared a guttural laugh.

'She does have talented hands. I was struck by her artistic skills using just chalk and slate. Quite impressive for a woman.'

'A tame game though, drawing birds and suchlike. If she were a man, we could have urged her to draw something more amusing.'

'Like what?'

'Bosoms.'

This was greeted with a snort of mirth. 'Indeed. Perhaps we could have set a challenge to see whether we could identify the lady just by the shape of the bosom?'

'Now *that* would have been good entertainment. I would suggest including Miss Hutchville's mother in the pictorial candidates. She might not be participating in the games in general but her contribution in this regard would certainly have been, ah, enormous.'

Emily was torn between humiliation at the shortfalls of her body and indignation at the infantile direction of the gentlemen's conversation. She withdrew from the terrace with quiet footsteps, leaving the two anonymous men none the wiser that they had been overheard.

Over the course of the morning, the other guests rose and partook of a late breakfast. Emily joined them, though she took care not to sit anywhere near Harriet. She glanced around surreptitiously at the gentlemen present but could not pinpoint who might have been the participants of the lewd conversation below the terrace. She even took a few discreet sniffs to see if she could detect a whiff of cigar smoke from any of them but to no avail. Perhaps she would discover the truth if the man who had called her a peach asked to dance with her that evening. Or perhaps she would prefer not to know at all.

A riding excursion had been planned for that afternoon and Emily was among the few who had to stay behind as she had not yet learned how to ride. She was glad to have an excuse to avoid the party for a few hours and thought she might go sketching in the gardens instead. She hurried up to her bedchamber to retrieve a pencil and her sketchbook from the belongings she had brought with her.

When she came back down, she found that the riders had begun assembling outdoors at the front of the house and that Mr Bertram and Mr Grover had just joined them. Emily watched Harriet give her brother an adoring hug, but her attitude towards Mr Grover was conspicuously reserved. She gave him a brisk curtsey and then asked him something with a steely expression and a curt gesture to the side. He frowned his assent.

As the pair stepped a few feet away from the rest of the group for a more private exchange, Miss Yates approached Emily.

'Miss McGovern, is that your sketchbook? Oh, I do beg your permission to see it!'

Pleased that she had not made an enemy of at least one person in the assembly, Emily obliged and handed it to her. Miss Yates flipped through it, exclaiming at intervals in admiration.

'Oh, a self-portrait—my word, the accuracy is astonishing...what a superb depiction of waves crashing against a ship, how marvellously lifelike...I notice several attempts to create a particular shade of green. You are quite the perfectionist!'

Emily smiled graciously while observing in her peripheral vision that Harriet and Mr Grover seemed to be having a somewhat heated argument. However, by the time the stable hands started bringing around the horses to the guests, Mr Grover appeared to have smoothed things over because Harriet accepted his assistance to mount, an honour which she could easily have bestowed upon her brother if she had remained unhappy with her suitor. The arrival of the stable hands also prompted Miss Yates to recollect the afternoon's scheduled activity and she reluctantly gave the sketchbook back to Emily.

'I must praise you once again for your remarkable gift,' she said warmly before departing to mount her own horse.

No sooner had she left Emily's side than Mr Grover strode over. 'What did you say to Harriet?' he flung at her by way of greeting.

She bit her lip. 'Nothing that wasn't the truth.'

He looked livid. 'She asked me if my affections had been engaged by another woman and whether I viewed her as a last resort for marriage. This is your doing, God damn it.'

He loomed over her but she stood her ground. 'If her eyes have been opened to the fact that you don't afford her enough respect, then I can only consider that to be a positive circumstance.'

'I've managed to convince her that you were lying, but you caused a lot of mischief, you little chit.' He glared down his nose. 'You shouldn't have interfered,' he said ominously, before spinning on his heel and walking away from her.

CHAPTER 22

Cormac wasn't sure whether to expect his visitors to return to Bewley Hall following his warning to Patrick about his conduct, but he glanced out of a window shortly after noon the next day and perceived two figures riding up the avenue towards the house. As they approached, he discerned Patrick's hunched shoulders and wondered whether it was coercion on Garrett's part or curiosity on his own that had compelled him to come back.

By the time the knock came on the study door, Cormac had rearranged the furniture so that his chair was on the near side of the desk along with two others, the three set up in a loose circle. He didn't want to sit formally across a desk from his nephew while they discussed the boy's family history and complicated identity. Sheppard conducted Garrett and Patrick into the study and, after a slight hesitation, Cormac extended his hand to Garrett. They shook gravely while he privately thought that twenty-four hours ago he would never have entertained the notion of such civility with the man. Nevertheless, he was willing to tolerate it for Mary's sake. He offered his hand to Patrick too and the boy shook it languidly.

Bracing himself for the challenging conversation ahead, he asked Sheppard to send David up with some refreshments. The butler withdrew and Cormac, Garrett and Patrick sat down, the

181

angles of their three chairs subtly stating that no one person had greater authority here. Cormac wanted to command his nephew's respect but he also needed to be approachable. Patrick's gaze darted around, his jaw locked tight, and Cormac sensed the need to tread carefully or the boy would bolt like an unnerved horse.

He cleared his throat. 'Do you have any particular questions as we begin? Or would you prefer me to talk?'

Patrick shrugged. Cormac decided to give him the benefit of the doubt for the time being regarding his manners.

'I'll talk then,' he said. 'I'd like to tell you first about your namesake: my brother, Patrick. He was the second of our siblings. Your mother was the first. In fact, they were born only ten months apart. She and Patrick were very close as children so I wasn't one bit surprised that she named you after him. He was a stable hand like me.'

Patrick's lip curled at that last piece of information.

'There is no dishonour in a life of honest labour,' Cormac said, his voice tight. 'Your uncle was decent and hardworking. There wasn't a bad bone in his body.'

Patrick flinched and Cormac suddenly recognised a potential problem in praising his brother – perhaps his nephew didn't feel he could live up to his namesake. There was already a precedent for this in the family: Cormac and Bridget had shortened their younger son's name to Gus so that he wouldn't have to bear the full weight of his admirable grandfather's name before he was ready.

Lacing his fingers in his lap, Cormac carried on smoothly, 'No one expects you to be the same as him, Pat. I'm just telling you about him so you know what kind of person he was and how much he meant to your mother.'

Both Garrett and his son blinked. Patrick narrowed his eyes. 'My name is Patrick. I'll thank you to remember that.'

Only for the vehemence in his tone, Cormac might have chuckled at how the boy's words and haughtiness matched the way he had responded that day at Anner House when Cormac had told him he was his uncle and Patrick had denied their connection and insisted that he be addressed as Master Whitmore. Would it be worth reminding him of that encounter?

But the opportunity passed by as David entered just then with the refreshments: a pot of coffee and several slices of honey cake. He laid out the cups and plates on the desk and left. Once the door had closed, Patrick, who was sitting closest to the desk, reached idly for a slice of cake as though he had no greater concern than that of satisfying his belly.

'Your uncle was your age when he died,' Cormac said quietly and Patrick froze in the motion of bringing the cake to his mouth. His Adam's apple bobbed. After a moment, he took a bite but Cormac suspected by the boy's grey pallor that he couldn't taste the flavour at all.

'Eighteen years old,' said Cormac. 'Far too young. He died in a stable fire.' He recounted what had happened, how the fire had probably been started by an abandoned rushlight, how the men and boys had rushed to save themselves and the animals, how Patrick had ended up dying only three weeks after their father. 'Our father was your grandfather, Jack McGovern, and he was a stable hand and a carpenter. The older of your two cousins you met yesterday is named after him.'

Patrick continued to say nothing.

'I understand that all of this doubtless makes you feel quite uncomfortable,' Cormac said. 'You probably don't want to claim any affinity to stable hands or carpenters, not when you were raised to believe that you were far superior to such simple folk. Lady Anner did much damage to you in that regard and I presume your father did not make any effort to rid you of that conviction.'

Garrett shifted in his chair.

'But the fact of the matter is that you are not better than the lower classes. You are equal to them because you came from them. And you are equal to the upper classes because you came from them too. You straddle both worlds but do not wholly belong in either. This truth is something with which you will need to reconcile yourself if you are to move forward with your life in a meaningful way.'

Patrick's hazel eyes had become troubled. He opened his mouth but, before he could speak, they heard a commotion outside the room and the door burst open. Mr Sandler staggered in with Sheppard and David close on his heels looking dumbfounded. Cormac shot to his feet as he took in Mr Sandler's bruised, dishevelled appearance. Though a hundred questions came to mind at the agent's unexpected return, he started with the most vital.

'Where is Bridget?' he demanded. 'Did she come back with you?'

Mr Sandler shook his head, breathless and pale. 'Taken,' he said hoarsely. 'By Irish bandits. On the road to Oakleigh.'

Cormac's heart lurched as Garrett exclaimed, 'Good Lord.'

'Has she been hurt?' Cormac asked Mr Sandler urgently.

'No, sir. They know she is too valuable. But they won't release her without a ransom.' Mr Sandler fished in his pocket and withdrew a folded note. 'They allowed her to write a letter to you. You will know her writing. You'll recognise its authenticity.'

Cormac took the letter at once and unfolded it. He could tell immediately that Bridget's hand had penned it and he read it quickly, frantic with worry.

My darling Cormac,

I know you will be alarmed when you read this but please be reassured that I am unharmed. Hawkins, too, is safe. Unfortunately, our carriage was waylaid by starving highwaymen on the road between Dublin and Carlow. They discovered the chest of rent money and realised that their victims came from even greater wealth than they had supposed. Now they refuse to release us, expecting that they can reap an even larger reward from their ambush. They have housed us in comfortable circumstances at a farm and will hold us there until Mr Sandler returns from the Bewley Estate with a sum of £30,000 in his possession.

Darling, Mr Sandler can be wholly trusted. He resisted the bandits valiantly but they had the advantage of numbers in three against one. They beat him quite severely but permitted him to leave in order to take my message to you and to collect the ransom. They insist that Mr Sandler must return to the farm alone. If you attempt to contact the authorities or send additional men to apprehend our captors, they have warned that our lives will be the price. I believe their threats and I beg you to heed them too.

I reiterate that we are being well looked after and I urge you to pay the ransom without delay. You and I both know that money holds little value in comparison to freedom.

With all my love and hope,

Bridget

Cormac's blood ran cold in his veins. He reread the letter more slowly, noting every single word. Then he just stood there as he tried to absorb its implications. He sensed everyone else's eyes upon him but he didn't move.

Eventually, Mr Sandler said, 'Sir? I believe we should make haste. I am prepared to do what is requested, despite my injuries.'

Cormac raised his gaze from the page to look around him. Mr Sandler winced in pain, his arms wrapped across his midriff, before heroically straightening his shoulders. Beyond him, Sheppard and David wore identical expressions, their eyes wide and their jaws slack. Garrett had risen to his feet and was frowning expectantly at Cormac. Patrick remained seated but his usually torpid mien had converted into a taut wariness.

'Yes, we need to make haste,' Cormac said in a low voice. Louder, he continued, 'David, can you seek out Mr Comerford? And Sheppard, please fetch Mrs Sandler. Tell them to come here at once. Speak to no one else.'

The footman and the butler departed from the study in a hurry. Mr Sandler looked questioningly at Cormac.

'We require the presence of both to discuss what will happen next,' Cormac said briefly.

Garrett put out his hand. 'May I see Bridget's letter?'

Cormac paused and scrutinised him intently before handing it to him. Garrett glanced down through it. His frown eased a little.

'At least she won't suffer anything more than boredom while she waits for you to play the champion. Even if you must do it from afar for once.' He clicked his tongue. 'How brazen of them to demand such a sum though. Do you even have that much readily at your disposal?'

Cormac didn't reply. He took the letter back from Garrett. Then he rounded his desk to the far side which was empty since he had moved his chair earlier. The desk was not so neat as it had been in Lord Bewley's time: the coffee cups and plates of honey cake accompanied a sprawl of assorted items that he had left discarded upon its surface, including the book on inheritance law and the penknife he had used to slit apart its pages. He pushed them all aside and placed the letter flat on top of the desk. Pressing a fist into the wood on either side, he stared down at it and read it again.

'Sir?' said Mr Sandler, sounding nonplussed. 'Ought we not to begin making a plan to gather the money?'

'We'll wait until everybody is here,' Cormac replied.

Sheppard returned first with Mrs Sandler. She sucked in a breath at the sight of her battered husband but, never a demonstrative person, she did not rush forwards to clutch him, nor did she break down in tears. Instead, she demanded, 'Who did this to you?'

'Irish bandits,' he said with an air of virtuous suffering. 'I might have had a chance against two, but there were three to best me. They have kidnapped the Lady Courcey and seek a ransom in exchange for her release.'

Mrs Sandler's gaze shot to Cormac. 'And will you pay it, sir?' she snapped. 'After what they have done to my husband and to your wi—your lady?'

He imagined what Bridget had been through and, as his initial shock thawed, an icy rage began to grow inside him. 'I will take the appropriate action,' he said.

David took longer to appear; Mr Comerford must have been out and about on the grounds. When at length they came in, Cormac could tell by Mr Comerford's lack of surprise that David had already informed him about what had happened.

'My niece?' he asked gruffly.

'She's as safe as she can be, given the circumstances,' Mr Sandler reassured him.

Cormac nodded at Sheppard and David. 'Thank you both. You may leave for now but please remain close by and ensure that we are not disturbed here until our business has concluded. Do not let word of this reach Jack and Gus. They don't need to be burdened with worry about their mother.'

After Sheppard and David had exited the study, their faces solemn, Cormac swivelled his attention to Garrett. 'Would you prefer Pat to leave too? He could go find Rory and tell him what's going on.'

'I want to stay,' Patrick said with perhaps the most animation Cormac had yet seen from him – in fact, he seemed so engrossed in the situation that he didn't even object this time to being called Pat.

Cormac didn't push the matter of sending him off; he would fill Rory in himself soon enough. Garrett shrugged, seeming content with his son's preference, and sat down again.

Straightening up off the desk, Cormac crossed his arms. 'It's vital that we analyse every minute detail of the ambush. Tell me, Mr Sandler, where on the road did it happen?'

'I'm not familiar enough with the Irish countryside to say for certain but we were a few hours outside of Dublin.'

'Would you know how to find your way back?'

'Yes, I'll recognise the spot when I come upon it.'

'Why did you not travel by rail down to Carlow?'

'The tracks were closed due to an accident, a most unfortunate coincidence.'

'Can you describe the perpetrators of the crime?'

'They looked no different to the other starving wretches we saw along the road. I do pity their plight and their desperation that led them to take such drastic measures.'

'In what condition did you leave the two ladies?'

'In satisfactory health, if in poor spirits. I assured them that I would return as swiftly as possible to liberate them.'

Mr Sandler had an acceptable answer for everything and Cormac nodded his acknowledgement of each one.

Then he said, 'Before we discuss how we are to proceed, I feel compelled to reveal some hidden details about my past that may be pertinent to the forthcoming situation. You are all aware of my fraudulence regarding the persona of Oliver Davenport. Prior to that, however, I was an even worse criminal. I worked for a moneylender in Dublin and carried out his despicable orders, threatening his borrowers and inflicting physical harm when they did not comply. A dagger was my weapon of choice.' Unfolding his arms, he casually picked up the penknife from the desk and twirled it, weaving it back and forth between his fingers as he used to do with the dagger Henry Munroe had given him. 'I hurt many people with it,' he said calmly. 'I even committed murder.' There was no need to tell them that the only person who had actually died from a dagger wound by his hand had been the moneylender himself, a man who had deserved death more than most.

Mr Sandler's brow furrowed. 'Why are you telling us this? You don't mean to involve yourself in delivering the ransom, do you? If so, I strenuously advise against it. You would put your lady in grievous peril. The Irish savages are dangerous enough to do anything.'

Cormac twisted his mouth. 'You're right, of course. I must heed their demands. And I regret that I spoke of such violence in the presence of your good wife.' He rounded the desk again and bowed towards Mrs Sandler. 'I do apologise, Mrs Sandler, for my indelicacy. Perhaps it would be best if you leave us? Could I prevail upon you to remove the refreshments as well?' He waved at the cups of coffee, long cold by now, and the plates of uneaten cake. 'We will need space on the desk to count out the money.'

Though she looked a touch peeved, her eyes were also alight with anticipation. She stepped towards the desk.

As soon as she came close enough, Cormac reached out to grab her by the arm and pulled her to him, her back to his front, trapping her body against his in an iron grip and bringing the penknife up to her throat.

'What the—?' Mr Sandler cried out. Garrett and Patrick both jumped out of their seats, eyebrows raised in mirror-image expressions of surprise. Mr Comerford uttered an inarticulate noise of shock. Mrs Sandler struggled in Cormac's grasp.

'What on earth are you doing?' she said angrily.

'Unhand her at once!' Mr Sandler commanded.

'I will not,' Cormac said evenly as the icy rage spread right through him to every extremity, hardening his stance and his resolve. 'I have her precisely where I need her to be.'

'Have you taken leave of your senses?' Mr Sandler spluttered.

'I feel obliged to ask the same question,' Garrett said cautiously. 'What can you mean by this?'

Mr Sandler took a step forwards and Cormac dragged Mrs Sandler backwards until the desk was in front of them.

'If you value your wife's life, you will not come any closer,' he warned. 'I have already explained my past acquaintance with a blade. I'm capable of doing plenty of damage, even with a mere penknife.'

Mr Sandler threw his hands up in bewilderment. 'I am at an utter loss here. Why are you threatening her?'

'It is in retaliation for what you have done to Bridget,' Cormac growled.

'That was not my doing! I told you how it transpired. I cannot be blamed that we fell foul of a highway robbery by chance.'

'You're lying,' Cormac said through clenched teeth. 'I know that you are responsible for all of this. I know you cannot be trusted.'

'What can possibly make you think that?' Mr Sandler exclaimed.

'Because Bridget told me so herself.' Cormac jutted his chin at the letter on the desk without slackening his hold on Mrs Sandler. She continued to squirm within his grasp but to no avail.

Mr Sandler gaped. 'But Lady Courcey explicitly said that you could trust me. Those are her words. It was her hand that wrote them.'

'And yet she also managed to communicate to me that her words were lies. I'm convinced she wrote them under duress.'

Mr Sandler's eyes bulged. 'What proof is there of that?'

Cormac ignored the question. 'What remains now is to establish the truth of what really happened. And you *will* tell me the truth, given that I hold a knife to your wife's throat right now.'

'But this is preposterous! I have already told you the truth. There is nothing else to tell. You will release my wife at once.'

Cormac shook his head in disappointment. 'On your head be it.'

Keeping an unyielding grip on Mrs Sandler with one arm, he extended the other that held the knife and plunged it down towards the centre of her chest.

'Wait, it was me!' Mr Sandler screamed. 'I made her write the letter!'

Everyone stared, horrified, at the hilt of the knife pressed against Mrs Sandler's sternum. She looked down at it in shock.

'No!' Mr Sandler shrieked. 'You Irish bastard!'

Cormac pulled the knife away from Mrs Sandler's body with absolutely no resistance, no tug of flesh or spurt of blood. He displayed it for all to see, showing clearly that he had folded the blade just before he had thrust it against her chest. Mr Sandler emitted a bleat of relief. Then he glowered at Cormac. The other eyes in the room, all of which had been so intently focused on the knife, now swivelled to behold Mr Sandler's guilty countenance. Cormac snapped the knife open again and waited for his confession.

However, it was Mrs Sandler who spoke. 'You son of a bitch,' she hissed over her shoulder at Cormac and he swallowed at the venom in her voice. Her bony body trembled against him with fury. 'You've ruined *everything*.'

Garrett cleared his throat. 'Madam, I have had many an occasion where I felt justified in bestowing that appellation upon him,' he said wryly, 'but for what reason would you wish to address him thus?'

'Bewley Hall should have been ours!' she snarled at Garrett. 'Three decades we worked on this estate, doing everything in our power to ensure that my husband would be the natural choice to inherit. We thought this upstart had destroyed all our plans when he showed up as Oliver Davenport, but fortunately he obliterated his own entitlement once his fraud was exposed. All we needed after that was patience. And then, at the very last, Lord Bewley chose to forgive him and name him as his heir! We've been cheated out of our just reward by this swine and his whore. Instead of dwelling right here in the earl's residence, we've had to watch the estate fall into the undeserving hands of those who fornicate on the hearthrug like beasts.'

Garrett gave Cormac an appraising look at this but Cormac had no time for embarrassment. He was floored by Mrs Sandler's vitriol and his own blindness in not having recognised the danger sooner. He had thought he had amply appeased Mr Sandler the day he offered those generous terms to him regarding the increase of his and Mrs Sandler's incomes and the promise of a substantial pension on top of the refurbishing of their house. Evidently, no terms would have been generous enough, given that the Sandlers believed they were owed the entirety of the Bewley Estate. But Mr Sandler in particular had been canny at concealing his dissatisfaction. He had bided his time. And Cormac had placed Bridget directly in the path of jeopardy when he had agreed to let Mr Sandler accompany her to Ireland.

'So the ransom demand comes from you?' he barked at the agent, masking his fear with every ounce of hostility he could muster. 'Do these Irish bandits even exist? Tell me, where is Bridget? If you've harmed her, I swear to God I'll make you a widower.'

Mr Sandler's eyes narrowed. 'Then we appear to be at an impasse. Because if you kill my wife, you'll never find your own woman.' A shadow of an ugly grin crossed his face. 'We shall have to bargain if either of us wishes to get what we want.'

'You're in no position to bargain,' Cormac retorted. 'You forget that you are outnumbered here.'

It was only after he said it that he realised he had made an absurd assumption that Garrett and Patrick would stand by his side in this matter. Jesus Christ, he had lost his head. It was folly to expect any kind of backing from a man who had wronged him so greatly in the past and a boy who cared only for his own profligate interests.

And yet, when he flicked his gaze to Garrett, the gentleman gave him a subtle nod and said to Mr Sandler, 'Indeed, you are at a distinct disadvantage, sir.' Beside him, Patrick folded his arms in an attempt to look intimidating. Cormac didn't know how much of their act was genuine but he was grateful nonetheless.

Mr Sandler looked at Mr Comerford. 'What about you? You've said plenty of times that this blighter had no right to be here.'

'I said he didn't deserve to inherit the estate after the way he treated Lord and Lady Bewley,' Mr Comerford said slowly. 'I always considered you to be the right fellow for the job and agreed with you that you'd been hard done by. But not anymore.' His jaw clenched. 'I thought it mighty surprising that you volunteered to accompany the lady to Ireland, but I assumed you'd managed to overcome your own resentment. Now I see that you were hatching your plan and didn't care if my niece became caught up in it.' His hands curled into fists. 'What have you done with my Polly?'

At this blatant shift of support in Cormac's favour, Mrs Sandler emitted a feral sound from deep in her gullet. 'You said this would work!' she screeched at her husband.

'I was sure it would,' he said defensively. 'There's nothing in Lady Courcey's letter to communicate a grain of doubt. I dictated it to her myself.'

'We should have just taken the rent money and run,' she lamented. 'We could have been long gone by now.' She let out a groan. 'After everything we did, the extreme lengths we went to with the Bewleys to make sure nothing stood in our way. It's all been for nothing.'

Cormac frowned. 'What extreme lengths?' When she didn't reply, he shook her. 'What did you do to them?'

'We were convinced Lady Bewley was barren,' she said unwillingly. 'But then one day she confided in me that she believed she was with child at last. An heir would have ruined our ambitions entirely.'

'What did you do?' he repeated, his voice hoarse with horror.

'I slipped her juniper berries in her tea. She thought she lost the babe of her own accord.'

A black hole of despair opened up inside Cormac, grief and wrath pouring out of it. He pressed the blade of the knife right against Mrs Sandler's skin. 'You deserve to burn in hell for that,' he choked out. 'All the lady ever wanted was a child. You stole that joy from her.'

'Take that knife away,' Mr Sandler said in a menacing tone, 'or I'll never tell you where your woman is. If I don't return to the farm, the savages will probably kill her. No doubt they'll have their way with her first.'

Cormac endeavoured to control his fury. Mr Sandler was right. He still had power here until Cormac could ascertain Bridget's whereabouts. He pulled the penknife back a couple of inches but still left it hovering above Mrs Sandler's throat.

'Where is the farm?' he asked tightly.

Mr Sandler scoffed. 'I'm not telling you anything until I get some reassurances.'

'What reassurances do you seek?' Cormac said with deadly calm.

'You will not involve the authorities,' said Mr Sandler. 'You will let my wife and I go free with enough money to keep us in comfort. In exchange for that, I will tell you where Lady Courcey and Miss Hawkins are.'

'No, you will *show* us,' said Cormac. 'I'm prepared to leave the authorities out of this but you shan't have your freedom until I see both women in front of me, alive and unharmed. Only then will I let you and Mrs Sandler go.'

Mr Sandler agreed quite readily to this, which gave Cormac a scrap of relief. If Mr Sandler or the bandits had already inflicted harm on Bridget or her lady's maid, then surely he would have baulked at this condition.

'In what circumstances will we find them?' he asked. 'Be truthful. Your wife's welfare depends upon it.'

'They're being kept in a barn,' Mr Sandler muttered.

Cormac ground his teeth. 'And there are three men guarding them?'

'Two. The third travelled with me back to Dublin and awaits there for my return.' Mr Sandler looked like he regretted having told the truth about the number of men involved – perhaps if he'd had the forethought to lie, he could have played up the danger and made Cormac think twice about confronting a dozen abductors.

'We need to make preparations to head for Ireland as soon as possible,' Cormac said tersely. 'You will take us to the place where Bridget and Miss Hawkins are being held captive, and I will bring Mrs Sandler to ensure your cooperation. It goes without saying that I officially relieve you both of your duties as land agent and housekeeper at Bewley Hall. Mr Comerford, I know you have been considering leaving this employment, but are you willing to take on the role of land agent in Mr Sandler's stead, at least on a temporary basis?'

Mr Comerford cast Mr Sandler a glare of contempt before giving Cormac a brusque nod. 'I am, sir.'

'Very good, but I'm afraid your first task is an unpalatable one. I need you to fetch Sheppard and David and with their help confine Mr and Mrs Sandler in two separate rooms until we are ready to depart. That is, if you trust that Sheppard and David will not side with the Sandlers?'

'I don't believe they will, sir,' said Mr Comerford. 'Not when I tell them what they've done to Polly and to Lady Courcey. I know David in particular has grown very fond of her ladyship.'

Mr Comerford strode from the room. After he had gone, Cormac turned to Patrick.

'Pat, will you go seek out Rory and bring him here? I think you'll find him up in the attic. He agreed this morning to indulge Jack and Gus in their mission to visit Lady Dorothea's haunting place.'

To his credit, Patrick didn't demur. Looking rather stunned by all that had taken place, he left the study as well.

Mr Comerford returned with Sheppard and David; both wore steely expressions. Cormac at last lowered the penknife and relinquished Mrs Sandler into Mr Comerford's clutches, while the butler and the footman each took hold of Mr Sandler's arms. He felt very uneasy as he watched the fuming Sandlers being escorted from the study, but he needed to take a moment to breathe and process this unforeseen, terrible turn of events.

Snapping the penknife closed, he dropped it onto the desk and threw Garrett a wary glance. 'I'm surprised you didn't take the opportunity to weigh in on the Sandlers' side. It would have been a chance to exact revenge on me, if in an unorthodox manner.'

Garrett shrugged. 'For the sake of my son, I need to try to get into your good graces, don't I?' He twisted his mouth. 'And for all my failings, I draw the line at incarcerating two women in a barn like animals.'

Cormac grunted. What a revelation to learn that Lord Wyndham actually possessed some basic morals buried deep beneath his conniving nature.

'I'm curious,' Garrett went on. 'How did you know that Bridget's letter wasn't authentic? Her words seemed entirely sincere to me.'

Cormac chewed the inside of his cheek for a moment before deciding to tell the truth. 'She told me long ago that she detests

197

the endearment "darling" because it's what you used to say to her. She deemed it to be empty of any true feeling and, for that reason, it's not a word that we have ever used between us. So when she addressed the letter to "my darling Cormac" she could only have intended it to relay to me that something was amiss. And then she repeated it when she said that Mr Sandler could be wholly trusted. I understood immediately that I had to be on the alert and that Mr Sandler ought to be the target of my distrust.'

Garrett looked discomfited and, rather astonishingly, contrite. 'I see.'

'In all honesty, I also suspected you at the outset. There was every possibility that "darling" was a clue that you were somehow involved as well, especially considering the coincidental timing of your arrival at Bewley Hall.'

Garrett lifted his chin. 'And what allayed your suspicions, pray tell?'

'No motive,' Cormac said with an arched eyebrow. 'You had nothing to gain from the situation.'

'How fortunate that my self-serving character saved me from your accusations,' Garrett said dryly. After a beat, he said, 'Patrick and I will come with you to Ireland.'

Cormac opened his mouth to object but no words came out.

'You know you need allies in this endeavour,' Garrett said. 'And I feel a disagreeable urge to make amends. Bridget is, after all, still my wife. No one but you knows her better.'

Cormac would have liked to point out that there were a great number of people who knew Bridget better than Garrett, not least her own daughter. But now was not the time, not when Bridget was in peril and Cormac ought to be accepting all the help he could get, no matter the dubious source of it.

'Are you sure you want your son to come too?' he asked.

'Yes,' said Garrett. 'I think this might be exactly what he needs.'

He didn't elaborate any further as Patrick came back into the room at that point with Rory. Rory looked mystified, so it appeared that Patrick had restrained himself from spilling the bad news before Cormac could break it to him.

Cormac briefly told Rory what had happened to Bridget and then said, 'I need to go to Ireland to rescue her, but I have to know that the rest of my family is safe while I do so. Will you take the carriage to the Hutchville Estate right away and bring Emily home? I don't want to leave here until she's back. She might resent me for taking her away from the entertainment but you'll have to insist upon it. After that, I must ask a further service of you. Will you remain here at Bewley Hall to watch over her and Jack and Gus until Bridget and I return?' He would be leaving Mr Comerford in charge of the estate, but there was no one better than Rory to look out for Emily and the two boys.

'Yes, sir, I will,' Rory agreed without hesitation.

It gave Cormac comfort to know that he could implicitly put his faith in Rory, particularly when the past hour had blurred the line between the people he thought he trusted and those he believed he could never trust.

CHAPTER 23

'May I have the next dance, Miss McGovern?'

Emily caught a whiff of cigar smoke as the young gentleman bowed to her and became instantly on her guard. Past his shoulder, she espied another gentleman leaning against a wall nearby and eyeing their interaction with interest while pretending to watch the dancing couples out on the floor who were twirling to the energetic music of the small orchestra. These were doubtless the two participants of the indecorous conversation about bosoms that she had overheard on the terrace beyond the ballroom's French doors. Indeed, when the man in front of her straightened, his gaze lingered too long on the slight dip at the centre of her neckline before it rose to her face. Her lavender gown was styled off the shoulder with a pretty panel of lace hanging from its neckline, wide enough from arm to arm to cover her bust and her short sleeves. She had adored it, but now she felt that this young man's stare had cheapened it.

She did her best not to reveal her disdain for him as she said, 'I'm afraid I have already promised the next dance to Lord Dartry.' When she dipped her head with feigned disappointment, several ropes of her curls bounced lightly on either side of her face; the rest were bundled up into a bun at the back of her head.

He offered her an amused grin. 'That is my grievous loss. Rest assured, I shall seek you out again later.'

Curtseying, she privately resolved to make every effort to ensure that this was one 'peach' he would not lay his hands on.

She supposed his amusement stemmed from the notion of her dancing with Lord Dartry after refusing his proposal. But in truth, Lord Dartry had continued to be quite pleasant to her since that conversation on the lawn, and when he took her hand for the next dance, it was with a charming smile, which he retained even when she stumbled through the dance steps. Part of her wondered whether he was holding out hope that his unfaltering decency might encourage her to change her mind and accept him, and another part wondered whether she ought to do just that. In fact, she nearly opened her mouth to say it. By not exhibiting any vindictiveness towards her, he had demonstrated that he was not a spiteful man. Still, that made it all the stranger that he would put his foot down about her art exploits. Perhaps he was just too obsessed with society appearances to allow it. And that would stifle her in the long term, she was sure of it. She kept her mouth closed and they carried on dancing amicably, although without any heat of attraction.

After the dance ended, she curtseyed to Lord Dartry and made her way purposefully off the dance floor, hurrying away lest the young gentleman return to renew his request. She stepped through the French doors out onto the terrace, where she came upon Harriet Bertram and Miss Hutchville deep in conversation. Hesitating at the sight of Harriet, she started to move towards the other end of the terrace so as not to cause any unpleasantness, but Miss Hutchville beckoned her over.

'Oh, Miss McGovern, isn't there the most magnificent moon tonight?' she gushed. 'I do very much want to dance but I simply cannot tear my eyes away from the sky.'

Emily glanced up; the night sky was cloudless and the moon full, casting its silvery sheen upon the gardens below the terrace, almost as bright as day itself. It was, in fact, quite breathtaking.

'I'm sure your painter's eye appreciates it even more than I can,' said Miss Hutchville. 'No doubt you are noting how all the details we take for granted in the sunlight become so changed in the moonlight. I wager you would disappear into the gardens with your sketchbook right this minute if given half the chance.'

Her laugh tinkled on the night air while Harriet offered a false smile.

'Indeed,' she said. 'Let us go inside to allow Miss McGovern to enjoy a moment of solitude in this painter's paradise.'

They went back into the ballroom, leaving Emily alone. She crossed to the far side of the terrace and leaned on the balustrade above the place where the two men had enjoyed their smoke that morning. Gazing out over the gardens, she perceived that Miss Hutchville was right; the moonlight altered a great deal, eliminating colour but adding rich layers of shadow and light. She truly did long for her sketchbook. Perhaps she could try to commit some of it to memory and render it on paper the next morning as well as she could. When she heard a nightingale burst into song somewhere among the trees, her feet pursued its call, her mind's eye already picturing how the silvery rays might look on its plumage.

Descending the steps from the terrace into the gardens, she passed beneath a trellis draped with ivy and followed a gravel walkway lined with tall laurel hedges. There, she espied the nightingale perched atop the hedge, its plain brown feathers made exquisite by the ethereal moonlight, and she excitedly began to consider which of her watercolour cakes would best aid her in her depiction of the beautiful creature. It fluttered away as she approached and she lost sight of it beyond the tall hedge, left only with an impression that she had been gifted a privileged glimpse into the marvels of nature. What a spectacular birthday present.

Suddenly, she heard footsteps on the gravel behind her and whirled to see Mr Grover coming along the walkway. A shiver of revulsion rippled over her skin, augmented by wariness. What was he doing here? He came to a stop in front of her, a smirk dancing around his mouth.

'What brought you out here all by yourself, Miss McGovern?' he drawled.

'I sought a breath of air,' she said, her voice tight. 'I am going back inside now.' She moved to stride around him but he shifted so that he remained in her way. 'Please allow me to pass,' she said with icy politeness.

'No,' he replied just as coldly, his casual demeanour gone in a flash. 'My moment of retaliation is at hand.'

She took a step backwards, her wariness growing into fear. 'Retaliation?'

'Yes. You damaged my good standing with Harriet. So now I shall irrevocably damage yours.' He closed the gap she had just created between them. 'In the eyes of all society.'

Horrified, she tried to draw back again but he grabbed onto the panel of lace at the front of her gown. She continued to jerk away but he didn't let go and the lace ripped. She stared down in disbelief at her chest where the material now hung in front of her bodice in two torn pieces.

'I can't go back to the party looking like this!' she exclaimed.

He chuckled meanly. 'You won't be going back to the party at all. After what happens next, you'll want to retreat to your bedchamber in disgrace.'

Now she was truly frightened. Though her chin trembled, she lifted it boldly. 'Do you mean to force yourself upon me?'

He appraised her as a butcher might scrutinise a slab of meat. 'I don't think you'd be worth the effort,' he finally said in a cutting tone. 'Besides, that's not my purpose here. Although I suppose there's no harm in getting a little taste.'

He planted his two palms on her bare shoulders and pulled her roughly to him. She managed to turn her face just in time and his clammy mouth landed on her cheek. Repulsed, she struggled in his grip.

'Let go of me!' she demanded.

When he didn't comply, she gathered her saliva and spat at him. The wet globule hit his chin. He grunted and released her in surprise. She reeled around to run away but she wasn't fast enough; he seized her viciously by the elbow while he wiped his chin with his other hand.

'Now we see your true breeding shining through,' he remarked. 'Makes my job all the easier, not to be hampered by any compunction whatsoever.'

'Your job?' she said, bewildered.

He grinned. 'I've already started with the dress. Now let's see, what else can I do?'

With his free hand, he tugged on several pins in the bun at the back of her head, causing her hair to fall into disarray. Then he plucked a couple of leaves from the nearest laurel hedge and slipped them into her tumbling curls. She reached up to brush them away but he batted her arm back down.

'No, no, you of all people must know that you shouldn't disturb an artist at work.'

She scowled. 'What are you trying to do?'

'I'm preparing you for your audience. In just a few short minutes, a group of ladies from the party will take it into their heads to get some air in the gardens. They'll come along this path and what will they see but a young lady who has clearly been involved in a scandalous tryst. Your reputation will be left in tatters, just like your dress. No one, not even Dartry, will entertain a connection with you then.'

She stared up at him, aghast. 'But if they see you here too, they will assume that you are my lover. There will be an expectation that you will do the honourable thing and offer for my hand. Surely you do not wish that?'

He snorted. 'I certainly do not. I will make my escape further into the gardens shortly before their arrival. But not before' – he delved into his pocket and pulled out a white cravat – 'the final piece of damning evidence that you were enjoying a gentleman's company.' He clicked his tongue. 'Such a terrible scandal. Your family's name, poor as it was to begin with, will never recover.' He dropped the cravat onto the gravel at their feet.

'This is outrageous!' she cried. 'All because I told Harriet the truth about your low opinion of her? You wretch. If you behaved with a bit more decency towards women, you would not find yourself in the position of resorting to these cowardly measures to exact revenge.'

His eyes flashed. 'I will not be upbraided by a chit of common blood,' he said with contempt. 'You deserve everything that's coming to you.'

She attempted once more to pull herself free but he held fast, crushing her to him. Although his face was perilously close to hers, he didn't try to kiss her again. Instead, one hand snaked up between their bodies and clutched brutally at her breast. She yelped in pain.

Then she heard crunching gravel further back along the walkway and realised that the ladies from the party were about to arrive to witness her in a compromising position. Except Mr Grover had not yet vacated the scene, which meant he would be obliged to propose to her out of so-called honour. Well, she would refuse him outright, reputation be damned. She would shout that he was taking advantage of her and if they chose not to believe her, then to hell with them all.

In the next moment, Mr Grover was wrenched away from her. Shocked, she saw him stumble and fall onto his knees as a shaggy-haired figure towered over him, breathing hard.

'Put another finger on her and I'll end you,' Rory snarled.

Rory? Emily gaped, utterly stumped as to how he had shown up at the Hutchville Estate, and at this time of the night.

Mr Grover grimaced and stood upright. 'I'd like to see you try,' he sneered foolishly.

Without hesitation, Rory swung at the gentleman and his knuckles elicited a satisfying crunch as they connected with Mr Grover's nose. Mr Grover gasped and blood spurted out onto his upper lip. He drew back but Rory didn't relent. He punched Mr Grover again, delivering a blow to his chin and then another to his nose. Mr Grover fell onto his backside with an agonised groan. He put his arms up defensively over his battered head.

'Call off your dog, for heaven's sake!' he snapped at Emily.

She crossed her arms over her ripped gown and said nothing.

Rory loomed over Mr Grover, his fists still raised. 'You don't get to look at her again,' he panted. 'You don't get to talk to her either. If you do, you'll end up with no eyes or teeth left in your skull. D'you hear me?'

At first, Mr Grover seemed inclined to be mutinous, but then he tried to breathe in and winced. 'I hear you,' he said sullenly, his face bloody and his gaze incensed. He scooted backwards on the gravel and climbed to his feet. Pressing the back of his hand to his nose to stem the flow of blood, he turned and lurched away along the path further into the gardens.

Rory swivelled back to Emily. His green eyes were ablaze with anger. 'Did he hurt you?'

'No,' she wavered and then said more strongly, 'No, I'm all right. Rory, what on earth are you doing here?'

'I'll explain,' he said. 'Are you sure you're all right though? I saw him—'

She cringed at the memory of Mr Grover's hand grabbing her breast. 'It was...unpleasant, but I'll be fine. Thank you for getting him off me.'

Rory still looked furious. 'I heard two girls talking in a corridor outside the ballroom. They were planning a trap for you in the gardens. One of them said she'd already sent a fella out after you and that they just needed to wait a few minutes before following.' He glared down the path where Mr Grover had disappeared. 'They were all plotting to ruin your reputation.'

Much to her own surprise, she laughed and threw her hands up into the air. 'Honestly, they don't need to. My reputation is already sullied beyond redemption.'

'How?' he said, taken aback.

'Mr Carruthers was wrong—I'm not really considered an eligible match at all. No matter where I go, people make mention of my family's scandal and my lower-class blood. Some of them tolerate me while others are downright abusive. Frankly, I'm tired of waiting for the next insult to be thrown at me. I'm either viewed as dirt under their boots or a means of gaining wealth and, having witnessed the pitiable struggle of one girl to retain the attentions of a contemptible man, I've decided to have more self-respect than that.' She put her hands on her hips. 'I shall not settle for someone less than I deserve. I thought I would be helping my parents, but in reality I would just be doing them, and myself, a disservice. I'm far better off being a spinster.'

He stared at her. 'But...' He swallowed. 'It can't have all been for nothing, what we did.'

She blinked. 'What *we* did?' She was all too conscious of the choices she had made and suffered from, but what had he done? She frowned. 'Rory, what do you mean by that?'

He glanced away. 'Nothing,' he muttered.

Something tickled her neck and she realised it was one of the laurel hedge leaves still stuck in her hair. Plucking it out, she let it fall to the ground beside the discarded cravat. When she returned her gaze to Rory, her breath caught in her throat. He was looking at her again and there was a *want* in his expression that hadn't been there a second ago. It exuded from him like he had just taken a damper off a furnace. She meant to reach up to her hair to seek out the second leaf but her hand faltered in mid-air. She felt exposed under his intense stare. She sensed his hunger and, if she wasn't mistaken, it seemed to be directed towards her.

Her pulse pounded. 'Rory—'

'I've been an idiot,' he said. 'And I'm worried 'tis too late to fix what I did.'

That made her worried too. 'What did you do?' she demanded. 'Just tell me!'

He heaved a breath. 'I lied to you. I thought it was the right thing, that I was giving you the best chance. But it sounds like it hasn't made a blind bit of difference, and now I wish—' He broke off awkwardly.

An inkling of comprehension dawned on her and, with it, not a little anger. Striving to control her temper, she said evenly, 'Tell me it all.'

Even in the moonlight, she could discern the flush creeping up his neck. 'I overheard the lawyer talking to your da back in Boston. He said you needed to marry well to help your family and for your own sake too, and that it had to be a gentleman with influence and connections. Sure, that wasn't me. On top of that, I'd started to wonder whether your feelings might have cooled while you were away because you only talked about your studies in the letters you sent from New York. But I figured you'd be too nice to tell me that you'd lost interest or that I wasn't good enough for you, so I reckoned it was probably best for you to believe that I didn't, uh, feel the way I used to.'

Her ire rose even further. 'Your relationship with Emmeline?' she bit out.

'We made it up,' he said, guilt written all over his face. 'I went to her 'cause she was your friend and I thought she'd be willing to help you in a roundabout way, but I actually think she did it out of jealousy.'

Emily could believe that. It wouldn't have been the first time Emmeline wanted to take something away from her.

'I'm really sorry for the way you found out though,' he said. 'I didn't know you were coming to Broad Street that day. I'd been planning to introduce Emmeline to my ma, to plant a rumour that you'd hear later through your own ma. I didn't mean for us to meet like that. It must've hurt.'

'It did,' she said, seeing no reason to lie about it.

His features twisted with remorse. 'Hurting you was the last thing I wanted. I was honestly trying to do what I thought was best for you, even if it meant we couldn't be together.'

Her heart skipped a beat. 'Then you didn't think I'd been gone away to New York for too long?' she said, attempting to keep her voice steady. 'You had been waiting for me?'

His throat bobbed. He nodded.

She launched herself towards him. He put his hands up as though to ward off an attack but she pushed them out of the way, grabbed him by his ears and tugged his head down towards hers. Their mouths met with a fierce impact. She pulled away to say breathily, 'I agree: you have been an absolute idiot, Rory Carey.' And then she was kissing him again, harder than before.

He clutched her to him and his grasp was so different to Mr Grover's, not rough or overbearing but ravenous and worshipful. His tongue was greedy while his fingers were gentle, and his body pressed against hers, combining possessiveness and tenderness in the most exhilarating way. Her legs started to tremble, just as they had done when they'd first kissed so long ago in the workshop.

The gravel crunched nearby and a chorus of female gasps rose up. Emily and Rory broke apart. Standing there staring at them with slack mouths were Harriet Bertram and Miss Hutchville, along with Miss Hutchville's mother, Miss Yates, and even Lord Dartry. The latter gawked with palpable disappointment, while Harriet and Miss Hutchville seemed confused. Genuine shock filled the faces of Miss Yates and Miss Hutchville's mother. Emily pictured how she must appear to them with her torn gown, her tousled hair and a laurel leaf still trapped in her curls.

'Oh, my dear girl,' Miss Hutchville's mother lamented. 'You have utterly ruined yourself.'

Emily looked up at Rory. 'I have never been so happy to be ruined,' she said, beaming.

CHAPTER 24

In a matter of hours, Emily and Rory were in the Bewley carriage, the driver urging the horses as fast as he dared in the darkness, two lanterns at the front of the carriage illuminating the road ahead. Rory had told her what had happened to her mother, and Emily's things had been packed haphazardly into her trunk, which sat now by her feet. She was horrified and enraged at the Sandlers' despicable conduct. How she feared for her mother's safety.

Overwrought with fright and fury, she hunched within her cloak, which covered the evidence of her ripped gown. When Rory informed her about the unexpected arrival of Garrett and Patrick, her blood boiled even further.

'As if we didn't already have enough trouble,' she seethed.

Needless to say, all of this dreadful news had dampened the passion that had risen so swiftly between her and Rory in the gardens of the Hutchville Estate. However, she had desperately seized his hand at her initial shock and, when she didn't release it, he seemed entirely happy to leave it there too.

They didn't let go of each other until they reached Bewley Hall. Emily scarcely waited for the carriage to stop moving before she jumped from her seat. When she and Rory got out, the night was still dark, though a grey tinge to the sky showed that dawn was not far off. All the inhabitants in the house ought to have been asleep at this late hour, but light glowed from many of its windows and Sheppard was ready to receive them at the front door.

'Where is my father?' she asked the butler at once, but there was no need for him to reply because her father was already striding across the entrance hall towards her. She ran to him and buried herself in his arms.

'I'm sorry for cutting short your trip away,' he said and she perceived the strain in his voice. 'I just needed you back here. I had to know you were safe before I left.'

She pulled back to look up at him. 'I understand, Papa, and I'm glad you did,' she assured him. 'But I want to come with you to Ireland and help you rescue Mama.'

He shook his head emphatically. 'I have to be able to put all my focus into finding your mother. I can't worry about you too.'

'Surely you cannot mean to travel alone?' she exclaimed. 'It's too dangerous!'

'I'm not going alone,' he said, glancing over his shoulder. That was when she noticed Garrett lingering at the far end of the hall, Patrick just beyond him.

'You're not serious,' she said incredulously. 'Why would you trust him?'

'He has given me his reasons,' her father replied, his tone weary.

She gaped. This was inconceivable. He had to be too exhausted and anxious to think straight.

Letting go of him, she stamped across the hall and stood in front of Garrett, arms akimbo. 'What game are you playing this time?'

Garrett grinned. 'No game. I am here entirely in earnest.'

'Stop smirking,' she snapped. 'My mother is in danger. There's no room here for your sarcastic remarks.'

His face sobered but her skin still crawled.

'You somehow have a hand in this, don't you?' she said, hurling the accusation at him like a javelin.

'I do not,' he said. 'Your father and I have already had this discussion. I've been blameworthy in the past but in this I am guiltless, and I will continue to vehemently swear so.'

She pointed a finger at him. 'If you plan to interfere rather than help, then we have no use for you.' Her finger swivelled to Patrick. 'The same goes for you. I can't imagine why you would even agree to go. The boy I met three years ago wouldn't lift a finger to warm himself. Have you so dramatically changed since then?'

'No,' he admitted. 'If anything, I'm worse.'

She whirled around. Her father and Rory had by now crossed the hall too. 'Papa, this is a terrible idea. They will be a liability.'

'They bring an advantage in numbers.'

'You ought to ask Mr Comerford to accompany you instead then. You can trust him.'

'The fact that I trust him is why I want him to remain behind. I need to leave the estate in reliable hands. But you can rest easy, *a stór*. David is coming with us too.'

She did feel a measure of relief at that. The footman was a strapping young fellow and he, at least, bore no antagonism towards her parents.

'Where are Mr and Mrs Sandler?' she asked.

'Detained downstairs,' he said grimly. 'We have negotiated an agreement to allow them to keep their freedom in exchange for the liberation of your mother and Miss Hawkins.'

It sounded like he was struggling to keep a lid on his wrath. She gulped as she glimpsed his balled fists; here was a hint of the violent side of him that she had witnessed so many years ago when he had assaulted Garrett in the townhouse in London. This time, however, he could not release his rage. It was galling

213

that the Sandlers would go free, but her mother's welfare, and that of her lady's maid, had to be the priority.

Emily bunched her own hands into fists as she imagined what condition her mother might be in when her father finally found her. 'When will you depart?'

'Now that you're here, we leave at first light.' The fingers of his right hand slipped under the cuff on his left wrist in a fidgeting gesture. 'We have already packed the necessary provisions. We'll take the carriage to Bedford and then travel by rail on the first train departing for Liverpool. With any luck, we'll get overnight passage on a ship and reach Dublin tomorrow.' He glanced at Rory and back at Emily. 'Rory has agreed to stay here with you and the boys until your mother and I return.'

He said it cautiously as though he expected the arrangement to cause some friction, and she remembered that he had no inkling of what had happened at the house party. Now was not the time to tell him, not when he was so consumed with worry for her mother.

'That's fine,' she said, trying not to appear too enthusiastic as she avoided Rory's eye. 'How much do Jack and Gus know about all of this?'

'Nothing,' her father said. 'Before they went to bed, I told them I would be gone to Ireland in the morning. That was always meant to be the plan after the court case was settled, after all. The only difference is that the three of you aren't coming as intended. They might question why you have returned early from the Hutchville Estate—if they do, perhaps you could say that your hostess became ill and all the guests were obliged to leave. I know it will be hard, but please try to keep things as normal as possible for the boys. I don't want them to hear that their mother has been kidnapped, not after what happened to them in New York. I will write to you as soon as I have found her to let you know that she is safe, and you can tell them then.'

His blue gaze connected with her own, and she discerned the fine lines at the corners of his eyes and the dark circles below them. She embraced him again.

'Be careful,' she choked out, fully conscious of the two individuals behind her in whom she simply could not place her faith.

Chapter 25

By the time the ship left the Liverpool estuary, Cormac had been awake for more than thirty-six hours and he was mentally and physically shattered. As he covertly touched the precious leather band beneath his cuff on his left wrist – two braids of leather entwined with a third braid consisting of strands of Bridget's hair mixed with his own – he could not suppress a jaw-cracking yawn in spite of his unease. He would be of no use to Bridget if he reached Ireland in this state, so it was with only a small degree of reluctance that he accepted David's suggestion to get some rest on the overnight crossing.

He had secured two cabins for the voyage. Mr and Mrs Sandler had been confined to one and Garrett and David agreed to watch them while Cormac and Patrick went into the other. It was well appointed and contained two beds positioned against opposite walls. It even had a porthole, though the view from it was as black as ink at present. As he dropped onto one of the beds still fully clothed, his last thought before unconsciousness hit him was that the days were long gone when he was so poor that he could only stow away on a ship.

When he woke, the pale light of dawn filtered through the porthole. He had slept much longer than he had intended but felt all the better for it. Judging by the passage of time, he and Patrick ought to go now to the other cabin and relieve Garrett and David so that they could also rest before the ship docked. He glanced over at the opposite bed to find that Patrick was already awake and sitting up with his back against the cabin wall. Cormac couldn't see his nephew's face clearly in the dimness but his slouched figure spoke volumes.

He rose up on his elbow. 'Did you sleep?'

Patrick's silhouette shrugged. 'A little.'

'What kept you wakeful?' When Patrick didn't reply, Cormac said, 'You can tell me, Pat. I'm willing to listen.'

'You keep calling me that,' Patrick said irritably. 'It's not my name.'

'It could be if you wanted it to be.'

'I've already changed my name once. Why would I do it again?'

'Because maybe you haven't found the name that's right for you yet. There's still time to figure out who you really are and to tell us who that person is.'

There was a long silence from the other bed.

'What kept you wakeful?' Cormac asked again, endeavouring to coax his nephew out of his reticence.

Patrick sighed. 'I was thinking about my mother.'

That brought Cormac to full alertness. He sat up too, swinging his legs over the edge of the bed. 'What about her?'

Another pause. At last, Patrick said, 'I don't know anything about her. I mean, it's been impressed upon me from several quarters that she was lower class and that seemed to be sufficient information. But I find myself wondering...what was she like?'

For a second, Cormac was struck by the similarity of this situation to Henrietta asking him about her mother. Summoning himself back to the present, he appraised Patrick's slumped posture.

'I loved her as fondly as a brother could love a sister,' he said, 'but she was quite a temperamental sort. As a family, we never knew what mood we might find her in. She could be laughing one minute, and irritable the next. If you ever feel like that, she's where you got it from.'

Patrick's head twitched but he didn't speak.

'I think it's because she experienced everything so deeply. Her joys had her soaring to the skies, but her sorrows brought her down very low, to a point where she struggled to climb out of her despondency.' Cormac hesitated. 'Do you know how she died?'

It was so quiet in the cabin that he heard Patrick swallow. 'No.'

Cormac gathered his courage. 'She...took her own life, I'm sorry to tell you.'

Patrick went very still.

'She hanged herself,' Cormac said in a low tone, 'in the woods behind our family's cottage. I found her and cut her down, but it was too late.'

After a long beat, Patrick asked, 'Do you know why she did it?'

In a flash of anger, Cormac wanted to tell Patrick that his own father had driven his mother to the extreme act when he had abandoned her and her child. There was nothing to stop him declaring it. It might be in conflict with Garrett's original purpose in acquainting his son with Cormac, but the man ought to have foreseen that facilitating that connection would give Cormac a substantial opportunity to turn Patrick against him.

Still, now probably wasn't the right juncture for such a revelation – not for Garrett's sake, but for Patrick's. Moreover, Cormac had to admit that, while Garrett had played a significant role in the circumstances that had led to Mary's death, other critical factors also had to be taken into account.

In truth, she had been more unstable than Cormac or anyone else had known.

Before he could speak though, Patrick asked another question. 'Was it because of me?'

'Jesus, no,' Cormac said, shocked. 'She loved you, don't ever doubt that. She was just very...troubled in her mind. I've thought about this a great deal over the years. I can't say for certain, and God knows how much I wish I could talk to her to find out the truth, but I think she didn't know how to cope with despair. When she was in the midst of her worst pain, it was like she had no hope of coming out the far side. And that last time it got the better of her.'

In the ensuing silence, the ship creaked and rocked as the light grew a little brighter, touched now with a faint pink hue.

'Do you ever feel like that, Pat?' he asked gently.

Minutes passed but he remained patient.

Eventually, Patrick responded. 'Yes.'

The single word was full of a tortured misery and Cormac's heart twisted to hear it.

'Will you make me a promise?' he said. 'When you feel like that, don't suffer alone. Come to me or tell your father or, hell, share it with your duchess if that will help. Whatever you do, don't keep it inside because it will only fester and grow worse. Will you promise?'

Even as he made his sincere appeal, he wondered whether Patrick would scoff at him, and thus he was disappointed but unsurprised when his nephew said offhandedly, 'Right. Whatever you say.'

He waited to see if the boy might rethink his flippant response and retract it, but not another syllable issued from the opposite bed. At length, he conceded defeat.

'It's time to relieve David and your father,' he said and, getting up, he headed to the cabin door.

Patrick followed mutely.

CHAPTER 26

Shivering in the pre-dawn gloom, Bridget reached up to touch a crossbeam supporting the roof of the barn above her head and then peered over the edge of the loft, calculating the distance from the beam to the shadowy floor. It would require a lot of material but perhaps, by tying together strips of their clothing, she and Hawkins could create a rope long enough to suspend themselves over the edge and drop to the lower level. She felt annoyed at herself for not thinking of this idea sooner but her head was fuzzy from exhaustion, cold and lack of food. Would their makeshift rope be strong enough to hold the weight of a body without snapping? It was risky but there were no other options available to them. They had to try. If she and Hawkins could succeed in escaping, they would remove the only leverage Mr Sandler had and his kidnapping scheme would be in tatters.

She woke Hawkins with a gentle shake of her shoulder. The woman's hair had long since fallen loose from its pins and it surrounded her face in a matted cloud of dirty wisps. Bridget cautiously proposed her plan, conscious of her companion's continuing resentment. Hawkins considered it with her upper teeth clamped on her chapped lower lip.

Finally, she said, 'Let's try it.'

After assessing their clothes, all of which were in a filthy state after five days of captivity, they settled upon their cotton

221

petticoats as the best candidate for their rope. The fine fabric of their dresses was too delicate and, while the fichus tucked into their bodices were made of strong linen, there was not enough of the material to provide the length they needed. They each pulled back their outer skirts to expose the top layer of their petticoats and set to work, Hawkins picking at the seams with her nails while Bridget tore at them with her teeth. Once they had ragged edges to grasp, they began ripping the material into long strips. They moved quickly, energised by purpose despite their hunger. There was no knowing when either of the Sullivan men might appear to bring them their meagre water rations, and some bread crusts if they were lucky.

When they had several strips laid out, Bridget paused to survey their labours. 'I suggest we conduct an experiment at this point to test their strength.'

She tied the strips together end to end, trying to make the knots as tight as possible. Then she threw the makeshift rope over the crossbeam above, looping it three times before letting it dangle in front of them.

'Right,' she said nervously, 'here we go.'

Keeping her feet planted on the floor of the loft, she tugged lightly on the rope. It seemed secure. She exerted more weight upon it, bearing down as heavily as she could. For an instant, she thought it had worked. Then her stomach dropped as she heard the slither of material and two of the knots came completely apart. She landed hard on her knees, the looped section swinging above her and the remaining strips of petticoats flopping uselessly into her arms.

'Damn it!' she burst out.

Hawkins exhaled, looking dispirited.

'We can try again,' said Bridget, trying to gather her determination even though her temporary burst of energy was already draining away.

'There's no point,' Hawkins said sourly. 'It's not going to work.'

Before Bridget could find anything encouraging to say, the barn doors opened below. Panicked, she tried to unwind the pathetic scrap of rope left hanging on the crossbeam but it was too late. The elder Mr Sullivan stood staring upwards, his gaze riveted on their failed escape attempt. He shook his head. Then he bent down, lifted the ladder with a grunt and set it up against the edge of the loft. He stepped back and motioned at Bridget and Hawkins.

'Let's go,' he said. 'Hurry.'

Bridget goggled down at him. Flabbergasted, she exchanged a perplexed glance with Hawkins but didn't dawdle to debate. 'Come on,' she said.

Hawkins gestured that Bridget should go first and there was no time to speculate on her motivations. Bridget descended the ladder, staying vigilant for any sign that this might be some sort of trap. Her legs felt like jelly, though, and she lost her footing a couple of rungs from the bottom. She slipped off the ladder but Mr Sullivan darted forwards to catch her. Trembling, she found her feet on the floor of the barn and he made sure she was steady before he released her.

As Hawkins climbed down the ladder next, he said, 'Johnny's had enough drink to flatten a bull. With any luck, he won't surface for hours.'

Bridget put out her hands to help Hawkins down the final few rungs. 'Why have you changed your mind?' she asked Mr Sullivan.

He lowered his gaze, shamefaced. 'You were right. If I let this go on, I won't be able to face my wife when we meet again.' He jerked his head towards the barn doors. 'I can take ye as far as the road. Ye'll need to make your own way from there.'

They followed him to the doors. When they emerged outside, the rising sun was turning the sky from grey to deep rose.

'Red sky in the morning, shepherd's warning,' Hawkins muttered.

Mr Sullivan began to lead them across the farmyard in the direction of the track they had come down five days ago in the carriage. 'There's an inn called The Bells out on the main road, about a mile to the south. The innkeeper's a decent fella—he'll take ye in when he sees you're in trouble. And I know 'tis a lot to ask but I'm begging you not to report me and my son to the authorities. We've done wrong, but it was only out of sheer desperation. We had no other options.'

'We won't report you,' Bridget promised, prepared to make any bargain to get away from here.

'You also swore you could get us money if I set ye free?' he added in a tentative manner, plainly aware that he was pushing his luck.

'It may take some time,' she said, 'but I assure you that aid will come.' How quickly would she be able to get a message to Cormac to tell him that she and Hawkins had been released from their captivity and also that she needed more money? She would need to act with all speed to foil Mr Sandler's plans.

They had nearly reached the track when they heard the scrape of a door opening. Bridget glanced over her shoulder. Weak candlelight spilled from the farmhouse into the strengthening daylight, framing a figure in the doorway.

'Da, what the hell are you doing?' came a slurred voice full of anger.

Frightened, Bridget swivelled back to Mr Sullivan.

'Run!' he barked.

They didn't need telling twice. She and Hawkins took off, making it to the far end of the yard and dashing along the track. The younger Sullivan was drunk. They could outrun him.

The track was dusty and pitted with holes. Bridget coughed and urged her shaky legs to keep going. Sullivan's shouts and pounding footsteps thundered in their wake. Perhaps if they could get out of sight around the approaching bend, they could hide themselves in a ditch.

Then Hawkins let out a shriek of pain. Bridget whirled around to see that she had fallen to the ground a couple of yards back and was clutching her ankle. Dismayed, she looked past Hawkins at Sullivan charging towards them, then back up the track to the bend. Caught in indecision, her gaze landed on Hawkins again. Her shoulders were hunched and her face was full of dread. Heart hammering in her throat, Bridget hurried back to her and put her hands under her elbows.

'Come on now, up you get,' she encouraged her.

Hawkins tried to put her weight on her ankle and collapsed with a groan. Bridget threw another anxious glance behind them. Sullivan's dark shape was silhouetted by the red sunrise, his knife visible in his hand.

'I need you to get up, Hawkins,' she said desperately.

But it was too late. Sullivan had reached them and his face was a mask of rage. 'God damn ye!' he snarled thickly. 'I'll murder my da for this.'

He yanked on Hawkins's matted hair to force her to stand. She yelped, unable to rise.

'Leave her be!' Bridget snapped and shoved him away.

He was so drunk that he lost his balance and fell onto his hip with a curse. She bent over Hawkins, urging her to try to crawl away, but Sullivan staggered to his feet again.

'You bitch!' he hurled at Bridget and his hand swung up towards her.

The one holding the knife.

The blade swiped her left cheek. She saw it happen and yet she didn't feel it. Not at first. A whimper of shock escaped her.

Sullivan jerked his hand back and the knife came away with a tug at her flesh. In the next instant, she sensed the wetness on her jaw and a sharp sting, followed by a wave of pain so powerful it made her dizzy. She emitted a stuttering gasp.

Still on the ground, Hawkins blurted in horror, 'Oh, my lady!'

Bridget's cheek felt like it was on fire. She reached up shakily to touch it and found her fingertips soaked in blood. Weakly, she dropped to her knees. Next to her, Hawkins fumbled with the fichu she wore, wrenching it from the confines of her bodice. She bundled it into a ball and pressed it against Bridget's cheek. Bridget cried out.

'I'm sorry, my lady,' Hawkins moaned. 'But we need to stop the bleeding.'

She kept the fichu in place and Bridget grimaced but didn't draw away. Sullivan loomed over them, his breath ragged, the knife dangling loosely from his hand. He swayed a little as his father finally caught up with them.

'What have you done?' the older man exclaimed.

'They need to get back to the barn,' Sullivan muttered in reply.

'You fool!' his father flung at him. 'The rich fella will never pay the ransom now, not with his woman looking like that.'

'He wasn't going to pay it anyway if she escaped!' Sullivan retaliated. 'You're the damn fool. If you hadn't let them go, I wouldn't have had to do this.'

He gestured with his knife and a few droplets of blood landed on the dusty ground in front of Bridget. She stared at them dazedly. The dry dust absorbed the blood at once, leaving a spatter of dark spots in a fascinating pattern almost like a love heart. Then it appeared to blur. She slumped but Hawkins kept her upright.

'The lady needs a physician,' she said in a pleading tone. 'This wound is grievous.'

'There'll be no physician,' the younger Sullivan growled. 'Get on your feet, both of ye.'

It seemed like an impossible command to obey. As Bridget strove not to black out, she heard the older Mr Sullivan say, 'We have to help them. They can't do it on their own.'

His son cursed. There was a flash of metal as he stowed his knife in his pocket. Then he hunkered down and Bridget smelled the liquor on his breath as he lifted her into his arms. She had no power to resist. Hawkins's hand and bloodied fichu fell away from her. Her head lolled against Sullivan's chest and pain ricocheted through her, shooting out from the gash on her cheek.

'Please,' came Hawkins's desperate voice. 'We need to keep pressure on it.'

The older Mr Sullivan's face hovered over Bridget and he pressed the wet linen to her cheek. She whimpered.

'Try to hold it there as best you can,' he murmured. She clasped her hand weakly over the material.

The younger Sullivan started to stagger back towards the barn; she couldn't tell if he was struggling due to her weight or his inebriation. Behind them, his father said, 'Stand on your good ankle, miss, there you go. Now lean on me. We'll go slow.'

By the time they made it to the barn, Bridget was sobbing with agony. Energy utterly depleted, she let the sodden fichu fall into her lap. Blood seeped down her jaw and onto her collarbone. Sullivan deposited her on the hay-strewn floor near the door and stepped back, eyeing the ladder up to the loft in the centre. Tossing his head in vexation, he seized the rope from the nail on the back of the door and cut off a length of it. He bound Bridget's wrists and feet right where he had set her down and was securing the last knot when his father and Hawkins came hobbling in. With a final puff of effort, Hawkins stumbled to the floor beside Bridget. She stretched out her hand for the fichu but Sullivan caught her by the shoulder.

'Get back,' he ordered. 'I'm putting you over at the opposite end of the barn.'

'I beg you to have mercy,' she said. 'If you must tie us up, at least let me stay by the lady's side.'

He scowled. 'Fine,' he said grudgingly.

Slicing off another length of rope, he knelt and bound her feet, not paying much heed to her injured ankle judging by the sound of her hiss. When he grabbed her wrists next, she implored, 'Please keep my hands free until I've tended her. She will continue to bleed if I do not see to her wound.'

He grunted and stood back. Hawkins scuffled closer to Bridget and plucked the bunched-up fichu out of her lap. Bridget had stopped sobbing by now because it hurt her face too much. Hawkins shook her head at the saturated fichu.

'This is useless. May I use yours, my lady?'

Bridget was afraid to nod in case it made the throbbing worse so she just blinked a couple of times. Hawkins understood and eased Bridget's fichu out of her bodice. Putting the bloodied fichu aside, she pressed the fresh one over the wound and gently applied pressure to it. Bridget gasped feebly.

Sullivan's features were red with fury as he watched them. He rounded on his father. 'This is all your fault! Why'd you help them escape?'

His father flinched. 'Our women died on this farmstead, Johnny. Their spirits are still here and they can see what we did. They won't forgive us.'

Sullivan spat on the floor. ''Tis too late for regrets. We're in this for better or worse and we have to see it through. Except I can't trust you anymore, Da.'

'Don't worry,' his father said bitterly. 'They're in no shape to escape now.'

'No, but 'tis like you said, that fella isn't going to want to give us the ransom once he sees her. We're going to have to force his hand.'

Bridget's thoughts were woolly but she comprehended that much with misgiving. What did Sullivan mean?

Hawkins lifted up the second fichu to peer beneath it and clicked her tongue. 'Please, we need water and bandages,' she said to the two men.

They looked at each other. 'I'm not leaving you alone with them again,' Sullivan said.

His father trudged out of the barn. While he was gone, Sullivan surveyed Bridget and Hawkins without a word, his face gradually paling to grey. He seemed to be sobering up as the weight of what he had done hit him.

His father returned presently with a basin of water and some rags that looked clean enough. 'I'm sorry,' he said. ''Tis all we've got.'

Hawkins washed out the wound. Bridget watched her companion's countenance turn green as she worked and perceived that the injury must be very bad. She wanted to weep again. Hawkins placed a bandage made up of rags onto Bridget's cheek and carefully wrapped the second fichu under her chin and over her head, knotting the ends of it together to keep the bandage in position.

As soon as she was done, Sullivan gesticulated at her and she reluctantly offered her hands to him. He tied her wrists and then used more of the rope to wrap around her and Bridget's waists, securing them back-to-back and fastening them to an upright beam nearby. He tossed the remainder of the rope aside. Hawkins was left facing the barn doors while Bridget ended up looking across the ground floor of the barn at the mound of unfinished netting against the far wall. Sullivan leaned over them, tugging on their bindings to make sure they were secure.

'They're not going anywhere,' he said to his father. 'And now you're coming with me.'

He shoved on his father's arm and the two of them headed towards the doors, Sullivan still complaining about the mess his father had made.

Hawkins slumped despondently against Bridget's back. After a minute, she said, 'You had the chance to keep running, my lady. You could have left me behind.' She swallowed audibly. 'You should have left me behind.'

Bridget tried to speak but the dust still clogged her throat. She coughed to clear it and the left side of her face burned. 'Thank you for looking after me, Hawkins,' she managed to rasp.

'Oh, my lady. Please call me Polly.'

After that, Bridget slipped into a sort of dream state where nothing felt real to her, apart from the ache in her cheek. Polly endeavoured to talk to her on numerous occasions and Bridget did her best to mumble back, but she wasn't sure if anything she said was coherent.

She had no idea how much time passed before the younger Sullivan re-entered the barn, but his appearance revived her more effectively than any of Polly's attempts because he came in with no less than five other men, and none of them were his father.

'She's our ransom,' he told them, standing in front of Bridget and pointing at her. 'The English fella isn't going to be happy when he sees the state she's in. We're going to have to put up a good fight to get our money. If we're successful, I promise ye'll all get a fair share.'

He started talking about the need to post scouts at the edge of the farm and to guard the two women at all times. Bridget was aghast. She had told Cormac in her letter that there were only three men to contend with. Now the odds had dramatically changed.

If he was on his way, he was well and truly outnumbered.

CHAPTER 27

Emily was feeling agitated and uncertain and excited and worried and, with so many conflicting emotions churning inside her, she sensed her need to withdraw from the world to a place that was familiar and uncomplicated, so she had retreated to her parlour to paint. Her easel was set up in such a way that she could look out the windows at the lawn, and she thought perhaps it would be most straightforward to simply paint the scene in front of her. But as she rooted through her watercolour box on the table next to her, she found herself idly mixing paints on her palette to create various shades of green and realised that she was once again striving to match the colour of Rory's eyes.

With all the upheaval of her father's hasty departure in the early hours of the previous morning, and then her need to retire to her bedchamber for half the day to catch up on sleep, followed by an earnest effort to maintain a normal atmosphere at dinner with Jack and Gus, she and Rory had not had a minute to themselves to discuss what had happened between them in the gardens at the Hutchville Estate. And the longer that time frame widened, the more she anticipated the impending conversation with apprehension. Did he want to stay here in England? Or would he prefer to go back to America? Were these choices they now ought to make together or did she assume too much? They had shared a kiss, yes – a kiss so wild that her knees went weak again just thinking about it – but it had not been a promise of marriage. What was to happen next for them?

She added a little more blue to her palette, but it made the green too dark. Screwing up her face, she tried to picture the precise colour in her mind. As she did so, the parlour door opened and the owner of the eyes in question walked in. She quickly rearranged her features but suspected he had caught sight of her contorted expression. He didn't comment on it; he just closed the door and stood with his back against it.

'You disappeared after breakfast,' he said. 'But Jack said I might find you here.'

She smiled timidly. 'Indeed. I've come to think of this parlour as my sanctuary.'

He blinked. 'Should I leave so?'

'Gracious, no,' she said, dismayed. 'I didn't mean that. You are of course always welcome here.' Was that saying too much? 'That is to say, if you wish to. Be here, I mean. Um...' She trailed away into self-conscious silence.

He regarded her from across the room without reply. Then he pushed away from the door and approached her. She was perched on her high stool which gave her a little more height than usual, but he was still so much taller than her.

He peered at the blank paper clipped to the drawing board on her easel. 'What're you painting?'

She glanced furtively into his eyes and averted her gaze. 'I haven't quite decided yet.'

Another silence rose between them. He took a breath. 'I'm not very good with words. So I don't know what are the right things to say. And I know you're really worried about your ma, so maybe the right thing to say right now is actually to not say anything.'

She couldn't help but glow with affection at his tongue-tied speech. 'It's true that my mother is at the forefront of my thoughts,' she admitted before adding tentatively, 'but I think we can say some things. If we are ready.'

He hesitated. 'D'you remember the night we had to share a bed at the inn in Liverpool?'

She chuckled. 'How could I forget?'

The details of that excruciating encounter were burned forever into her memory: the innkeeper insisting, since they had proclaimed themselves brother and sister, that they share one bed because accommodation was tight; the pair of them lying side by side fully clothed, mute and painfully aware of the scandalous nature of their situation; Emily spreading herself out like a starfish in her sleep and Rory pinning her down with his arm across her waist to prevent her from encroaching on his side of the bed.

The corners of his eyes crinkled briefly with amusement but in the next instant he became sombre again. 'I want to own up that I touched your hair that night. When you were asleep.' She raised her eyebrows in surprise and he hurried on, 'It was spread out over my pillow and I just meant to brush it back to yours, only I left my fingers there longer than was proper.' His face turned a guilty shade of red. 'I know I shouldn't have. It was disrespectful of me. But it was even softer than I'd imagined.'

Her stomach fluttered. 'You'd been imagining what my hair felt like?'

He shrugged, casting his gaze downwards.

She licked her lips, apprehensive and eager. 'Would you like to touch it now?'

He looked up quickly. After a moment, he said, 'I would.'

She turned on her stool to face him straight on. He stepped closer so that their knees were touching. She had not taken particular care with her hair that morning, since she had no plans to leave the house and they were not expecting any visitors, so her curls hung loosely, apart from where she had pinned them back at her temples to allow her to view her easel. Rory reached out and brushed a knuckle against the end of one long lock of hair. Then he slid his hand into the tresses at her neck, gliding through her curls until he cupped her nape. Her breath snagged in her throat. Given his customary awkwardness, this caress was more delicate than anything she could have anticipated from him.

His head lowered to hers and his mouth grazed her lips. A tremor ran through her and her knees knocked against his.

He laughed and drew back. 'That seems to keep happening.'

She blushed. 'I'll try to control it better next time.'

He contemplated her nervously. 'So you do want there to be a next time?'

Gathering her courage, she gave him her completely honest answer. 'I want there to be lots of next times. An infinite number.'

Relief flooded his countenance, but still he said, 'Even though I'm not rich? And I don't have a title or influential connections or a massive estate?'

'I couldn't care less for any of those things,' she said seriously. 'I only care about you.'

He coloured. 'Me too. About you, I mean.'

It was her turn to feel relief. How terrifying it had been to lay herself bare and hope he would reciprocate.

He kissed her again, more fiercely, and she tensed the muscles in her legs to prevent them from shaking. She didn't want the odd compulsion to interrupt their kiss this time. She opened her mouth to him and their tongues met while his other hand reached up to her nape so that both were plunged deep into her curls. His grip and his kisses were reverential, as though he were sipping from a holy chalice. Her heart sang in exultation.

When they finally drew apart, they spent several moments just breathing and staring at each other with unabashed fascination. She had never felt so exposed, nor so understood.

The corner of his mouth tilted up. 'I don't suppose you'll be making it into any library books so.'

Her forehead creased. 'What?'

'I found a book in the library all about the English peerage and its important families. It lists names going back generations, people who inherited titles or married into them.' She expected him to get embarrassed about mentioning marriage, but in fact he continued to hold her gaze steadily. 'What I mean is, if you stick with me your name won't be included in those kinds of records.'

She felt nearly ready to burst. He might not consider himself very good with words but, goodness, he could still say a lot without using many of them at all. She beamed at him so widely her cheeks hurt. Then she swivelled away to rummage inside her watercolour box for a pencil before hopping down off her stool.

'Come with me,' she said.

Taking his hand, she led him from the parlour through the house. The skin on his fingers was rough, but she thrilled at the eager pressure of his grasp. Even though it probably wasn't decorous of them to be holding hands, she yearned for someone, anyone, to pass them in the hallway and notice them together. She longed for their actions to be witnessed so they could declare the giddy truth: she was his, and he was hers.

When they reached the library and she pushed open the door, a wheezy cough told her that it was already occupied. Entering, she discovered that Gus had dragged a chair from the table over to the fireplace and was standing on it, his tricorne askew as he tried to peer behind the picture frame that hung above the mantelpiece. Jack hovered next to the chair. He whirled at Emily and Rory's entrance and his blue eyes widened in alarm. Gus spun around too, his tubby figure wobbling on its perch.

'We haven't damaged it,' he said at once. 'We were just trying to see how to get it down.'

She was already aware of the significance of the painting, as he would not stop talking about it at the dinner table the previous evening. 'Didn't Papa tell you to wait?'

'He did, but then he left. It'll be ages before he's back. We can't wait that long to solve the mystery.'

She heard the desperate plea in his voice but shook her head. 'It has to be done under proper supervision. We'll ask Sheppard or Mr Comerford if there's a convenient time to do it, but you'll have to come down from the chair for now.'

He did so with a pout and flopped into a nearby armchair, staring dispiritedly up at Lady Dorothea's uncommunicative face. Jack sighed and gazed up at her too before glancing back at Emily and Rory. He blinked when he noticed their joined hands. She gave him a small smile and he returned it, looking quietly pleased. She didn't know why but the approval of her ten-year-old brother made her even happier. After he turned back once more to the painting, she squeezed Rory's hand.

'Show me the book,' she murmured to him.

He surveyed the bookcases and led her over to a shelf where he tugged a hefty volume out from among its companions. Reluctantly releasing his hand, she took the book and flipped through its pages. It appeared to discuss at wearying length the various ranks in the English aristocracy and, as Rory had said, it listed the principal families who held them. She discovered the Bewley title recorded in the section on earldoms. Out of amusement, she checked for Dartry and found it there too, the author praising the Dartry name for its longevity and nobility. She grinned and kept turning the pages.

There were a few blank leaves at the back of the book. She crossed to the table in the centre of the room and sat down on one of the chairs, a gap next to her where Gus had dragged his one away. Rory didn't sit but he observed her with a frown as she began writing on the first blank page with her pencil.

'Isn't that vandalism?' he asked.

'Papa owns this library and I can't imagine he would mind,' she replied vaguely, distracted by her task.

When she was finished, she shyly held the book out to Rory. He accepted it from her and scanned the page. She watched his face carefully and identified the instant his gaze fell on the most important part.

She had sketched a simple family tree for the humble surname McGovern. Her father's name was there with a line connecting him to her mother's name, even though they were not married. Descending from her parents were the names of their three children: Emily, Jack and Angus. And Emily had drawn another line to link her name to Rory Carey.

He raised his eyes from the page and her cheeks flushed at the warmth in those green irises.

'I really wish we were alone right now,' he murmured.

The flush spread throughout her body until her fingertips and toes were tingling. 'Let's go back to the parlour,' she breathed.

'Wait a second,' Jack said suddenly in a louder voice than was customary for him. Startled, Emily wondered if he had heard the suggestive exchange between her and Rory, but he was staring up at the portrait of Lady Dorothea. 'The clue we need could be right in front of us.'

'What do you mean?' Gus said moodily, still slouched in the armchair.

Jack pointed at the painting. 'Look. Where is she?'

Gus glanced idly at it and then sat up straight very fast. 'The woods!'

'Not just any woods,' said Jack. 'Those are beech trees, aren't they?'

'They are!' Gus exclaimed. 'It's the place where Da nearly shot us with his rifle!' His forehead wrinkled. 'But we never saw any bench there.'

'Well, the portrait was painted one hundred and fifty years ago,' said Jack. 'The bench could have rotted since then or been moved somewhere else. Anything that was buried beneath it though...'

'...could still be there!' Gus finished with excitement. 'The iron ring, and her lover's bones! That *has* to be where they are. It was probably a special meeting place for the lovers.'

Jack tapped his chin, musing. 'And maybe Lady Dorothea's father knew that and made it the secret grave out of spite?'

'I bet that's it!' Gus leapt to his feet. 'But there are a lot of trees in that grove and they've kept growing all this time. How will we know the exact spot without the bench?'

Jack assessed the painting with squinted eyes. 'The trees will be bigger but at least they'll be in the same place. See, on the left of the bench there are four in a row almost in a straight line, and those two behind the lady look like they're standing at either shoulder as her guards. If we can find that arrangement of trees in the grove, then the burial spot should be just in front of the roots of the two guards.'

Gus turned his animated face to Emily and Rory. 'Are you coming?'

Though part of her wished very much to return to the parlour, the rest of her knew it would be best to be present to soothe Gus after he was inevitably disappointed in the coming venture. She glanced at Rory. He seemed to read her thoughts because he gave her a resigned grin and put the peerage book on the table.

''Course we are,' he said to Gus.

Gus whooped. 'Let's go ask Mr Comerford for his shovel!'

It took a while for them to locate Mr Comerford, but eventually they found him below stairs, his gruff voice issuing from the butler's pantry as they approached it.

'My sister's worried sick about poor Polly,' Emily heard him say.

Through the gap in the pantry's open door, she caught sight of Sheppard's sympathetic expression. 'Put your faith in Mr McGovern,' he said. 'My gut tells me he has the mettle to prevail.'

Gus pushed past Emily and burst into the pantry. 'We need your shovel, Mr Comerford!'

Jack scurried in after him. 'Please,' he added.

Emily and Rory entered too as Mr Comerford regarded the boys suspiciously. 'What for?'

Gus answered him at top speed. 'We wanted to look at the back of the painting but then we realised we only needed to look at the front because the lady is sitting in a grove of beech trees and there's a beech grove where you gave out to us that time Da nearly shot us and we think her lover's bones are buried right in that spot and you said we could borrow your shovel once we figured out where the burial place is!'

Sheppard looked nonplussed, but Mr Comerford stared hard at Jack and Gus. 'Very well then, let's go get it.'

Surprised by his lack of resistance, Emily appreciated him indulging the boys even while he remained so concerned for his niece.

After paying a visit to the tool shed to collect the shovel, they made their way across the sunny grounds, Gus running ahead and holding onto his tricorne so it wouldn't fall off. By the time they had crossed a number of fields and reached the grove of beech trees, he was already darting among the trunks, his gaze swinging around him as he counted aloud.

'One, two, no, only three there, and it's not quite a straight line. Maybe over here...' He raced further into the shady grove, calling behind him, 'Come on, slowcoaches!'

Jack hurried to follow him. Emily and Rory hung back with Mr Comerford, who emitted a rare chuckle, the shovel propped on his shoulder. 'He deserves some success after all his perseverance.'

They wandered through the grove, which wasn't very large, examining the layout of the trees without expectation but in the spirit of adventure. None of them were impervious to Gus's enthusiasm, not even, it seemed, Mr Comerford. He was just conjecturing about the possibility that some of the trees in the painting may have been uprooted in the intervening decades when Gus let out a shout up ahead.

'I found them!'

Exchanging looks of astonishment, Emily, Rory and Mr Comerford hastened to catch up. They came upon Gus skipping along a straight line of beeches, yelling triumphantly as he tapped each trunk, 'One, two, three, four!'

Jack, meanwhile, was standing in front of a pair of trees adjacent to the line of four, goggling up at them. 'The two guards,' he proclaimed in awe. He swivelled when Emily, Rory and Mr Comerford drew near, his countenance bright with exhilaration. 'I think this is it!'

Emily scanned the trees herself. Indeed, their arrangement was remarkably similar to the one in Lady Dorothea's portrait. There was even a space right where Jack stood that might have been suitable for a bench once upon a time. He peered down at the ground beneath his feet.

'It makes sense to start here,' he said. 'Mr Comerford, may we use your shovel now?'

Mr Comerford wordlessly handed over the tool. He looked astounded and shot an uneasy glance around the grove. Was he wondering whether the restless ghost of Lady Dorothea's lover lingered nearby?

Gus dashed to his brother's side as Jack jabbed the shovel into the grassy earth. Not fully grown yet, he wielded the long-handled implement awkwardly.

Rory stepped forwards. 'Here, let me.'

Jack gratefully gave him the shovel and Rory set to work turning over the earth. Emily tried not to picture his muscles rippling beneath his shirt. Gus hopped about exuberantly but Rory dug up two feet of nothing but soil.

'Try over here,' Gus said, undeterred, and he directed Rory to a spot a little closer to the pair of trees that had supposedly stood as guards over Lady Dorothea. Rory started digging in the new location. Jack and Gus scrutinised the ground, while Emily and Mr Comerford hovered behind them, observing over their shoulders. Gus was wheezing with anticipation.

Then Jack exclaimed, 'I think I see something!'

Rory paused in his labours and Jack and Gus dropped to their knees around the hole, raking their fingers through the soil. Emily wondered if she should berate them for getting dirty, but she didn't have the heart to spoil their fun, even if they weren't likely to unearth anything but animal droppings—

She blinked. Jack was holding up a piece of rolled canvas.

'Let me see!' Gus cried and seized it from him. He unrolled the canvas and two objects fell out onto the upturned earth: a circle of metal and something that looked like an ivory-coloured twig.

Emily gasped. 'Is that a bone?'

Gus picked it up gingerly, his jaw slack. 'It's a finger,' he said in wonderment.

Jack scooped up the other object, which glinted in his palm. 'The iron ring,' he said in a hushed tone.

'Goodness gracious,' Emily said weakly.

Rory had propped the shovel in the soil and was leaning on its shaft, wide-eyed with amazement. Mr Comerford coughed next to Emily; she sensed he was trying to mask some sort of emotion. Was he fearful at this discovery?

Gus tore his gaze away from the bone to look back down at the earth. 'Is there anything else hidden there?'

Rory scraped away more of the soil but didn't uncover any more buried items.

'I wonder what happened to the rest of the lover's bones,' Gus said. 'I hope the finger will be enough to bring the lady peace.'

'What do you plan to do with it?' Emily asked warily.

'We have to bring it and the ring to her haunting place in the attic and leave them there. If the lover's ghost follows, then Lady Dorothea will be able to reunite with him at last. Isn't that the best thing to do, Mr Comerford?'

Mr Comerford cleared his throat. 'Yes,' he said. 'You certainly paid attention to what the servants told you.'

Gus beamed proudly. 'A good detective needs to have an excellent memory for details.'

After Rory used the shovel to refill the two holes he had made, Jack wrapped the bone and ring back in the piece of canvas and Gus cradled it in his cupped hands. They all left the beech grove, dumbstruck by their discovery. Gus was still wheezing slightly from the exertion and the excitement.

When they returned to the grounds of Bewley Hall, Mr Comerford took the shovel from Rory. 'I'll put this back in the shed,' he said and strode away. Perhaps he felt most comfortable ending his involvement there.

The rest of them made their way into the house and ascended several flights until they reached the entrance to the attic. They crowded together on the narrow stairs, staring at the closed door.

'Who wants to go first?' Gus whispered.

He and Jack looked up at Rory in unison. Emily scratched at the corner of her mouth to hide her smile. Rory raised his eyebrows at her and then climbed the final few steps to the attic door.

'You should knock first,' Gus advised him in a low voice, 'so she knows we're coming in.'

Rory obediently rapped his knuckles on the door and waited a moment before opening it and entering. Emily, Jack and Gus filed in after him, Gus still carefully clutching the wrapped canvas.

The heat inside the attic was stifling. A narrow window at the far end let in a long shaft of sunlight, and dust swirled in the rays below the sloped eaves. Rory had to stoop to avoid hitting his head.

Jack pointed to a small door set into the nearby wall, his expression sombre. 'That leads to the roof.'

Gus chewed on his lip. 'Maybe that's the place where we should leave this,' he said, holding up the wrapped canvas. 'To help replace her bad thoughts with good ones.'

'Good idea,' Emily said encouragingly.

Gus crossed to the small door and laid the canvas down on the floor in front of it. He unfolded it, leaving the ring and the bone visible. The simple iron band gleamed in the sunlight.

'Be at peace, Lady Dorothea,' he said, his tone fervent.

Then he motioned meaningfully to the others and they all retreated to the attic door. They slipped back out onto the stairs and into slightly cooler air. Rory was last and shut the door softly behind him.

'Well done, Detective McGovern,' Emily said.

Gus puffed up proudly. 'I wouldn't have been able to do it without Jack. He figured out the vital clue.'

Jack coloured with pleasure.

Gus cocked his head to the side, looking thoughtful. 'Now that the ghost won't be troubled anymore, I think I'm going to be brave enough to sleep in my own room from now on.' He tugged on Jack's elbow. 'Let's go and move my things out of your room. Jennie will help with the clothes.' He grinned at Emily and Rory. 'Jennie is one of the scowly maids, but she's not as scowly as she used to be.'

With that, he and Jack descended the stairs and rushed out of sight.

Emily glanced back at the attic door. 'I have gooseflesh after all that,' she said with a shiver. 'I don't believe the ghost part, naturally, but the buried ring and the bone seem to prove that Lady Dorothea's tragic story was true. I wonder where the rest of her lover's remains ended up, poor man.'

Rory grimaced. 'Whatever happened to him, they both paid the price for trying to marry someone they shouldn't.'

She read the worry in his gaze. With a confidence that thrilled her, she linked her arm with his, right where it belonged. 'How fortunate for us that I don't have a father who will disapprove of our match and murder you to keep us apart.'

His grimace didn't entirely dissipate. 'So you think he'll be accepting of it?'

'I absolutely do,' she reassured him. 'He and my mother will both be delighted. They cherish you as a son just as much as Jack and Gus.'

Her heart stuttered as she thought of her mother and wondered how she was faring. Had her father reached her yet? Rory's bashful grin drew her back to the present.

'I'm glad to hear that,' he said. 'They're good people. I don't want to let them down.'

'There is no fear of that at all, I promise you that.'

As the final trace of apprehension faded from his eyes, she contemplated their green colour and pondered over the paints she had been mixing earlier before he had entered the parlour.

'Rory,' she said shyly, 'will you help me with something?'

'Anything,' he said at once.

'I've been trying to paint your eyes, but I'm struggling to establish the precise colour. Would you perhaps sit for me sometime so that I can paint them from life?'

He blinked in surprise and embarrassment, and she expected him to refuse. But at last he said, 'All right so.'

Chapter 28

The ship had finally docked in Dublin. As the passengers disembarked, Cormac made Mrs Sandler take his elbow so that he could keep her under his watchful eye. Garrett, Patrick and David stuck close to Mr Sandler, although Cormac was reasonably certain he wouldn't try to escape without his wife.

Mr Sandler had already told them that he was expecting his accomplice, Duffy, to be waiting for him at the docks. Charged with keeping the chest of rent money safe while Mr Sandler went to England, the man was to be ready to accompany him back to the farm as soon as he returned. With this in mind, Cormac halted before they started down the gangway, making them all stop.

'If this Duffy fellow sees us, he'll bolt,' he said. 'We need to allow Mr Sandler to go ahead by himself and give Duffy time to approach him. Then, once he gets near enough, we'll seize him. David, can I task you with that?'

'Yes, sir,' said the footman, assuming a zealous look of determination.

'Don't even think of fleeing,' Cormac warned Mr Sandler. 'We'll be ten feet behind you all the time. You understand?'

'Yes, sir,' Mr Sandler said in a contemptuous echo, before shooting a miserable glance at his wife.

He went down the gangway first and stepped onto the wharf, walking to the end of it where he paused in full view of the crowds bustling around the docks. Cormac and the others followed at a safe distance and waited, scanning the throng for any sign of Mr Sandler's accomplice. They lingered a full quarter of an hour but no man approached him.

Eventually, Mr Sandler marched back to Cormac. 'I can't see him,' he muttered. He let out a disgruntled huff. 'What's the betting he's absconded with the money?'

Garrett snorted. 'Or he's drunk himself into a stupor with it and forgotten all about your arrangement here. He's an Irishman, after all.'

Ignoring the slur, Cormac shrugged. 'Either way, it's easier for us to have one less bandit to deal with. We can't afford to dally any longer, so let's move on.'

He glanced back at the ship where the sailors appeared to be dawdling over the unloading of its cargo. He winced. They had travelled with one trunk, and its contents would be vital for the journey ahead – they would need to exercise patience until it had been unloaded.

'We'll organise our transport while we wait for the trunk,' he decided.

'Rail is by far the speediest option,' Mr Sandler chimed in at once.

Cormac threw him a dark look. 'We will hire a private carriage.'

He had already come to this conclusion before they docked. Travelling by train, though quickest, was regrettably out of the question; their ability to confine the Sandlers without drawing attention would be limited on a public form of transportation, giving the pair too much opportunity to slip away. A carriage would take longer, but it would be an easier environment to control. Besides, they would need a carriage anyway to get from the railway station to the farm. This way, they could travel directly there without scrutiny or interference.

They located the premises of a hackneyman near the docks. Passing the custody of Mrs Sandler over to Garrett, Cormac entered it to arrange the hiring of a carriage and a pair of horses.

'A driver too, yes?' said the hackneyman.

'No, thank you,' Cormac replied. 'I'll drive it myself.'

The hackneyman grew suspicious at that. 'The driver's my guarantee I'll get my property back,' he said, peering askance through the window at the other five waiting outside.

'I'll pay more,' said Cormac, too impatient to argue, 'and you have my word that your property will be returned to you in due course.'

Gleeful at the additional compensation, the hackneyman accepted Cormac's money before barking orders at a loitering employee. The carriage was brought around to the front of the premises and Cormac went out to check the saddles and bridles of the harnessed horses. Rubbing their noses, he hoped they would prove to be swift beasts.

'Get in,' he said to Mr and Mrs Sandler, 'and don't try anything stupid like jumping out while we're moving.'

They complied with resentful expressions, Mrs Sandler grumbling about his insolence towards them. Garrett, Patrick and David followed them into the carriage, while Cormac climbed up front and took the reins. Although he didn't have a lot of experience in this area and reckoned that four horses might be too many to manage, he felt relatively confident driving two.

They returned to the docks to find that the sailors had finished unloading the ship's cargo. Cormac collected their trunk and stowed it at the rear of the carriage, but not before extracting a rectangular case from within it, along with a coil of rope.

He got into the carriage and shut the door behind him, pulling down the blinds so that no one outside could see in. It was a tight squeeze with all six of them inside.

'Hold out your hands,' he commanded the Sandlers.

They had no choice but to obey. Binding their wrists with the rope, he used the whole of it in one length so that they ended up bound to each other too. Then he opened the case to reveal two pepperbox pistols nestled within, courtesy of Mr Comerford. His hunting rifles would have been too unwieldy for this venture but he had happily offered the pistols instead. They had handsome walnut grips and short barrels. He had shown Cormac and Garrett precisely how to use them before they departed from Bewley Hall, explaining in a loving tone how the pistols could discharge five shots and needed to be rotated by hand.

Cormac now gave one to Garrett, who aimed it warningly at the Sandlers, and took the other for himself, tucking it inside his coat.

'We don't stop now for anything,' he said grimly. 'I'll bang on the roof once we're out of the city so you can open the blinds. Mr Sandler, you will observe the road through the window and inform me when we are getting close to our destination.'

He cast a meaningful glance at Garrett's pistol as a reminder that it was in the Sandlers' best interests to comply, and then he got out of the carriage and climbed up front again. He checked his right boot for the small knife he had kept hidden there since they had left Bewley Hall – he had learned that his boots were a useful hiding spot three years ago when he had secreted money in them to keep it concealed from the untrustworthy passengers he had met on the ship to Liverpool.

'Hold on, Bridget,' he murmured, taking the reins. 'We're nearly there.'

***

Every part of Bridget's body hurt. Her shoulders and spine had grown unbearably stiff from sitting for hours tied up back-to-back with Polly, unable to shift position. The rope chafed at her wrists and ankles, its knots so tight that her hands and feet had gone numb. Her empty stomach ached.

But the very worst was her cheek. The initial fiery pain had dulled to a constant, simmering throb that blazed up instantly whenever she ventured to open her mouth. Polly's makeshift bandage had successfully stayed in place but when Bridget raised her bound hands to gingerly touch the material she could feel how much blood had soaked through the rags and fichu before it had hardened. What would happen if she attempted to remove the bandage? Would the wound begin to bleed in earnest again? How long before it started to fester?

Her knees were drawn up; she wanted to rest her forehead against them but couldn't bend forwards enough. She tried not to picture her mutilated face but she couldn't help imagining how hideous she must look. How would Cormac and her children bear to look at her? How would she be able to go on with her life when the sight of her would be repulsive to everyone she met? She didn't think she wanted to be rescued anymore.

'Don't say that, my lady,' Polly hissed at her back and Bridget realised that she must have voiced her last thought out loud. 'You need to keep up hope, do you hear me?'

She sounded fretful. Bridget told herself not to surrender to her despair, if only for Polly's sake. 'Yes, I hear you,' she mumbled, trying to move her mouth as little as possible.

'Quiet, you two!' barked another voice.

She craned her neck carefully to get a better look at the pair of men who were standing near the closed barn doors watching them. She and Polly hadn't been left unattended since Sullivan had appeared with his five new companions; at least two men stayed with them at all times. She didn't know why the men were so reluctant to leave them alone – clearly, they hadn't a prayer of escaping now.

But the men were taking no chances. Even as the second man reiterated the first's command to be quiet, the doors opened and a new pair entered the barn. Neither of them were the Sullivans; one was a skinny young fellow with red hair and the other looked a little older with a thin beard growing in patches across his chin and cheeks.

'Our turn,' he said. 'Sullivan says to go join him and the others in the farmhouse. He's cooked a shoulder of mutton.'

The first two men left eagerly and the new ones took up their post by the barn doors.

Bridget stopped craning her neck but she heard the bearded man say, 'Can't believe Sullivan's luck in getting that money, and our own that he's sharing his good fortune. How great does it feel to have a full stomach?'

'The best,' replied the red-headed man. 'I'd forgotten what it was like.'

The bearded man's voice turned pensive. 'Brings back a hunger for other things, doesn't it? Once your belly's satisfied.'

'What d'you mean?'

Bridget didn't hear any response from the bearded man, but she felt Polly's body stiffen against her back.

The red-headed man laughed. 'Ah, I see.'

Heavy footfalls came across the barn floor and Bridget glanced up to find the two men staring down at her and Polly appraisingly.

The red-headed man pointed at Bridget. 'She'd obviously be the prettier one only for that gash on her face.'

The bearded man hummed contemplatively in his throat, surveying Polly. 'But this one's got no ring. Which means she's probably untouched and therefore likely to be very tight you-know-where.'

Bridget's stomach rolled at his undisguised leer.

'You're right,' said the red-headed man. 'The virgin's the better choice. How do we decide who goes first?'

Even in the midst of her disgust, Bridget experienced a perverted sense of rejection, and her disgust intensified towards herself.

'I'm going first,' the bearded man said matter-of-factly. 'You can have the damaged one while you wait if you want.'

'Fine,' the red-headed man muttered.

Polly uttered a whimper and Bridget's anger rose. 'Stay away from us,' she hurled at the men, flinching at the spike of pain in her cheek.

The bearded man ignored her, dropping to one knee. She strained to look over her shoulder and glimpsed him cupping Polly's face roughly in his hand. Polly wrenched her head out of his grasp.

'Leave us be,' she snapped.

The red-headed man crouched in front of Bridget. She recoiled, but there was nowhere to go. He reached out to her bent knees and pushed down hard to force both her legs flat. Then his hand moved and pressed on her groin over her skirts. There were layers of material between his palm and her body, but it still felt like a horribly intimate invasion. She shuddered and tried to jerk away from him. All she achieved was to inadvertently thrust herself further into his hand and he emitted a throaty laugh.

Behind her, Polly was struggling against her binds. Bridget heard the wet sound of lips mashing together and a muffled protest from Polly, which was swallowed by the bearded man's insistent mouth.

Tears of fury sprang into Bridget's eyes. This could not be happening to them on top of everything else they had already endured. It was too unfair.

Suddenly, the barn doors banged open. Disregarding the shooting pain in her cheek, Bridget twisted to see who it was. The younger Sullivan strode in, along with—

She sucked in a breath. Sullivan's companion was missing three fingers on his left hand. Duffy. What did this mean? Had Mr Sandler returned? Had he successfully deceived Cormac? Were she and Polly about to be released, or was worse yet to befall them?

Sullivan noticed what the two men were doing to Bridget and Polly, but he exhibited no outrage. He just said, 'Lads, we need ye to stop. There's been an unexpected development.'

There was a slurping noise as the bearded man pulled away from Polly's mouth. The red-headed man also reluctantly took his hand away, although Bridget's skin still crawled.

'What development?' asked the bearded man.

Duffy marched up to Bridget and gesticulated at her with his undamaged hand. 'Your fella,' he said. 'What does he look like?'

She goggled up at him, dumb with bewilderment.

'Is his hair silver?' he pressed. 'Or does he have yellow hair maybe?'

'Wh-why?' she stuttered.

He clicked his tongue. ''Cause I think he's coming for you.'

Her heart leapt.

'I'd been waiting for Mr Sandler at the docks in Dublin, just like he'd ordered,' Duffy went on, not to Bridget and Polly but to their two abusers. 'Watching every ship that arrived from

England, keeping an eye out for himself. Mighty boring work after doing it for a few days, let me tell ye. So I popped off today for a mid-morning pint at the quayside tavern where I'd been staying and was nearly finished it when a pair of fellas with Liverpool accents came in. I hurried back out and spotted himself standing on the docks. I was heading towards him when he turned and walked back to join some other folk—those two men I'd described, as well as a woman and two younger lads. That's when I realised he hadn't come alone. That wasn't part of the plan, so I scarpered back to the tavern, grabbed his chest of money and got the train down here, quick as I could. I reckon the whole lot of them are on their way to stage a rescue.'

'And thanks to your warning, we'll be ready for them,' Sullivan said grimly. 'We know how many are coming and we've got more. 'Tis time to make a plan.'

He jerked his head at the other men. They gathered over near the barn doors and started muttering among themselves, looking back at Bridget and Polly every now and then. Bridget was utterly relieved that the two men had been interrupted in their assault but her relief was subsumed by terrible anxiety and more than a little confusion. The man with the yellow hair was Cormac, without a doubt. But who were the other people with him? A man with silver hair? She had no idea. It wasn't a description of Mr Comerford or Sheppard, and she could think of no one else Cormac might have asked to accompany him from Bewley Hall. And a woman and two younger lads? Surely he had not brought Emily, Jack and Gus with him. That would be preposterous – he would never involve them in such a dangerous situation. Unless he meant to leave them in Dublin and travel down to the farm with just Mr Sandler and the other mysterious man. But why bring them at all then? She could not make head nor tail of it.

A small sob emanated from behind her.

'Oh, Polly,' she murmured, trying to keep her voice low. 'Are you hurt?'

Polly shook her head and drew in a trembling breath. 'I just desperately want to wash out my mouth,' she mumbled. She spat on the barn floor beside them. 'I suppose that will have to do for now. What about you?'

Bridget recalled where the red-headed man had put his hand and shuddered. 'I'm fine,' she attempted to lie, though she was betrayed by the quiver in her voice. 'I'm just glad they got no further.'

'Until they try again,' Polly said dispiritedly. 'We won't be able to stop them. It's hopeless.'

Bridget wished she could squeeze her hand. 'Only a few minutes ago, you told me I had to keep up hope. Now I say the same to you. Sullivan and Duffy have given us the gift of knowledge. We know that Cormac is coming for us. And I promise you he won't rest until we're safe.'

Before Polly could reply, Sullivan stomped back over to them. 'Right,' he said. 'We know what we're going to do with ye.'

CHAPTER 29

Cormac was heartsick as he drove the carriage through the ravaged Irish countryside. The fields were barren on all sides and the starving souls he glimpsed were pitiful to behold. He grieved for his suffering countrymen and for his homeland that had been so badly afflicted by the effects of the disastrous blight. What state was Oakleigh in, and its tenants? How did his old friend Liam Kirwan fare, and his wife Ellen and their children?

He couldn't think that far ahead. Right now, he could only focus on getting to the farm and rescuing Bridget and Mr Comerford's niece. Should he have made a surreptitious attempt to involve the authorities? No, it would have been too risky. Mr Sandler still retained power while he continued to withhold the farm's location.

There were so many unknowns about what lay ahead. Cormac's main advantages were numbers and the element of surprise. The two men guarding Bridget and Polly wouldn't be expecting them and, armed as they were, Cormac and his companions ought to be able to overpower them.

After a couple of hours had passed, he sat up straighter, on the alert for any indication from the occupants of the carriage that they were nearing the location of the farm. They had crossed the border from Dublin into the county of Kildare by this stage. It was mid-afternoon, warm but with heavy cloud cover. The two horses were decent animals and had kept up a good pace, but he knew he couldn't push them indefinitely and that they would need to stop and rest soon.

He was just beginning to sense their tiredness when he heard a knocking noise on the carriage ceiling behind him. He pulled on the reins to slow the horses down and leaned sideways to peer back over his shoulder as David stuck his head out the carriage window.

'Mr Sandler says the track to the farm is just up ahead on the left,' he called gravely.

Cormac nodded and faced forwards again. He spotted the place where a narrow track abutted the main road and guided the horses onto it. Driving the carriage along the bumpy track, he noted an expanse of fields on one side and a stretch of sparse woodland on the other. He went barely twenty yards before seeking a suitable gap in the trees and veering into it. Branches scraped the outer walls of the carriage; he was sure he would be obliged to pay a fee for damages when he returned the vehicle to the hackneyman. He halted the carriage once he was certain it was no longer in view from the track.

Jumping down, he strode around to the side of the carriage and pulled his pistol from inside his coat, pointing it in front of him before opening the door. Garrett radiated complete self-assurance within as he continued to aim his own pistol unwaveringly at the Sandlers. They both looked peeved.

'Why have we stopped?' Mr Sandler demanded. 'The farmstead must be at least half a mile further up the track.'

'This is as far as you go,' Cormac replied. 'Get out of the carriage. Slowly.'

They were still tied to each other so their exit from the carriage was ungainly. As soon as they emerged, Garrett followed in a hurry to ensure that both pistols remained trained upon them. Patrick and David hopped down too, surveying the surrounding trees warily.

'What are we doing here?' Patrick asked.

'Our guide doesn't need to come any further,' said Cormac. 'Stand over there,' he directed Mr and Mrs Sandler, indicating a tree whose bark was covered with lichen.

They shuffled over to it. He put away his pistol again, seized the end of the rope that bound them and started winding it around the tree trunk.

'Now, hold on!' Mr Sandler protested. 'There's no need for this.'

'We're not animals,' Mrs Sandler snapped.

Paying them no heed, Cormac secured the rope to a branch beyond their reach and double-checked the knots at their wrists. 'You'll stay here,' he told them, 'until we've scouted ahead and can confirm that we're in the right place.'

'This *is* the right place,' Mr Sandler whined. 'What do I have to gain from leading you astray? I want this to be over just as much as you do. The sooner you get your woman back, the sooner you give us our money and we can be on our way.'

'If what you say is true, then we'll know it soon enough,' Cormac said tersely.

Mr Sandler struggled futilely against the rope. 'Ideally, you should send me on ahead,' he said in a cajoling tone. 'I could prepare the savages for your arrival, smooth over the situation so that it doesn't get out of hand. That would be the smart thing to do.'

'I'm not convinced,' Cormac said dryly. He turned away from the Sandlers. 'Pat, David. Will you both stay here and watch them while Garrett and I go ahead to scope out the area? We will just be establishing the terrain and gathering information. We won't act until we have the cover of darkness later.'

David agreed at once, but Patrick twisted his mouth. 'Do you mean to leave us without any weapon? We ought to be able to threaten them so that they don't try to escape.'

'It's a valid point,' said Garrett. 'Here, you can have this.' He held out his pistol to Patrick. 'Take heed as it's a different beast to the hunting rifle you're accustomed to. This is how you cock the hammer. And this is how to rotate the barrel for the next shot. There are five altogether. Be sensible with it, won't you?'

He handed it over and Patrick appeared rather gleeful as he accepted it.

Cormac gestured at Patrick's and David's neckcloths. 'You have my permission to gag them if they make any noise above a whisper.'

Mr and Mrs Sandler both looked sour but said nothing.

'Look after the horses as well, will you?' said Cormac. The animals were already nibbling at some grass by their hooves, but they would need water. He showed David how to unhitch them. 'I can hear a stream bubbling nearby so you won't have to take them far. We'll try not to be too long.'

'Be careful, sir,' said David.

Cormac nodded and motioned to Garrett. They slipped away through the trees, going back the way they had come and then staying concealed within the woods while following the line of the dusty track next to them. Garrett carried his body awkwardly as he trudged through the undergrowth, patently unused to navigating such rustic surroundings, but he didn't complain.

'So this is reconnaissance only?' he said instead.

'For now,' said Cormac. 'We need to find where Bridget and Polly are being held and determine whether their captors are keeping a constant watch on them before we can figure out a practical plan.'

'We ought to be prepared for every eventuality,' said Garrett. 'I am mindful of the fact that I have given away my only weapon.'

Always looking out for his own interests, of course. Cormac clenched his jaw and withdrew his pistol from inside his coat.

'Here,' he said, passing it to Garrett who regarded him with surprise. 'I have a knife,' he added by way of explanation.

'That's fair then,' said Garrett. He didn't put the pistol away but maintained a firm grip on it in readiness.

They made their way between the tree trunks, keeping a wary eye out for any sign that the men on the farm might be alerted to their approach. All was quiet. The afternoon was muggy but the shade from the tree canopy kept the air within the woods a little cooler.

Finally, they glimpsed the farmstead through the trees. They could see the house and the barn and an enormous sycamore tree situated between them. Cormac experienced a quiver of anticipation – Bridget was close by. At least, he prayed that she was. If it transpired that she wasn't, he'd go back and unleash holy hell on the bastard who had brought them here.

'The woods skirt the whole farmstead,' he said in a low voice to Garrett. 'We'll circle around to the barn first and see if we can look inside.'

Garrett responded with a nod of agreement and they continued on through the woods, giving the farmstead a wide berth until they had looped around to the trees nearest the back of the barn. There, they halted and Cormac studied the structure. From their initial view of it on the far side, he had observed that it had double doors at the front, but they obviously didn't want to approach it via that entrance in broad daylight and in full view of the farmhouse. However, here at its rear, he spotted a narrow door set into the back wall. If it wasn't bolted, they might be able to ease it open and peer into the barn.

'The door?' Garrett murmured.

'Yes, I'll go first,' Cormac replied.

He glanced about in every direction, then darted out from the cover of the trees across the ground to the barn. Pressing up against the wall, he waited for a shout of discovery. When none came, he beckoned to Garrett who copied his quick dash over the exposed space. He, too, hugged the barn wall. Cormac sidled along it to the narrow door and, after a deliberate pause, tried to lift the latch. It rose without any obstruction. He rested a palm against the door and pushed on it gently. It opened inwards with a soft squeak. He held his breath but nothing happened.

'Let me go ahead this time,' Garrett said, indicating the pistol in his hand. It was a rational move so Cormac offered no dissent. Garrett slunk past him and warily stepped over the threshold, pistol at the ready. Cormac followed on his heels.

But then Garrett froze. His arm dropped and he said weakly, 'Good Lord, how could they do such a thing?'

'What is it?' Cormac said in alarm.

Garrett looked back at him, white-faced. 'I don't think you want to see—'

Fearing the very worst, Cormac shoved past him into the barn, his heart in his mouth.

Eyesight adjusting to the gloom within, he scanned the barn swiftly. There were no animals, only a hay-strewn floor, a discarded stool and a ladder leading up to a hayloft in the middle. His gaze was drawn immediately to the two figures directly below the hayloft: Bridget and Polly. Any relief he felt was obliterated as he registered their condition. They were slumped back-to-back, rope binding them together at their waists and lashed around their wrists and ankles too. But far worse than that was the sight of all the blood. He could make out the blood stains on Polly's hands, and on Bridget's too, on the bodice of Bridget's dress, on her shoulder, her throat, her face.

Jesus Christ, her face.

Horrified, he could hardly believe his eyes. The material wrapped around her head and chin held a bloody bandage in place over her left cheek that plainly covered a grievous wound. Her eyelids were closed but pain was etched across her forehead. Bile rose in his throat. He would crucify the brute who had done this to her.

He knew the plan right now was only to establish the circumstances of their captivity. He knew it was reckless to go any further into the barn. But he wanted to rush to her side...and he knew that he could not stop himself. He stumbled forwards.

'Wait,' Garrett rasped, but Cormac was deaf to his warning.

He lurched across the barn floor in staggering steps and Bridget's eyes flew open at the sound. Falling to his knees in front of her, he croaked her name.

'Oh no,' she moaned, wide-eyed with horror. 'You must get out of here. It's a trap.'

In the same instant, Garrett exclaimed, 'Look out!'

Cormac had no time to do anything but glance around at Garrett's pointing arm and then upwards to see a net descending over him. It entangled his limbs at once, causing him to topple backwards.

'Got him!' crowed a voice from the hayloft above and there was a flurry of drifting hay as two men burst out from the mounds they had been hiding beneath.

Cormac struggled against the net but only succeeded in pulling it tighter around himself – the damned thing was long enough to ensnare him from head to toe. Bridget strained to lean forwards to help him but she was hampered by her bonds. Polly peered frantically over her shoulder at what was happening. The two men slithered down the ladder as Garrett dashed towards them. Bridget's eyes nearly bulged out of their sockets at the sight of him.

'Stop right there!' he barked at the two men.

'You can't shoot both of us,' rejoined one of them, sporting a patchy beard and a wide grin.

As Garrett hesitated, the man sprinted out through the barn's double doors. The remaining one, a younger red-headed fellow, put his hands up in surrender.

'You've got me,' he said, but the mocking edge to his tone conveyed his confidence that Garrett wouldn't have the upper hand for long.

Garrett waved his pistol from the man to Cormac. 'Free him at once,' he ordered.

'No.'

Garrett cocked the pistol's hammer. 'If you don't, I will shoot you.'

Viewing the scene from his powerless position on the barn floor, Cormac wished Garrett could have concealed the shake in his hand better. The red-headed man folded his arms in scornful defiance.

'I repeat,' Garrett said more loudly, 'I will—'

But he didn't get any further because at that moment several men poured into the barn through both the double doors at the front and the narrow door at the rear. Two of them attacked Garrett from behind and he cursed as they twisted his arms behind his back, pinning him in place. One of his attackers was the man with the patchy beard – he wrested the pistol from Garrett's grasp and tucked it into the waist at the back of his shabby trousers.

Cormac's stomach turned over. They were surrounded by half a dozen men. Where had they all come from, and how had they been so prepared to instigate a coordinated ambush? Had

Mr Sandler somehow managed to get a warning to them before Cormac and the others had reached the farm?

One of them approached Cormac and stood over him. He carried a knife loosely in his hand and wore a smug expression. 'Walked right into it,' he said. 'Couldn't have been easier.'

'You blackguard,' Bridget spat at him.

He aimed his knife threateningly at her and she shrank back. Cormac narrowed his gaze at the blade and his insides seethed with rage. He tried once again to break free from the net but it was taut and unyielding. He yearned for his own knife hidden in his boot but he couldn't bend his body to reach down to it.

The man with the knife smirked. 'I've sent Duffy up the track. He was watching from a distance when your fancy carriage turned off into the woods. What's the betting you left our charitable English fella there before you came sneaking up to the farm?'

'We left no one behind,' Cormac said in an attempt to protect Patrick and David from discovery. 'The two of us came alone.'

'Don't believe you,' said the man. 'Hope you brought a lot of money with you. We all need paying for our hard work.'

Polly let out a snort of derision. 'Starvation, mutilation and molestation. Yes, you all exemplify the notion of hard work.'

The man's mouth compressed into an angry line. 'Still alive, aren't ye? All we want is our money and ye can be gone from here for good. You hear me?' He dug his booted toe into Cormac's side and Cormac grunted in pain.

An older, grizzled man was standing back and looking downright uncomfortable at the proceedings. Now he said, 'Don't goad him into fighting back, for God's sake. Let's try to end this as peacefully as we can.'

'He'll keep the peace if he knows what's good for him,' retorted the man with the knife. 'He'll leave with his life and his woman and he'll go back to his big house in England. That'll be enough for him.'

'This fella's Irish,' replied the older man. 'The lady told me so herself. You heard him speak—he doesn't even sound like an Englishman.'

'The other fella's definitely English though,' the red-headed man piped up. 'I heard his posh accent.'

'Indeed, and proud of it,' Garrett said acerbically. 'I certainly do not wish to be mistaken for an unsophisticated Irishman.'

'Precisely!' Bridget cried, wincing as she spoke. '*He* should be the target of your ire, not this man.' She stretched forwards as far as she could and Polly leaned back with her so that Bridget could put a protective hand on Cormac's shoulder, still shrouded by the net. She glared accusingly at Garrett. 'Shall I tell you who he is? His name is Lord Wyndham and, yes, he is an Englishman and he is just as arrogant as you might imagine. He lives in England and he looks down on the Irish people, on *you*, as a primitive race.'

Cormac gulped. How was he to communicate to Bridget that Garrett was actually, bafflingly, on their side in this altercation?

However, she had already raced on. 'But he is not above owning Irish land, oh no. He and his father came to this country many years ago and purchased a property which he has never once lived in. He is one of those absentee landlords who have caused so much damage to this country, exporting the land's wealth while the tenants die of hunger or disease or are forced to emigrate. And guess where his property is? Right here in Kildare, your own beloved county!'

A deadly silence greeted this passionate condemnation. Every gaze swivelled towards Garrett, piercing him with the collective weight of their blame. He grimaced, and Cormac was willing to lay a hundred pounds on a wager that Garrett was right now wholeheartedly regretting that he had ever suggested joining this rescue mission.

The man with the knife took a few steps in Garrett's direction, pointing the blade at him. 'We've lost our wives, our mothers, our children,' he said, grief cracking his voice. 'All because greedy landlords like yourself wouldn't pay us fairly and wouldn't help us when the blight ruined our crops and we couldn't feed our families. Ye all just turned away and counted your coins and left us to starve.'

Garrett opened his mouth but he found nothing to say.

The man's eyes glittered. 'Let's string him up, lads!' he roared.

As they hollered back their livid approval, two more bandits materialised at the barn's double doors. One of them, who was missing three fingers on his left hand, dragged David along by a rope wrapped around his torso, trapping his arms to his sides. Mr and Mrs Sandler appeared behind them, free of their binds, their expressions ugly with self-satisfaction. Mrs Sandler sneered when she saw Cormac restrained by the net.

'Oh, how the tables have turned, Mr McGovern,' she said snidely.

As the man with the missing fingers hauled David further into the barn, Cormac frantically tried to catch the footman's eye. 'Where's Patrick?' he mouthed at him.

David's jaw tightened. 'Ran away,' he mouthed back.

Mr Sandler strode forwards with a palpable sense of importance but he came to a standstill in shock when he caught sight of Bridget's face. 'What did you do to her, you fool?' he demanded of the man with the knife.

'She tried to escape,' the man retorted. 'Doesn't matter. The fella will still pay us to get her back alive. But that can wait.' He glared at Garrett. 'First, we need to deliver some well-deserved justice.' He picked up a length of rope discarded among the stalks of hay on the barn floor and gesticulated at the two men holding Garrett. 'Bring him outside to the sycamore.'

Garrett's eyes dilated and he struggled in their grasp. 'This is outrageous! You would not dare.'

The men shoved him forwards, heedless of his pleas.

'I have money!' he exclaimed, panicked. 'Plenty of it.' He glanced around wildly and his gaze landed on the grizzled old man, perhaps identifying him as having the most common sense of the lot. 'Money is what you all want, isn't it?'

The man shook his head. 'Looks like vengeance is what we want now,' he said mournfully.

The bearded man ripped Garrett's cravat from his neck and tossed it away, and then he and his companion forced Garrett to stumble onwards. He threw Cormac a desperate look before he was thrust through the double doors. The rest of the men charged outside as well, spurred on by the man with the knife who scooped up the discarded stool as he passed it. The man with the missing fingers followed them eagerly, dragging David behind him like a dog on a leash, seemingly unwilling to let go of his prize.

Mr Sandler surveyed Cormac, Bridget and Polly. 'You three aren't going anywhere,' he chuckled meanly and turned to escort his wife outdoors.

Bridget stared after them, her mouth slack and her chestnut hair dishevelled around her wounded face. 'Are they really going to hang Garrett?' she said faintly. 'On account of what I said? My God, I didn't expect—'

'My boot,' Cormac cut her off as he wriggled his ensnared body around in an awkward circle. 'Can you reach it between the gaps in the net?'

Frowning in confusion, she stretched out her bound hands. 'Almost. Could you lift your foot a little more?'

He raised his right foot as high as the net would allow, bringing it up to her waiting hands. 'I have a knife hidden in it. If you can retrieve it, we can cut ourselves out of our binds.'

Her confusion cleared. 'Polly, can you lean back to help me reach it?'

'Yes, my lady,' Polly replied and tilted her body as far back as she could.

Bending forwards, Bridget pushed her fingers into the net and slid them down into Cormac's boot. She felt about, grasped the knife's handle and withdrew it. Gripping it carefully between her two palms, she started to hack at the net around his body but her movements were sluggish and weak, so he took over as soon as she had freed his arms, slashing at the net until it was in ribbons on the barn floor. Relieved, he scrambled to his knees in front of her and swiftly sliced through the rope around her wrists.

He was just reaching down to the binds at her ankles when the crack of a pistol shot resounded beyond the barn's double doors. Polly emitted a gasp. Cormac's gaze connected with Bridget's.

'Go see what's happened,' she said, pushing feebly at his arm. 'My hands are free. We can cut the rest.'

He hesitated, but then he gave her the knife, leapt to his feet and dashed to the double doors.

Pulse hammering, he absorbed the scene before him. The men were gathered around the enormous sycamore tree, below which Garrett was perched on the stool. The man with the knife had tossed one end of his rope over a branch about eight feet off the ground and noosed the other end around Garrett's bare neck. Garrett's fingers scrabbled at the rope which was so tight at his throat that he could only make spluttering noises. Two of the other men had grabbed the loose end of the rope and wrapped it around a lower branch, pulling on it to make sure it was tied securely. But they had paused in what they were doing, frozen in place as everyone stared in one direction...

...at Patrick who was standing in the centre of the farmyard, pointing his pistol at them.

'That was a warning shot,' he shouted at the group of men. 'The next one will lodge in one of your skulls unless you release my father immediately.'

Mr Sandler laughed. 'You're hardly more than a boy. You don't have the guts to kill a man. Put that pistol down or these fellows might take it into their heads to string you up too. Isn't there a Bible quote that says "the sins of the father shall be visited upon the son"?'

Garrett's eyes widened with fear. 'No!' he managed to utter in a strangled voice.

Mr Sandler laughed again. 'Proceed, Mr Sullivan.'

'Let's hang him!' bawled the man with the knife, Sullivan, and he put his heel into the stool, knocking it over.

Garrett's legs kicked out, but his feet couldn't touch the ground and he was left swinging from the branch. The men cheered. Patrick's face blanched and he waved his pistol wildly. It fired but the ball hit nobody, whistling through the air and striking the side of the barn.

Still, it was a distraction and that was enough. As the men jeered at Patrick for his failed shot, Cormac ran headlong into the group and tackled the bearded man, shoving him face first into the dirt. Landing hard on his knees, he seized the other pistol still stuck into the waist of the man's trousers and, lifting his arm, he cocked the hammer and discharged it in one smooth movement.

Unlike Patrick, he had decent aim. And unlike Patrick, he had the guts to kill a man. But killing wasn't appropriate in this situation. No, maiming was more apt – maiming and, with any luck, lifelong agony.

The shot ripped through the air and a scream rang out. He knew he should have fired at Mr Sandler for being the architect of this whole abominable affair. But when he thought of Bridget his rage overflowed. And it was the man with the knife who crumpled.

Everyone stared as Sullivan fell to the ground, knife slipping from his hand and blood pouring from his knee. He shrieked and writhed in pain. Cormac rose to a standing position, surveying him with cold satisfaction.

'Good Lord,' said Mr Sandler, pushing his wife behind him to shield her from Cormac. 'You really are a savage.'

The bearded man scrambled to his feet while the red-headed man scuttled past him and foolishly tried to wrest the pistol from Cormac. He swung it around and struck the fellow hard on the head with its walnut grip. He dropped like a stone. The other men stepped back from Cormac nervously.

Nearby, Garrett continued to struggle and choke, his movements growing weaker. Darting forwards, Patrick scooped up Sullivan's knife from the ground and sprinted to the low branch where the hanging rope was wrapped. The two men who had tied it lurched towards him but Cormac rotated the barrel of his pistol and directed it at them.

'If you interfere, you'll get a ball in the kneecap too,' he barked.

They stumbled backwards, hands raised in identical placating gestures. Patrick slashed at the rope, once, twice, three times. On his fourth attempt, it shredded apart and Garrett's feet thumped to the ground. His whole body collapsed as the rope slithered over the branch above and trickled harmlessly to the ground next to him. Patrick dashed to him and dropped the pistol and knife to loosen the noose around his father's neck. Garrett gasped desperately for air. Vivid red marks stood out on the skin at his throat.

The grizzled man had staggered towards Sullivan and now crouched beside him. 'Johnny!' he cried. 'Johnny, my boy!'

Sullivan groaned in response and clutched his thigh above his wounded knee. The grizzled man glowered over at Cormac with palpable loathing but said nothing. After all, what could he say? He and the other men were just as ruthless as Cormac – they had all been about to hang a man in cold blood.

Cormac stalked over to Sullivan and glared down at him. 'You deserved that,' he spat, 'for disfiguring an innocent woman, you animal.' He raised the pistol. 'I'll do the same to your other knee if you don't tell your men to cooperate with everything I'm about to say.'

Sullivan's face was contorted with misery. He couldn't seem to form words, so the grizzled man answered for him. 'Fine, they will.' He looked around and said in a louder voice, 'We're all going to cooperate, all right?'

There were a few low grumbles but no audible dissent.

'Firstly,' Cormac said, pivoting to point at Mr and Mrs Sandler who were beginning to inch away from the group, 'you need to surround that man and woman. Do not let them escape.'

Mr and Mrs Sandler took off at a run but four of the men pursued them and latched onto their arms, dragging them back. Mrs Sandler released a demonic shriek of fury.

'Irish scum!' she cried at Cormac.

He ignored her, turning instead to the man missing three fingers who still had David pinioned by the rope. 'Free the lad at once,' Cormac commanded and the man reluctantly obeyed, unravelling the knots in the rope. When it fell away, David stretched his stiff arms, looking dumbfounded at all that had transpired.

'Go to the barn,' Cormac urged him. 'Help Bridget and Polly.' David hurried off at once.

Cormac shifted his attention to Garrett and Patrick. Patrick was supporting his father in a half-sitting position, while Garrett's breathing came in ragged pants. He attempted to speak but wasn't able to force out anything except a hoarse croak.

'Don't try to talk,' Cormac advised him, picking up the pistol and knife that Patrick had discarded. He pocketed the knife and dangled both pistols loosely at his sides, ready to raise them again in an instant if needed.

He gazed around at the group of men. 'I understand why you did this,' he said calmly. 'You and your families have suffered far beyond what anyone should be expected to suffer. The blight has destroyed your livelihoods, your landlords have abandoned you, and the government has not taken sufficient measures to alleviate the situation. This explains your actions, even though it cannot excuse them.'

There was silence apart from the sound of the leaves rustling in the sycamore tree.

'I want to offer you help in whatever capacity I can. And I believe the greatest impact I can have is by making a petition on your behalf. Through him.' He pointed at Garrett. 'That gentleman you were about to hang is a member of the House of Lords. He has a voice in the English parliament where he can present a case to send far more substantial aid to Ireland. I am certain he will be able to convince his peers to provide assistance once he supplies first-hand details of the abject circumstances he has witnessed in this country. And I can exercise my influence to ensure that he does.'

He was very glad that Garrett couldn't speak just yet because he looked apoplectic at Cormac's words. The men, on the other hand, exchanged glances of wonder and bewilderment.

Still crouching next to his injured son, the grizzled man gawked up at Cormac. 'Why would either of ye want us to receive even a ha'penny after what we've done?'

Cormac avoided Garrett's eye as he replied, 'Because I genuinely wish to help you. And because he needs me to help him.'

'Sir!' David called from the barn doors. 'Her ladyship has fainted!'

Leaving the men goggling behind him, Cormac rushed to the barn.

CHAPTER 30

Emily sat at her easel, her paintbrush motionless in her hand as she stared despondently at her half-finished painting. It had been two days since Rory had agreed in principle to sit for her but she still hadn't plucked up the courage to suggest that they actually proceed with it. She wasn't sure if she was ready for the intimacy of it – how could she stare into his guileless green eyes and prevent her thoughts from veering wildly away from the purported task at hand?

Instead, she had taken solitary moments to paint the view of the lawn through the parlour windows, but her creation felt quite lifeless to her as she worried constantly about her mother. There had still been no word from Ireland, though her father had promised he would write to her with news as soon as he could. She tried to remind herself that only three and a half days had passed since he had left Bewley Hall and that it would take at least that length of time, if not longer, for him to reach her mother and for his subsequent letter to make it back to Emily in England. But her fears continued to mount like a shadow lengthening over her and the house. Her father had travelled in such untrustworthy company – what if he had been betrayed?

Jack and Gus were still not aware of the peril that had befallen their mother in Ireland. Having finally solved the mystery of Lady Dorothea's missing ring and her lover's bones, they had

275

now turned their attention to learning how to ride in earnest, taking instruction from Bewley Hall's stable hands while their father was away. Rory joined them in the paddock too but he hadn't yet managed to convince Emily to try. She had gone out to watch them but was too afraid to participate. Perhaps when her parents returned – yes, *both* of them, she thought adamantly – they would instil in her the confidence she needed to climb up on a horse.

Sighing, she dropped her paintbrush into the jar of water on the table next to her. Her levels of concentration, tenuous to begin with, had evaporated entirely. She would go seek out Rory and the boys and hope that their horseback antics would provide an adequate distraction from her mother's plight.

But when she left the parlour, she found Rory coming along the hallway towards her.

'I was just about to pay a visit to the paddock,' she told him.

He stopped in front of her. 'I left the lads to it. I wanted to come see you.'

Her whole being tingled with pleasure. He lifted a hand to touch one of her curls as he had done when he had kissed her in the parlour and she liked that he was brave enough not to wait for her invitation this time. His hand moved upwards and she thought he was going to cup her cheek but then they heard footsteps and a cough from further down the hallway. He dropped his hand and they both looked in the direction of the intrusion.

Sheppard was standing there. He offered them a quick bow. 'My apologies for interrupting,' he said, the censorious arch of his brow indicating that he could guess what he had interrupted and was not very sorry at all, 'but I thought it best to deliver this right away.' He approached them and held out a letter. 'The postmaster's boy came running up to the Hall immediately with it when the message on the outside was noted.'

Alarmed, Emily took it. The word 'URGENT' was written on the front above the address and it was in her father's handwriting. She gulped, frightened to read its contents. She glanced up at Rory. Expression solemn, he touched a supportive hand to her back and that helped to fortify her courage.

Heart in her mouth, she opened the letter and her gaze fell upon the crucial first line. *Your mother is safe.*

'Oh, thank goodness!' she cried.

Suddenly feeling ten times lighter, she raced through the letter. Her father declared that he had found her mother and her lady's maid and that they were both out of harm's way now and recovering from their ordeal. He asked Emily to pass on the good news to Mr Comerford. They were planning to travel on to Oakleigh in due course and would write again from there.

Emily threw her arms around Rory's neck and he grabbed her waist and swung her in a circle. Then she let go of him and impulsively hugged Sheppard too. Startled, he froze within her grasp.

'I'm so sorry!' she exclaimed, releasing him with a blush. 'How inappropriate of me. I'm just so happy and relieved!'

'Very good, Miss McGovern,' he said stiffly. 'Your father was successful in his mission, I take it?'

'Indeed, he was!'

The butler's rigid demeanour cracked as he smiled. 'I'm very glad to hear it.'

'Do you know where Mr Comerford is? I must tell him at once that his niece is safe.'

'I believe he is below stairs in Mr Sandler's office.' Sheppard's lip curled. 'I shall hereafter only refer to it as Mr Comerford's office. I do not intend to utter that blackguard's name ever again.'

Emily thanked him and, tucking the precious letter into her pocket, she and Rory made their way down to the servants' quarters. They first came across the empty housekeeper's room and she reflected that her parents would also need to employ someone new in that role. In the room next to it, they found Mr Comerford seated at a table with an assortment of documents spread before him and a frown on his face as he chewed on the end of his dip pen. He glanced up in surprise at their entrance.

'Mr Comerford, we bring good tidings,' said Emily.

He sucked in a breath. 'From Ireland?'

'Yes,' she said, beaming. 'My mother and your niece are out of danger. All is well.'

He released his breath in a long whoosh of air. 'Do you know what exactly happened?'

She shook her head. 'My father's letter was rushed in his haste to send us news. He says he will write again from Oakleigh.' She turned to Rory. 'I wonder whether we ought to travel with the boys and join them there? That had been the original plan, after all.'

Before he could reply, footsteps approached outside the office and Sheppard appeared in the doorway.

'I seem to be shadowing you today, Miss McGovern,' he said, the twinkle in his eye belying his stern tone. 'I wish to inform you that you have a visitor.'

'I do?' she said, startled. 'Who is it?'

'Miss Harriet Bertram.'

Emily gaped at him, amazed. She had never expected to cross paths with Harriet again, let alone receive a formal call from her.

'Shall I tell her you are not at home, miss?'

Emily paused. 'No, I'll receive her. Please show her to the drawing room.'

Rory looked askance at Emily. 'It will be fine,' she reassured him. 'I'll come find you afterwards.'

'I'll wait for you in the parlour,' he said.

She made her way to the drawing room and took a seat on one of the sofas, still bewildered. Presently, Sheppard entered and announced, 'Miss Bertram.' Harriet came in, her forehead creased as she wrung her gloved hands. Emily rose from the sofa and they curtseyed to each other.

'Thank you, Sheppard,' Emily said and the butler departed. 'Please sit,' she added to Harriet, who hesitated before taking a seat on the sofa opposite Emily. Emily sat again too with puzzled anticipation.

'Thank you for receiving me,' Harriet said quietly. 'You would have been well within your rights to turn me away.'

'I confess I am quite surprised to see you here,' said Emily. 'You gave me a very strong impression at the Hutchville Estate that you wished to end all association with me.'

Harriet smoothed out her skirts. 'I owe you an apology for that,' she said at last. 'In fact, I owe you several. My behaviour towards you has been...unconscionable and undeserved.'

Emily scrabbled for something polite to say but couldn't think of anything so she remained silent.

'I can hardly countenance what I did. Such conduct did not befit a woman of my station and, moreover, it was contrary to my personal morality. I have never considered myself a vindictive person. However, you had clearly incited Mr Grover's interest at the party at my parents' house and that stirred a jealousy in me that did not abate. When you planted doubt in my mind as to his genuine regard for me, I preferred to accuse you of telling falsehoods rather than give the notion any credit. And even when my conviction wavered and I decided to question him, he persuaded me most compellingly that you were a liar.' Harriet sighed. 'More fool me.'

Emily wanted to ask what had happened to awaken her to the truth, but Harriet had already carried on in her hurry to unburden herself.

'Mr Grover and I both took great exception to the insinuations you had made and so we conspired to demolish your already tenuous reputation. He had anger but no practical solutions. I regret to say that I was the one who concocted the scheme to entrap you in a compromising position.' She lowered her gaze to her hands which she had begun to wring again. 'I am so ashamed,' she said, her voice low. 'Whatever wrongs I believed you had committed against me, none of them were worthy of such spite. I intended to entirely ruin your character and your marriage prospects—the very idea is appalling. And all on account of an unwelcome disclosure on your part, which I now know was well meaning and j-justified.'

'How do you know that?' Emily asked.

Harriet gulped. 'The day after you left the estate, Miss Yates and I shared a private conversation. We were still in shock over what had occurred in the gardens the night before. She expressed her pity for you and her disgust for men who seem to think they can just take whatever they want without a second thought for the females they will wound. She really was quite bitter. I joked that there was at least one man who had been denied what he wanted after she refused his proposal and she said that the cad had tried his hardest to persuade her to change her mind. He had been repulsively arrogant and impertinent with his advances before a servant interrupted them. She had dreaded seeing him again when she heard he was to attend the party at the Hutchville Estate. And then she revealed that the scoundrel in question had been Mr Grover.'

Emily only barely managed to restrain her gasp from spilling out.

'You tried to tell me the truth about him,' said Harriet. 'And in return, I insulted you and attempted to ruin your standing in society. How I loathe myself for having done you such a disservice.'

To Emily's dismay, a tear trickled down Harriet's downturned cheek. It dripped from her chin and soaked into her glove. Despite what this woman had endeavoured to do to her, Emily was moved to compassion.

'Please do not be upset on my account,' she said. 'I assure you that I am unscathed by the incident that occurred at the Hutchville Estate. In fact, I am deliriously happy.'

Harriet peeped up at her, more tears glistening on her eyelashes. 'Yes,' she said thickly, 'you said as much that night. I must admit I am greatly confused by how events transpired. I had confided in Miss Hutchville about your unfounded allegations regarding Mr Grover and, indignant on my behalf, she had assisted in my scheme by encouraging her mother, Miss Yates and Lord Dartry to come walking with us in the gardens. She and I had expected to find you alone and in a state of disarray after Mr Grover had set up the appearance of a scandal. We did not expect to stumble upon...' A faint flush bloomed in her pale cheeks. 'Who was that man you were with?'

Although it was not apt for Harriet Bertram to be the first person to whom Emily made this declaration, she said proudly, 'He's the man I love and I'm going to marry him. He may be lower class but so am I for the most part and I don't care if society shuns us because of it. I know that we are meant for each other.' Her heart thumped in her chest. She could not wait to say the same to Rory.

Harriet managed a watery smile. 'I am so pleased for you. And I do hope that society will not spurn you. You have shown me that gentle birth has little correlation with honourable conduct. I, for one, would gladly extend a hand of friendship again if I was not convinced that I had no entitlement to your forgiveness.'

Emily hesitated. 'You have it anyway,' she said. Perhaps on another day she might have felt less inclined to be magnanimous, but not today. Today was only for joy. 'My forgiveness, at least. I'm not sure if I can stretch to friendship but I don't wish to bear a grudge. I shall not snub you if we meet in the future.'

She stood and offered her hand. After a faltering moment, Harriet rose too. She clasped Emily's hand with her own and Emily's fingers grazed the patch of moisture where Harriet's teardrop had fallen onto her glove.

'That is far more than I deserve,' Harriet said, her astonishment and her gratitude palpable as she squeezed tightly. With renewed spirits, she lifted her chin. 'I want to tell you that I have also implored my brother to cease his association with Mr Grover. Alfred didn't promise that he would, but he did express his bafflement at Mr Grover's abrupt departure from the Hutchville Estate with what looked like a broken nose.' She shot Emily a wry look. 'Was that courtesy of your young man?'

Emily grinned. 'Maybe.'

'I'm glad you have found a companion with such loyalty.' Harriet's eyes turned sad again.

'I hope that you will find the same someday,' Emily said and she squeezed Harriet's hand in return.

CHAPTER 31

When Emily entered the parlour, she discovered Rory standing at one of the long windows looking out onto the lawn. His head turned at her entrance.

'How did that go?' he asked, his expression wary.

'Surprisingly well,' she said, shutting the door behind her. 'Harriet acknowledged her mistakes and apologised most sincerely for them. We have put the quarrel behind us.'

'You forgave her?' he said in disbelief.

She contained a smile at his incredulous reaction. 'I reconciled with her to a certain degree. We have not become bosom friends by any means, but I am willing to remain acquaintances. It felt like the gracious thing to do.'

He knitted his brows. 'You don't think it was too gracious?'

'I have no room inside me today for anything other than joy and thankfulness,' she replied, thinking giddily of her father's letter. What a relief it had been to receive that welcome news conveying her mother's safety. She was so elated that, without planning it, she blurted, 'May I paint your eyes now?'

He reddened and glanced around the room. 'Right so. Where d'you want me?'

Pulse quickening, she pointed at the sofa. 'Will you sit there?'

He crossed from the window to the sofa and sat down. She went to her easel, perched on her tall stool and judged the distance.

'I think we need to bring the sofa a little closer,' she said.

He got up, circled to the back of the sofa and pushed it forwards several feet. Then he sat again.

'Could you move a little further to your left?' she asked.

He shifted position so she had a more direct view of him from the right side of her easel. He was now only a yard away from her and she could look straight into his eyes.

She swallowed. 'Yes, that's better.'

She switched her attention to the drawing board on her easel and her half-finished painting of the lawn. She knew she would never complete it – it was soulless, nothing more than a distraction from her anxiety. There was still empty space in the foreground where she had not even begun to develop the picture. She would use that area to experiment with colours until she had established the exact shade of Rory's eyes.

Feeling self-conscious, she busied herself with laying out her palette and the watercolour cakes she would most likely need. Next, she plucked her paintbrush from the jar of water where she had left it earlier and tapped it against the rim to shake off the excess liquid. Finally, she peered back at Rory. His gaze was upon her face and her self-consciousness grew, even though of course he had to be looking at her from a purely practical point of view.

'D'you need me to do anything?' he asked. He was holding his arms stiffly at his sides like he didn't know what to do with them.

'Just...relax,' she said.

His body loosened a little and he spread his broad hands flat on the seat on either side of him. She recalled their calloused texture and longed to feel their touch again.

Blushing, she picked up her palette. She glanced between him and her watercolour cakes, selecting colours and mixing them together. Testing the results on the paper on her easel, she continued to experiment with colour combinations. She added a touch more cobalt blue and another tint of yellow ochre. All the while, her blush did not fade away. Rather, it intensified each time she took a glimpse into his eyes. His gaze never strayed from hers and she began to feel like it was burning her skin, even from a yard away.

Struggling to keep her focus, she concentrated as hard as she could on the mixture of paints and, after several more adjustments, she realised with triumph that she had identified the right shade at last. She dashed her paintbrush across the paper and there it was, as vivid as fresh clover.

She looked back at Rory, meaning to exclaim, 'Success!' However, the word caught in her throat and never escaped her lips. His eyes were still riveted on her face, but he was leaning forwards now, his forearms resting on his thighs. Her own eyes drifted downwards, taking in his whole body. A ripple of excitement shivered through her and, with it, a sense of daring.

'Rory,' she said, her voice a little husky. 'May I ask you to help me with something else?'

He raised his eyebrows and nodded.

'A vital skill for an artist is learning to draw people in a lifelike manner. The opportunities to develop competency in this area were...limited back at Brubaker. I wonder would you be willing to oblige me?'

'What d'you want me to do?' His own voice was raspy too.

'I should like to draw your arms, if you might be willing to roll up your sleeves?'

He cocked his head to the side. 'I'd have to remove my coat to do that.'

'Yes, I suppose you would,' she said, demurely lowering her eyelashes.

After a beat, he said, 'Then I have a request in return.'

She peeked up at him.

'For every item of clothing I remove, you have to take something off too.'

Her eyelids sprang wide. His green gaze was positively scorching now and she felt her core growing hot with tantalising yearning. She simply had to explore this sensation further.

'Very well,' she said and his mouth dropped open. Evidently, he hadn't expected her to agree. 'If you remove your coat, I shall take off...my shoes.'

It was perhaps not the fairest exchange but he didn't utter a syllable of protest. He shrugged out of his coat and laid it on the sofa next to him, revealing his plain waistcoat and the loose sleeves of his white shirt. As she slipped off her left shoe, he rolled up both of his shirt sleeves to his elbows. She couldn't help but stop and stare. His forearms were muscular, the veins standing out and the skin covered with a layer of light brown hair. Her body's reaction to the sight of them was dizzyingly visceral. Making a concerted effort to gather her wits, she realised she still had one shoe on and kicked it off. Her skirts hung over her stockinged feet, leaving them barely visible. She had definitely benefited the most from this arrangement.

'What should I do now?' he asked.

She coughed. 'Can you lean on your arms again like you did before?'

He obliged. She dug in her watercolour box for her pencil and started to sketch on a corner of the paper still clipped to her drawing board. She noticed the powerful build of his muscles but she wasn't thinking about how to make a realistic depiction of them. Instead, she was imagining those attractive arms wrapped tightly around her.

Her mind was losing the run of itself. Before she could prevent the words from streaming out, she said, 'You know, the torso presents quite a challenge for an artist too. It needs just as much practice as arms do, possibly even more.'

He looked at her steadily. 'And what do I get in return?'

'My stockings,' she said at once.

'Deal,' he said.

She watched in anticipation as he unfastened the buttons of his waistcoat. He slipped it off and then he tugged his shirt over his head, revealing his stomach, chest and shoulders in one smooth move. Her mouth went dry and her heart pounded rapidly against her ribs. He dropped his shirt on top of his coat and waistcoat beside him.

'Your turn,' he said, his voice practically a croak.

She placed her pencil on the table next to her. When she bent down to her stockings, she found that her palms were sweaty. Reaching up underneath her skirts, she sought out the ribbons of her garters, untying them with trembling fingers. She rolled her stocking and garter down one leg, then the other, and discarded them on the floor at the foot of her stool, letting her skirts fall again to her ankles.

When she peeped up at Rory for his reaction, his mouth was a lopsided line. 'I didn't get to see much there,' he said ruefully.

She emitted a breathy laugh. Grasping her skirts in both fists, she hoisted them up and gathered the material into her lap, exposing her bare legs all the way to the tops of her knees. He stared hungrily at them and her heart beat even faster.

'This will make it rather harder to sketch with my hands full,' she said, striving for a light tone.

He dragged his gaze upwards to her face. 'Jesus, forget about that and come here to me.'

She dropped her skirts and slid off the stool, stumbling in her haste and plunging forwards. He caught her in his strapping

287

arms and pulled her into his lap. In the next instant, their mouths were locked together. Her whole body was aflame with desire and she tried to tell him so with the eager stroke of her tongue against his. He responded in kind and a deep groan rumbled in his throat, prompting a wave of heat that sizzled through her from head to toe.

She touched a palm to his naked chest, thrilling at the skin-to-skin contact. He kept one arm wrapped across her back but the other reached down to her hem and beneath her skirts. His big hand caressed her ankle with calloused fingers and then glided up her leg, cupping her behind her knee.

She gasped as his mouth slipped from hers and he pressed hot kisses along her jaw and down her neck. Her head tipped back with pleasure and it was at that point that her eye landed on the parlour's long windows. Anyone who happened to stroll across the lawn and glance in would see them. And that reminded her that the door was unlocked. One of the servants or, God forbid, Jack or Gus could walk in at any moment.

'Rory,' she moaned as his lips and tongue addressed the hollow at the base of her throat. Gracious, the sensation of it was incredible. No, she could not allow herself to be distracted. 'We must—'

His hand skimmed up past her knee to her thigh, stealing beneath her drawers, dangerously close to the place between her legs that felt like it was on fire.

'Oh, Rory, we must stop!' she bleated, even though stopping was the very last thing she wanted to do. She clasped his cheek and compelled him to look up at her. He was panting and his eyes were smouldering with a patent craving for more...

'This is terribly improper,' she breathed. 'We could get caught.'

'I thought you didn't care about reputation anymore,' he said, his gaze focused on her mouth.

'There is a difference between public image and private respect. Imagine if Sheppard came into this room right now! Do you think we would ever get over the mortification of it?'

He blinked. 'Probably not,' he admitted. With enormous reluctance, he drew his hand down from her thigh and brought it back outside her skirts, making sure the material fully covered her legs. His heavy breathing slowed. 'It's just...that was feeling so good.'

'I know,' she said. 'But we need to act with more prudence.'

She bit her lip, considering the implications of what she might suggest next. They weren't married, not yet. They ought to be sensible and wait until a more appropriate time, after he had obtained her father's permission and they had made a vow before God and she had a ring on her finger. But how could they possibly hold out against this irrepressible yearning? Who knew how long they would have to wait? It was too much to endure. And there were no parents here to forbid them.

Casting all caution to the wind, she said, 'Will you come to my bedchamber tonight?'

She felt his torso tense under her hand.

'Jesus Christ, I don't have the strength to say no,' he murmured.

CHAPTER 32

When Bridget woke, she expected to be cold, stiff and sore. To her surprise, however, she felt warm and comfortable and she sensed surprisingly little pain. Carefully, she opened her eyes. She was lying in a bed, and there seated by her bedside was Cormac, looking at her with anxious blue eyes.

'Are you real?' she whispered, echoing the question she had asked him a lifetime ago when he had shown up in London dressed as a gentleman and bearing the name Oliver Davenport.

The corner of his mouth lifted as though he, too, remembered that night. 'Indisputably so.'

'I knew you would come for me,' she said with a sigh.

His expression dimmed. 'I'm only sorry I didn't get there sooner.'

'Am I in a hospital?' she asked, her words somewhat slurred.

He shook his head. 'The hospitals are all overrun with fever patients. It would have been too risky. We're in an inn called The Bells. I engaged a physician to come tend to you here. He gave you laudanum which is why you might be feeling a touch disorientated right now.'

'A physician,' she repeated. That was when the fog in her brain cleared and she recalled why she would have needed a physician. She raised her hand and tentatively touched her left cheek. It was wrapped in a bandage that felt fresh and clean but

290

she knew what it concealed. A small sob escaped her and she turned her face away from Cormac. 'Please don't look at me.'

'I'm never not going to look at you, *a rún mo chroí*,' she heard him say gently.

'But it must be ghastly,' she whimpered.

'It's not as bad as you think it is.'

She swivelled back to him, grimacing when the residual effects of the laudanum could not dull the sharp pain. 'You've seen it?'

'I insisted on being here while the physician looked after you.'

'Tell me the truth then.' She pursed her lips. 'And I'll know if you're lying.'

He glanced downwards and then back up at her. 'It's deep,' he admitted, 'and about two inches long. You will have a scar. But the physician washed it and sewed it and he believes it will heal cleanly. He said the scar will hardly be noticeable in time.' Cormac's gaze was honest and he held hers without wavering.

She swallowed. 'I feel...changed. Damaged, like I've lost something vital and it can't be replaced. Oh, listen to me.' She scrunched her eyes shut. 'I never realised before how vain I am.'

'You're not vain,' he said firmly. 'That man robbed you. He didn't take your beauty—he could never take that—but he took your self-esteem. And I understand that it will be hard to get it back. But I'm going to remind you every single day that you are beautiful, and I'll keep saying it until you believe me. And I'll continue to say it even after that because I will always believe it.'

She let her eyelids tremble open. He rose up off his chair and leaned over her but he just hovered there, waiting for her permission. She nodded and he lowered his head to kiss her, his lips brushing hers softly.

'I love you,' he murmured against her mouth. 'And I'm so profoundly sorry for what you have been through.'

He sat back down again and she read the tortured guilt in his countenance.

'It's not your fault,' she told him. 'Neither of us suspected that Mr and Mrs Sandler could be capable of such wickedness.'

'Nor those men.' He grimaced. 'Polly told me how they mistreated you, the way they starved you both and t-took advantage.'

It was not often that Cormac stammered over his words but she perceived how distraught he was now in the way he faltered. She shuddered as she recalled the red-headed man's touch.

Veering away from the unpleasant memory, she asked, 'What has happened to the Sandlers?'

His gaze darkened. 'They're currently being detained at Naas Gaol, the nearest prison in this county. I had made an agreement with Mr Sandler not to involve the authorities but that had been upon the understanding that I would find you and Polly alive and unharmed. Once I discovered that the latter was not the case, I considered our agreement null and void. I have requested that the gaol keep them incarcerated until I'm in a position to return them to England. There, I'll have them both put on trial and I'm certain that Mr Carruthers will have no difficulty in ensuring their convictions. I'll ask him to seek a sentence of transportation to Australia, although a part of me feels that even execution would be too good for them.' An expression of anguish filled Cormac's face. 'Mrs Sandler confessed that she gave Lady Bewley a poisonous tea to end her pregnancy the one time she managed to conceive.'

'Oh, good gracious, no,' Bridget murmured. 'The poor lady. How could Mrs Sandler have been so cruel?'

'Like I said,' Cormac said through gritted teeth, 'death's too good for them. But transportation will have to be sufficient.'

'And what about the men on the farm?' Bridget asked unwillingly. 'What will happen to them?'

His expression turned cautious. 'I have made a choice in that regard. But I place it in your hands and you may reverse it if you so wish.'

Her body tensed. 'What choice did you make?'

'I promised to take steps on their behalf to get aid to them and their families while the effects of the blight continue to cripple the country. I'm aware that the Sullivans have regrettably lost their womenfolk but the other men have wives and elderly parents and children who are starving and blameless.' He swallowed. 'I'm very conscious of the fact that it seems like I am choosing to reward the men rather than punish them for their actions. But once I took revenge on the brute who hurt you, I tried to rein in my anger. Because I know better than most what hunger will drive a man to do.'

In the ensuing silence, she pictured the desperate young man who had been homeless on the streets of Dublin until he had accepted a job working for a ruthless money lender.

'Still,' he said, looking sick, 'their behaviour was monstrous. If you would prefer me to withdraw my promise of aid to them, or to exact a greater punishment, I will do it instantly.'

She hesitated. 'Did you ask Polly for her opinion?'

'She said she would abide by whatever decision you preferred to make.'

Bridget stared up at the ceiling. After a long moment, she exhaled. 'Don't withdraw your promise. Their families don't deserve to suffer on account of what they did. But the two who assaulted us...'

Cormac clenched his jaw. 'They're a different matter. Polly identified the two men to me and I arranged for them to be taken to Naas Gaol too. They will be sentenced to hard labour for what they did.'

Relief flooded her. 'And can we get any assurances that they will never mistreat a woman like that again?'

'As they were being taken away, I advised them that the local constabulary would be keeping an extremely close eye on their conduct after their release, and I also informed them which body parts they would lose if they ever took such vile liberties in the future. I deemed the wetness on their trousers to be an adequate response.'

That provided her with a level of grim satisfaction. 'What revenge did you take on Sullivan?'

'I gave him a limp for the rest of his life.'

'Good,' she said. Then she blinked. 'Is my memory faulty or do I recollect seeing *Garrett* there?'

He winced. 'Your memory is functioning correctly.'

'What on earth—'

Before she could expand on her incredulity, there was a soft knock on the door. Cormac went to answer it and revealed Polly standing on the threshold, a bandage around one foot as she leaned on a wooden crutch.

Her face brightened when she saw Bridget. 'You're awake, my lady. May I come in?'

'Of course,' said Bridget, summoning enough energy to raise herself into a sitting position. 'How is your ankle?'

Leaving the door open, Cormac assisted Polly as she hobbled across the room towards the bed. 'Your physician described it as a very bad sprain,' she said. 'If I keep my weight off it for two weeks, the worst of the swelling and pain should pass.'

'You're doing a marvellous job of following the physician's advice,' Bridget chided gently.

Polly smiled. 'I only came from a room further down the corridor. I wanted to check if you had woken yet. The laudanum really knocked you out.'

'Its effects are fading. I feel much more alert now.' Self-conscious, Bridget angled her head to obscure her left cheek from view as much as possible.

Cormac offered Polly his chair and she took it gratefully, propping her crutch up against the bed. 'Do you still mean to travel on to Oakleigh soon?' she asked.

Bridget glanced at Cormac. 'We haven't discussed it yet,' she said, 'but yes, that is what I wish to do, and with all possible haste.'

'You need to rest first,' Cormac interjected.

She shook her head. 'There can be no rest for me until we get there. I should like to journey on as soon as we can.'

He frowned but made no further objection, at least not in Polly's presence.

'I need to say to you, my lady,' said Polly, 'that I don't think I can travel further at present, not with the state of my ankle. Mr McGovern has already said he will cover the costs of my accommodation at this inn while I recuperate.'

'Yes, for certain,' Bridget said earnestly. 'And we will make arrangements for your return to England once it is suitable to do so.'

Polly gnawed on her lip. 'I will go back to England if that is your wish, my lady,' she said in a low voice. 'However, after my ankle is healed, I would be full of gratitude if you would allow me to return to your side as your lady's maid.'

Bridget's eyebrows jumped up with surprise. 'Oh yes, Polly—I mean, Hawkins—'

'Please continue to call me Polly,' Polly said, almost shyly. 'I would view it as a mark of affection.'

'And indeed it is,' Bridget replied, feeling a pleasant warmth spreading inside her. 'But then you must call me Bridget.'

'No, my lady,' Polly said in a firmer tone. 'I wish to address you with the respect you deserve, for you have gained both my admiration and my loyalty. You may consider it my own mark of affection.'

Bridget gulped back the lump in her throat and reached out her hand. Polly grasped it with her own and they clutched each other tightly.

A pointed cough came from the doorway. They all looked up to see Garrett standing there. Bridget suppressed a gasp. He was dressed impeccably, but he had dispensed with a cravat and the red welts visible across his neck were shocking. He twisted his mouth sardonically.

'May I seek a private discourse?' he asked, his voice coming out in a rasp.

'I'll leave you be,' Polly said, taking the hint.

She withdrew her hand from Bridget's and used her crutch to get to her feet. Cormac reached out to help her and, as she found her footing, Bridget took the opportunity to surreptitiously study Garrett. She hadn't seen him in many years. His black hair had turned silver in the intervening time but he was still strikingly handsome. He stepped into the room, held the door open for Polly and then shut it after she left. When he turned around again, his eyes were glittering with anger.

'Well?' he said hoarsely to Cormac. 'Have you anything to say for yourself?'

Cormac stood ramrod straight by Bridget's bed and surveyed Garrett with a shuttered expression. 'Do you want me to apologise for what those men did to you? Do you consider me somehow complicit?'

'No,' Garrett retorted. 'I want you to explain why you saddled me with an agenda at Parliament that I have no desire to raise, nor indeed any intention of doing so.'

Cormac crossed his arms. 'You're still in need of my assistance, are you not? And now my countrymen are in need of yours. You've seen the devastation here with your own eyes, you've witnessed the depths to which the people have sunk. They need an advocate at government level to save them from this deplorable situation. I would do it myself but I'm not a peer. If you go to London and speak for them at Parliament, I will agree to help Patrick.'

Garrett, too, crossed his arms. 'We already had an arrangement in place for that. I offered to obtain a divorce. Do you expect to have both?'

Bridget stared from one unwavering man to the other. 'Divorce?' she repeated. 'What is going on?'

Unfolding his arms, Cormac apprised her of the circumstances that had compelled Garrett to seek him out.

'Gracious, it sounds like Patrick is in a dreadful way,' she said. She was positive that Cormac would want to do all he could to help his nephew, but she understood that he could not say that straight out, not where Garrett was concerned. Everything had to be a negotiation with that conniving gentleman. She regarded Garrett with wariness. 'And originally you agreed to divorce me in exchange for Cormac's assistance with your son?'

He jerked his head mulishly. 'But now he is making further demands about parliamentary aid. So which is it to be?'

Bridget looked at Cormac, and he looked back. The unhappiness and resignation she read in his features mirrored what she felt within her. She broke their gaze to turn back to Garrett.

'You will speak to Parliament,' she said steadily. 'And you will convince them to send aid to the Irish people.'

Judging by his curled lip, he would have preferred to grant her a divorce. 'So be it,' he rasped. 'But I won't say a word to Parliament until I see some evidence that you are fulfilling your end of the bargain. How do you propose to do that?'

'Bring Pat here to me,' said Cormac, 'and I'll discuss it with him.'

'Very well,' Garrett snapped and marched from the room, no doubt torn between abhorring the idea of doing Cormac's bidding and conceding the undeniable fact that it was the quickest path to getting what he wanted.

As they waited for Patrick to make an appearance, Bridget's stomach grumbled. She had a vague memory of being fed gruel in a semi-conscious state before the physician tended to her, but now she thought she might be ready for some more substantial sustenance. She said as much aloud and Cormac promptly left her side to ask the innkeeper for a tray to be brought up.

As soon as he was gone, she released a whimper of sorrow. How close they had come to securing a happiness she had not believed possible. If only Garrett had agreed to uphold the original bargain, her future with Cormac could have been utterly transformed. They would have been able to marry and she would have been safe at last. That joy had actually been within their grasp.

But this new bargain would help so many more people. Countless men, women and children in this country desperately needed aid and Bridget and Cormac had found a means to give it to them, although Garrett was an unexpected path to providing it. There was no point in wishing he could have been generous enough to grant them both desires – he wasn't capable of such charity. It had to be one or the other and they had made the right choice, she was sure of it.

By the time Cormac returned, she had collected herself and not a moment too soon as Garrett and Patrick followed on his heels.

When Patrick entered the room, Bridget was struck dumb. He had been only a child of seven when she had last seen him, but now he was a young man of almost nineteen and he looked practically identical to the suitor who had charmed her long ago in the ballrooms of Dublin. She wished he was only like his father in looks but, from what Cormac had told her, it sounded like he was emulating Garrett in every respect. He held himself warily as he offered her a small bow.

'Lady Courcey,' he said, which surprised her, considering her legal name was Lady Wyndham and the man who had given it to her stood right beside him.

'It is a pleasure to see you, Pat,' she replied, imitating Cormac's manner of addressing him. He frowned but didn't protest. Waving at her bedridden state, she added, 'I'm sorry I cannot greet you more courteously.'

He tossed his head dismissively. 'Quite understandable, I'm sure we all agree.'

Well, so far he had been reasonably polite. She glanced at Cormac for a cue as to what should happen next.

'May we speak to Pat alone?' he asked Garrett.

Garrett scowled suspiciously. He seemed on the brink of objecting but then he tossed his head in the exact same way as his son. 'Fine,' he croaked and departed from the room.

'Would you care to sit?' Cormac suggested to Patrick, motioning to his chair.

'No, thanks, I'll stand.' Perhaps he preferred to hover in readiness for a quick escape if the forthcoming discussion became too uncomfortable.

Cormac remained standing too. 'Pat, do you know why your father brought you to visit me at Bewley Hall?'

Patrick's lip curled in just the same manner as Garrett's; the resemblances between them were uncanny. 'I suspect he thinks you can work some sort of miracle upon me.'

'That's right.' Cormac tilted his head. 'But I don't think it's possible, do you?'

For a split second, Bridget discerned Patrick's crestfallen expression before he covered it up with a nonchalant smirk. 'Of course not. I'm too far gone to be saved.'

'That's not what I meant,' said Cormac. 'I meant that *I* can't make you change. The onus is on you to do that. If you don't want to do it, then it simply won't happen.'

'I suppose this conversation will be pretty short then.'

Cormac shrugged. 'That's up to you as well. Before we end it though, I'd like to ask...how do you feel after what happened on the farm?'

Patrick arched an eyebrow. 'What do you mean?'

'I mean it was quite a harrowing experience,' Cormac said in a steady voice. 'You saved your father's life, but not before he was nearly hanged in front of you. Furthermore, he almost died in the same way as your mother. That must have been distressing for you.'

Patrick didn't respond but his Adam's apple moved up and down.

'I won't push you to speak about it now,' said Cormac, 'but I urge you to reflect upon it by yourself. You've confronted the reality of death—now consider what that means for the life you currently live.'

Bridget supposed they could interpret the tiny twitch of Patrick's head as a nod of acquiescence.

'We are going to be travelling on to Carlow soon,' she said. 'Would you like to accompany us to see where your mother was born?'

'Not on this occasion, thank you,' he replied stiffly.

'In that case, I'd like to extend an invitation to you to stay with us at a future stage instead,' said Cormac. 'Though I can't say for certain whether we are more likely to be at Bewley Hall or Oakleigh, you are welcome in either home. Perhaps after you complete your final two terms at Eton?'

Patrick looked at him sharply. 'That's quite an assumption,' he said, his tone just short of contemptuous.

Cormac didn't flinch. 'It is, based on the evidence I've seen to date. Still, like I said, the onus is on you to either perpetuate the dissipated existence that everyone has come to expect from you or to prove us all wrong.'

Patrick left the room shortly after that, his countenance inscrutable, and Cormac sat on the chair by Bridget's bedside. He blew out his cheeks.

'We are placing an awful lot of faith in an immature young man,' Bridget said worriedly. 'If he makes no effort to reform, Garrett will not lift a finger to hold up his side of your agreement. The Irish people will be left without support.'

'We'll still help them,' said Cormac. 'But obviously our own influence is limited, whereas he has the power to effect widespread aid throughout the country. If he can convince Parliament to act, then please God they will be able to save many from starvation and disease.'

'But we continue to speak in "ifs". All of this will depend on whether Patrick can mend his ways, or whether he would even care to. Do you believe he is capable of it?'

Cormac made a see-saw motion with his hand. 'It's difficult to say. He plainly enjoys indulging in a profligate lifestyle. But the events at Sycamore Farm might have given him pause. He very nearly lost both of his parents to the same death. I know for a fact that Mary has been preying on his thoughts. Perhaps it has occurred to him that he has been taking the existence of his remaining parent for granted.'

Much as Bridget had reason to loathe Garrett, she was glad for Patrick's sake that his father had not perished on that farm.

Cormac chewed the inside of his cheek meditatively. 'He also witnessed the wretched conditions of people who have had everything stripped away from them, people left without food, dignity, hope. It has to have occurred to him that such a fate might have been his had he not been taken from his lower-class family by Lord and Lady Anner. Will it spur him to better appreciate the privileges of his upper-class life, the education to which he is entitled and the incomparable opportunities that are afforded him by his father's peerage and wealth? I suppose only time will tell.'

'I sincerely hope he follows the better path,' she said. 'It would mean something worthwhile will have emerged from all of this.'

Just then, a servant girl knocked and brought in a tray bearing a bowl of soup and a cup of weak tea. Cormac took it from her and she left with a fascinated parting ogle at Bridget's bandaged face. Bridget cringed with mortification. As Cormac set the tray on the bedspread, she despondently wondered how long she would be restricted to liquid meals. She was reaching for the soup bowl when she noticed something that brought a fresh surge of anguish.

'Oh no!' she cried. 'My thread ring is gone!'

She held up her left hand in dismay. The gold ring still glinted on her finger but the circle of thread that Cormac had given her the day they had fled from London with Emily was missing. When had she last seen it? She recalled caressing it in the carriage as she left Dublin on the day of the ambush, but she had no memory of it after that. That meant she had almost certainly lost it during her captivity on Sycamore Farm.

Tears stung the back of her eyes. 'It must have frayed right through. It could be anywhere in that barn. Among all those stalks of hay!'

'I'm sorry,' Cormac said gently.

She gulped back a sob, devastated. It might have only been a tattered piece of thread but she couldn't convince herself that her reaction was silly, not when she had always looked upon it as his first wedding ring to her. Even so, neither of them needed to say that searching for it would be truly like looking for a needle in a haystack. It was yet another thing she had lost on that farm, and yet another wound to heal.

She would have to put aside her personal distress for now. Her original purpose in coming to Ireland still had not been fulfilled. She would devote herself to ensuring that they at least accomplished some good on this calamitous trip.

'Let's go to Oakleigh,' she said. 'Let's go home.'

CHAPTER 33

Emily had dithered over what to wear that night, but in the end boldness won out and she was clad only in her nightdress as she moved restlessly around her bedchamber, waiting for Rory to arrive. She wasn't even wearing any drawers. She didn't think she had presumed too much. She had seen the ardour in his gaze, she had felt it in his voracious touch. He wanted this as much as she did. Though what *this* was, she was not precisely sure. She hoped he knew more. She gulped. But that would mean he had engaged in it with another girl before her. No, she hoped he was as uneducated as she was. But then how would they know what to do?

There was a knock on the door and she hurried to it, not wanting to leave him standing out in the corridor. It was late enough that the boys were long gone to bed and the servants ought to have retired too, but there was no knowing who might take it into their heads to wander the halls of the house and witness her clandestine visitor.

She opened the door and her jaw dropped in dismay. Gus stood there in his nightshirt. He wasn't wearing his tricorne for once and his chestnut curls were tousled.

'Gus, what are you doing here?' she hissed.

'I had a worrying thought,' he said. 'I said it to Mr Comerford earlier but felt I should say it to you too.'

'A worrying thought about what?' she said, fretting that Rory would come along at any moment. Earlier, she had given Jack and Gus a distilled version of the events surrounding their mother's ordeal and had assured them that she was now out of harm's way, but perhaps Gus still feared for her safety.

'Lady Dorothea. I can't sleep because I keep thinking about her. What if the ring and the finger bone weren't enough? What if she can't rest until we find *all* her lover's bones? We might need to dig up the whole beech grove.'

'Oh, Gus,' she said, trying to conceal her exasperation. 'I'm sure you have already given her everything she needs. Go back to bed now, will you? We can talk about this again in the morning.'

Looking slightly dejected, he turned away. Feeling bad, she stepped across the threshold and pulled him into a hug.

'You are so good-hearted,' she murmured to him. 'But don't get too lost in the world of ghosts. I'm certain there are living people who are in great need of your detective skills too.'

He brightened at that. He squeezed her back and she cherished the fact that he was still young enough to show affection to his sister without inhibition. She kissed his mop of curls and let him go. He padded away down the corridor and back to his own bedchamber. She heard the door close and released a breath of relief before shutting her own door too.

She crossed over to her bed and sat on the edge of it, her gaze flitting anxiously over the candles lit on the bedside table. Were there too many or too few? Would Rory prefer the coming encounter to take place in darkness? Come to think of it, would she prefer that too? Her body was not exceptional; the cigar-smoking gentlemen at the Hutchville Estate had made it clear that she was lacking in certain important areas. All of a sudden, she was overcome by insecurity, convinced that Rory would be disappointed with what she had to offer.

Just as she was beginning to hope that he had come to his senses and decided to stay away after all, she heard another quiet knock on the door. She hiccupped. It could be Gus again, she supposed. She slid off the bed and went to the door. When she opened it and peeked out, Rory was standing there, barefoot and wearing only his untucked shirt and trousers. It was hard to tell in the shadowy corridor but she thought he looked nervous. Her heart thumped with her own nerves.

She stepped back and he slipped through the doorway. After shutting the door, she turned to him. The candles radiated enough light that she could better read his expression: there was nervousness, yes, but the hunger she had witnessed earlier was simmering just below the surface. That made her feel a little better. Perhaps he would find her minuscule breasts not entirely insufficient.

That aside, her other concerns still plucked at her, chief among them the fact that Rory should not be in this room. It had been so inappropriate of her to invite him. It would be best for her to call a halt to it before anything could begin.

She opened her mouth, meaning to say, 'Do you think we shouldn't do this?' And yet, what she actually said was, 'Do you know how to do this?' And she realised that, regardless of the enormous impropriety of it, she still wanted it to happen.

He coloured in the candlelight. 'I actually learned a good bit about it quite recently.'

'From whom?' she demanded.

'Your cousin.' He grimaced. 'We were left alone in the library for a while that day him and his da arrived, and he couldn't resist telling me about his exploits with some duchess in London. Seemed very proud of himself and shared a whole lot more of the details than he should've.'

Emily was embarrassed on Patrick's behalf and yet also a little grateful to him for providing some enlightenment for

306

this evening's proceedings. 'So you are informed but you do not have…practical experience?' she said, wondering whether he might not have had a tryst with Emmeline in the course of their deception.

He looked her straight in the eye. 'I've never done this before, Emily. You're going to be my first.' He paused. 'And only.'

Her stomach cartwheeled. 'Well then,' she croaked, 'I'm glad Patrick gave you a useful education.'

'There are some things he did with the duchess that we will *not* be doing though,' Rory said firmly.

She stared up at him, taken aback. 'Like what?'

'I won't say,' he said, his mouth a stubborn line. 'They didn't sound respectful at all.'

She didn't know enough about it for her imagination to run amok, but she said timidly, 'You'll be gentle with me, won't you?'

His features softened. He stepped closer to her and bent his head, touching the lightest of kisses to her lips. 'I will,' he said. 'I love you.'

Her heart hammered wildly. 'I love you too,' she breathed.

They kissed again, tenderly. His hand came up to caress her curls and she comprehended just how fascinated he was with them, given that he took every opportunity to touch them. He brushed them back off her shoulder and then stroked down her upper arm, his thumb grazing the side of her breast through her nightdress. Though she quivered with excitement at the contact, her previous apprehension returned. She drew away from the kiss.

'Rory,' she said tentatively, 'I want you to know, I'm not unaware of my…shortcomings.'

His eyebrows knitted together in confusion.

'I'm sorry if—if I won't be very pleasing to you.'

Now he gaped. 'What're you talking about?'

She glanced downwards, embarrassed. 'You don't need me to say it aloud, do you?'

'I honestly haven't a clue what you mean.'

She cringed. It was sweet of him to feign ignorance, but she wished she didn't have to be explicit. 'I know my womanly assets are not substantial,' she muttered. 'I do wish I had more to offer and I'm sorry that I don't.'

When she peeked up at him, his jaw was nearly on the floor.

'You're not being serious, are you?' he said. 'You're—' He floundered, his face scrunched in exasperation. 'Damn it, I'm no good with words.' He heaved a breath. 'Emily, you're stunning. There isn't a man on this earth as lucky as I am. You've no idea how much I'm trying to hold myself back right now. If you'll let me, I want to touch a-and kiss every single part of you. I don't know what else to say to make you believe me.'

Her pulse fluttered madly. 'You've said it,' she said, feeling a joyful warmth radiating from the centre of her body to the very tips of all the tiny hairs on her skin. 'And you may. You may touch and kiss every single part of me. If I may do the same to you.'

He didn't bother with verbal permission. He was done with words. Instead, he pulled her to him and, despite his earlier promise to be gentle, crushed his mouth to hers. To hell with gentleness. She responded with equal passion, aching for him to kiss her until they had no breath left. How had there ever been a time when she thought she couldn't stand to be in the same room as him? After all he had done for her – accompanying her to England when she had needed protection, waiting so long for her while she had worked and studied in New York, letting her go when he had believed it was the best choice for her – how could she not love him with every fibre of her being?

His hands started to roam, skimming over her shoulders and around to her back before gliding down to land on her hips. She felt him tug on the fabric of her nightdress and she halted their kissing to gaze up at him with absolute trust.

'Do you want to take it off me?' she asked.

His green eyes blazed. He bent to gather the hem and slowly drew the nightdress upwards. She raised her arms and he slid it up and over her head. After he pulled it free from her hair, he bunched it in his hands and stared at her body, an expression akin to awe on his face. She glowed with gratification; she was enough after all. She took the nightdress from his slack grip and dropped it on the floor. Then she nudged his still motionless hands.

'You may touch,' she reminded him with an encouraging smile.

He stretched out his right hand and cupped her left breast. His rough skin provided a wonderful friction on her sensitive flesh and his palm covered her perfectly. Those men smoking cigars below the terrace hadn't had a notion what they were talking about. His other hand moved and she expected him to curve it around her other breast but he slipped it behind her and slid down to grasp her right buttock. His eyelids flickered closed.

'Oh, my God,' he mumbled.

He let go of her breast to blindly reach for her other buttock and he pulled her against him, massaging the swells of her rear with reverence. It had not occurred to her that this part of her body might please him so greatly. Giddy with delight, she was overcome with a desire to taste the experience for herself.

She plucked at the material of his shirt. He reluctantly released her to let her tug it up. She had to stand on her tiptoes to drag it all the way off him until his shaggy head appeared again, tousled and grinning. Before she had even let the shirt fall to the floor, he was already reaching for his trousers. He yanked them down and stepped out of them, allowing his eager body to spring into view. She had not been prepared for the spectacle and it was her turn to stare. However, when she finally hauled her focus back up to him, she read the self-consciousness in his countenance.

She knew what a gift it was to have those fears assuaged. 'There isn't a woman on this earth as lucky as I am,' she said, and the momentary anxiety vanished from his face.

They came together again, their bare bodies pressing against each other. He grabbed her behind once more and she did the same to him, relishing the glorious firmness beneath her fingers. She brushed her lips against his chest and heard his heart beating, the thumps fast and fervent.

She wasn't sure who took the first step but, without any need for discussion, they both moved towards her bed. He eased her down upon it, not with her head on the pillows but perpendicular to them so that she lay back across the width of the bed. Prompted wholly by instinct, she parted her knees and allowed him to kneel between her legs. He lowered himself over her, bracing himself on his elbows, and kissed her like there would be no tomorrow. A hazy part of her thought that if there were no tomorrow, at least she would die very, very happy.

Taking his weight on one elbow, he slipped his other hand down to the apex between her thighs and touched her. She felt the slick movement and was startled to realise that she was wet down there.

'I d-don't know why—' she stammered but he shook his head to shush her.

'I think 'tis a good thing,' he said with a warm smile. 'Will we try now?'

Heart in her throat, she nodded. He took a hold of himself and guided his tip to her opening. Then he leaned over her again and, after a slight pause, nudged into her with a very gentle thrust. He waited for her reaction. She beamed to urge him to keep going, revelling in this extraordinary moment of their possession of one another.

But then, as he pushed in further and her body stretched to accommodate him, the pain came. It was slight but it stung and she couldn't help the tiny whimper that escaped her. He froze above her.

''Tis hurting you?' he said, eyes wide.

'No, it's fine,' she said. 'Don't stop.'

He didn't move. He looked shocked. 'I'm sorry. I didn't know it would hurt. We shouldn't—'

'Don't stop,' she repeated with more persuasion. She let her hands rove down to his backside and squeezed her encouragement. '*Please.*'

After an uncertain moment, he resumed, nudging himself forwards inch by inch until he was wholly inside her. She exhaled with relief – the initial pain had been sharp but now it had eased a little, reduced to an uncomfortable and yet pleasurable ache.

'Are you all right?' he asked anxiously.

'I feel wonderful,' she breathed. 'How about you?'

The corner of his mouth lifted. 'Like I'm about to explode,' he said frankly.

Once again heeding her instincts, she clenched a muscle deep inside her and it contracted around him. He emitted a sharp gasp. She clenched again and he began to move with intention. Watching his face, she gloried in the intensity of his rapidly mounting pleasure. At the crest of it, he groaned and a tremor shuddered through him. He almost collapsed on top of her but he caught himself just in time and, arms trembling, he hovered above her and pressed a clumsy kiss to the tip of her nose. She blushed up at him, delirious that she had been the one to give him such satisfaction. She looked forward to embracing that blissful duty for the rest of their lives.

When their bodies separated, she experienced a pang that was both a twinge of physical pain and a longing to be filled by him again. He rolled onto the bedcovers next to her and they lay like that for a while, just breathing, their arms and hips touching. At last, she turned her head to look at him. He looked back at her and in the same instant they burst into dazed laughter.

'Oh, we must hush,' she said, still giggling. 'Gus is awake, or at least he was a few minutes ago. Or might it be hours? I have no idea how much time has passed.'

'Neither do I,' he said, grinning widely.

She rose up on her elbow, disregarding the soreness below, and traced her fingertips over his bare torso. 'I'm so glad we didn't wait,' she murmured. 'But you understand it has rather expedited matters.'

'We'll make the arrangements as soon as possible,' he promised. 'I'd marry you yesterday if I could.'

She glowed down at him. 'Where would you like to live? Would you prefer to go back to Boston?'

'I want to be wherever you are,' he said, 'and I don't mind where that is.'

She felt relieved that she might not have to brave the sea journey back to America. 'What about the workshop though? And your family?'

The corners of his mouth curved downwards. 'My family's in Chicago. It doesn't make much difference whether I'm in Boston or England, or even Ireland for that matter. I'll still never see them. As for the workshop, 'tis suffered some blows over the past few years between your da shutting it to go to England and then me doing the same. Maybe 'tis run its course.'

That made her a little sad, considering her father had once envisioned it lasting long enough for his sons to take it over. But when he accepted the inheritance Lord Bewley had bestowed upon him, so many things had changed forever.

Rory turned on his side to face her. 'I'm sorry again that it hurt you.'

'Don't be. It was worth it.' She exhaled a contented sigh.

He put a hand on her hip and then slid it around to clasp her rear. When she saw his body stir, she was left in no doubt as to what stoked the fire of his arousal.

'You liked what we did?' he said bashfully.

'Very much so.'

'It can be better for you. At least, I think so, judging by the comments Patrick made about his duchess's reactions to the things he did. The way it was for me at the end—I think you can get that feeling too.'

'I can?' she said, powerfully intrigued.

He gave her an enthusiastic nod. 'Would you like to give it a go?'

'I don't think I can again tonight,' she said regretfully. 'I'm a little sore.'

'Not that,' he said quickly. 'There are other things we can try. I might not be very skilled at them yet but I'm willing to put in a lot of practice.' A more flirtatious man might have winked but he regarded her with solemn resolution.

'Like what?'

'Just lie back,' he said, and she shivered with anticipation.

CHAPTER 34

Bridget and Cormac departed early the next morning from The Bells Inn in a two-wheeled, one-horsed gig which they had hired from the inn for the final leg of their journey down to Oakleigh. Bridget had dreaded the very thought of going out in public with her wounded face, but there were other things more important than her pride.

Garrett and Patrick had elected to return in the carriage to Dublin, from where they would take a ship back to England. Certain that Garrett would not volunteer the money, Cormac had furnished them with extra funds to cover whatever damage the hackneyman would detect from the carriage's detour into the woods at Sycamore Farm.

'And you have my thanks,' he had said to them, his manner frank. 'You got much more than you had bargained for on this rescue mission.'

'Truer words were never spoken,' Garrett had replied dryly, the welts on his neck now hidden by a pristine cravat.

'We'll exchange correspondence in due course,' Cormac had added to Patrick, and his nephew had neither agreed to, nor opposed, the suggestion.

Garrett and Patrick had then taken their leave, their bows identical, cool and perfunctory. Bridget would have found it amusing if she had not known how much grief had come about to unite father and son.

Her parting from Polly had been much warmer, and she had also bestowed an earnest farewell upon David who would remain with Polly until she was able to walk again.

'Thank you from the bottom of my heart for the part you played in the rescue at the farm,' she had said to him fervently. 'I shall not forget it.'

He had gone red. 'I'd do it all again in a heartbeat, your ladyship. You and Mr McGovern are as decent as Lord and Lady Bewley and I can think of no higher compliment than that.'

Her eyes had welled with tears. 'We take it as such and are honoured.'

Now, she and Cormac were proceeding as fast as they could to Oakleigh with the chest of rent money – liberated from the clutches of a chagrined Duffy – at their feet, agitated and fearful of what they would find at the end of their journey. They changed horses along the way but did not stop for long, determined not to brook any further delays in getting there. They didn't speak much, although Cormac did tell her about Rory's appearance at Bewley Hall. She wondered how Emily had handled her emotions. With all that had happened, she longed to see her daughter again, as well as her two cherished boys.

That put her in mind of Henrietta. She vacillated for a while, but eventually she winced with resignation. 'I went to visit Mrs O'Hara while I was in Dublin,' she said. 'And I'm sorry to report that Henrietta has run away.'

Cormac's face fell. She relayed the conversation that had taken place at O'Hara's Tobacconist and Lodgings and watched him struggle not to reveal how upset he was.

'I wonder if there's anything that can be done to find her,' he said, his shoulders slumped.

Bridget sighed at the sight of the barren fields around them – they had just crossed into Oakleigh land. 'Let's face one problem at a time for now.'

At last, they reached the grounds of Oakleigh Manor as evening set in. Bridget's heart was in her mouth as Cormac drove the gig up the tree-lined avenue. He had described the reconstructed building to her, but her own memory of it was still as a burnt ruin. The horse's hooves crunched on the gravel and the house finally came into sight. She released a gasp of wonder. The red-bricked structure soared in front of her and, even though it was not quite the same as the home she had grown up in, it was similar enough that her throat choked up. For one sorrowful moment, she yearned to see her dear father step out the front door and to feel his burly arms envelop her in his protective embrace.

Blinking away the past, she focused her gaze upon the most unfamiliar part of the manor: the new wing on the western side that she had instructed to be built for the purpose of housing tenants in need. Ellen had said in her letter that many people had flocked here seeking relief. Therefore it struck Bridget as odd to find the place utterly quiet. The windows were shuttered and there wasn't a sign of life. Where was everyone?

But then, as the gig rolled to a stop, she perceived a sound at last. Weeping. It was coming from around the corner of the new wing. Distressed, she hastened to jump down from the gig, not waiting for Cormac's hand, and her feet thumped onto the gravel, jarring up through her body and making her cheek throb. She flinched but ignored the pain. Cormac leapt down from the gig too and together they hurried towards the corner.

They rounded it to discover a woman and a girl sitting on the stoop at the side entrance into the west wing. Their clothes hung loosely on their emaciated bodies and they had their arms wrapped around one another as they cried desolately into each other's shoulders. Bridget's heart cracked to hear their despair and then it cracked again when she recognised the woman.

'Ellen?' she croaked.

The woman's head turned and Bridget discerned the freckles scattered across her nose and gaunt cheeks. 'Bridget!' she exclaimed, astounded.

'Oh, Ellen,' Bridget lamented and rushed forwards with her arms open.

Ellen recoiled. 'No, don't come near us!'

Bridget faltered and stumbled back a few steps. 'Wh-what?' Her worst fear had been realised – Ellen believed Bridget had abandoned them and hated her for it.

But then Ellen said in a strangled voice, 'The fever. We're not sick ourselves yet but we've been inside the house. You mustn't come any closer or we could pass it on to you both.'

She kept one arm encircled around the girl beside her, who looked to be about ten years old. She stared up at Bridget and Cormac with sunken eyes and her own splash of freckles.

'Fever,' Bridget breathed. 'You said in your letter that you feared it would come. This is dreadful news.'

Ellen's cheeks were still wet. 'There is worse news,' she choked out. 'It has brought Liam to death's door—we're terrified that it will be only a matter of time before he succumbs to it.'

Bridget inhaled in horror.

'Oh, Jesus, no,' Cormac uttered next to her.

She so desperately wanted to embrace Ellen, enough to risk contracting the fever herself. But she held onto her common sense by a mere thread and stayed where she was, her empty hands seizing the folds of her skirts instead. 'This is devastating to hear,' she said thickly.

Ellen rubbed her palm into each of her eyes to wipe away her tears. That was when she seemed to take in Bridget's appearance properly. 'Y-your face,' she stuttered. 'What happened to you?'

'It's nothing,' Bridget said miserably. 'Absolutely nothing in comparison to your suffering.'

How could she have been full of anguish over what was no more than a cut on her cheek? She was so fortunate that she still had what was most important to her in her life – Cormac and her children, all healthy and well. Poor Ellen was on the brink of losing her husband, and her three children might soon be without a father.

Bridget swallowed a sob. 'Is this Bridie?' she asked, offering the girl a weak attempt at a smile.

Ellen gave a jerky nod and rubbed her daughter's arm. 'Bridie, this is Bridget. She's the lady we named you after.'

The girl mumbled a greeting, her damp eyes riveted on Bridget's bandage.

Hardly daring to ask, Bridget said, 'Where are Liam Óg and Aidan?'

Ellen dropped her gaze. 'Inside the house. Aidan also has the fever, though not as bad. We're praying that he at least will make it through.'

'We shall add our prayers to yours,' Bridget said, silently begging God not to inflict any more pain on this good woman.

'Ellen,' Cormac said cautiously. 'Are there many sick inside the house?'

She sniffed. 'Dozens. The fever has swept through it these last couple of weeks. Three poor souls succumbed to it overnight. That's why it's so quiet. Everyone is shocked and frightened by how fast it spreads and how mercilessly it takes lives, no matter if they're young or old or weak or strong. They are all huddled in separate rooms, clutching their families and not speaking to or even looking at anyone else.'

'Where is John Corbett?' Cormac asked. 'And Laurence Enright? How have they been trying to deal with it?'

'They're both gone to Tullow. John went to sell the last horse from the stables. It will buy some food but there are so many mouths to feed that it will be gone in a trice. Mr Enright headed there to seek a doctor willing to enter the house and treat the sick. Mr Abbott refuses to come. He claims that his old age puts him at too great a risk but we all know it's because the patients are lower class.' Bitterness filled Ellen's features.

'Oh, Ellen,' Bridget moaned, 'you must feel like the whole world has abandoned you.'

'The whole world,' Ellen muttered, 'and God most of all.'

'Please know that my thoughts and efforts have been focused upon you and upon Oakleigh for longer than it seems. A letter of mine went astray between Boston and Ireland and it was the most grievous misfortune as it contained my authorisation to sell Courcey House on Merrion Square. If only that had been done sooner, the estate would have had access to far greater funds to get through this crisis. But I have since visited the solicitors in Dublin in person and have requested them to facilitate its immediate sale. More help is on its way.'

'Furthermore,' Cormac added, 'we have brought money with us which can be used at once to purchase food and medicine and anything else the tenants need.'

Ellen's forehead scrunched in bewilderment. 'But where has that money come from?'

Cormac hesitated and Bridget guessed the reason behind his reluctance. Speaking the words here on the grounds of Oakleigh would somehow make it even more real, more permanent, and it would forever bury the humble life he had once led on this land. 'I inherited an earl's estate in England. I'm now a landlord at Bewley Hall.'

Ellen gaped. 'A landlord?' she said faintly.

'And I don't intend to be idle in that role,' he hurried on. 'I have a duty to my tenants there but the estate has much wealth and I mean to use it to help revive Oakleigh too. You're not abandoned anymore.'

Ellen burst into tears. Now she looked like the one who wanted to embrace them despite the risk of fever. Instead, she clutched Bridie to her and wept into her daughter's hair.

***

They did not rest for the next twenty-four hours. Ellen advised Cormac what food and medicinal supplies the starving tenants urgently needed and he drove off in the gig at once to make the necessary purchases in Tullow, the nearest town, even though night would fall soon and he would be obliged to bang on shuttered shop fronts. At least the shopkeepers and apothecaries would be grateful to take his money in exchange for their disturbed sleep.

By sheer luck, he encountered John Corbett and Laurence Enright as he reached the outskirts of the town – they were walking along the side of the road in the deep dusk, heads lowered in dejection, but he instantly recognised his former stable master's small, wiry form. He stopped the gig and called out to them. They both looked up at him in amazement.

'I think I must be seeing things,' John blurted. He had aged since the last time Cormac had seen him, far more than the intervening three years warranted.

Next to him, Mr Enright pushed his spectacles up his nose and squinted through them as though doubting whether they were functioning correctly.

'I'm really here,' Cormac said, 'and I've come to help. Mr Enright, did you locate a doctor willing to treat the sick at Oakleigh?'

Mr Enright shook his head, his whole demeanour infused with regret and weariness. 'He refused. He said it was a lost cause.'

Cormac summoned his resolve. 'You and I are going to pay him another visit without delay,' he said. 'John, could I ask you to obtain the supplies I came here to get? We must buy food and medicine for all the tenants back at the manor.'

'With what funds?' John said, looking wretched. 'I've sold our last horse today but that won't cover everything we need, not by a long shot.'

Cormac showed them the chest of rent money on the floor of the gig. Their eyes went as round as the coins within.

'I promise to explain where this came from,' Cormac said, 'but for now let's make haste. People we care about are suffering and they're depending on us to act as quickly as we can.'

Both men nodded grimly in agreement. After Cormac imparted Ellen's advice regarding the provisions that were most vital, John swapped places with him, taking the horse's reins and setting off for the town's market square. Mr Enright then led Cormac on foot along the road and down a side lane where they came upon a modestly sized house with dormer windows jutting from its upper storey. A stressed-looking maid answered Mr Enright's knock on the door.

'Didn't you just leave a little while ago?' she said, frowning at Mr Enright.

'I did,' he replied, 'but I wish to speak again with Dr Lynch. Is he still here or has he been called away to a patient?'

'He's still here,' she said. She gave him another frown but stepped back to let them both into the house. Striding ahead of them down the hallway, she stopped at an open door and stuck her head through the gap. 'That fella's back, sir, and he's brought another with him.'

Cormac didn't hear the response but she ducked back out and beckoned to him and Mr Enright. They approached and she waved them through the doorway. When they entered, they found themselves in a room lined with cabinets whose contents were visible through glass doors: surgical implements, a set of scales, a mortar and pestle, dozens of books, and an array of bottles, jars and vials. A man stood at a desk in the centre of the room poring over a massive tome lying open upon it. Cormac was surprised to see how young he was, perhaps no more than twenty-four or so. He was clean-shaven and neatly dressed, but worry lines creased his forehead.

He glanced up at Mr Enright. 'I'm afraid my answer has not changed, sir,' he said, his voice thin and tired. 'I wish I could help your tenants, truly I do, but my efforts would be wasted. You yourself told me that there is not enough food for all their hungry mouths. What good is it to save a person from fever if they don't also have the nourishment to bring their body back to health? It would be akin to patching up a hole in a bucket of water while another hole still remains. The water—or, in the patient's case, their life—will seep away regardless. No one despises the injustice of it more than I, but I must concentrate my efforts on those who have an actual chance of surviving.'

'Dr Lynch, the circumstances at Oakleigh have changed,' Mr Enright said. He gestured towards Cormac. 'By the grace of God and this man here, we are in the process of acquiring the necessary provisions to feed the tenants. All we need now is a doctor to minister to the sick.'

The doctor's eyes widened. 'You're speaking the truth?'

'Yes,' said Cormac. 'And we have the resources to pay you amply for your services.'

Dr Lynch winced. 'That was never as important to me as saving patients' lives. I would work for pennies if I had even the smallest hope of success. But I could not justify the futility of trying to heal the fever in the poor creatures when I knew with certainty they would never recover from the starvation.'

'And have we now provided you with that hope, sir?' asked Cormac.

A few of the worry lines eased on the doctor's forehead. 'Indeed, you have. Let me pack my medical case and we shall go at once.'

The doctor had a horse and gig of his own, which was just as well because John's initial purchases filled every available storage space in both vehicles. They would need to return to Tullow again for further supplies but they hastened back to Oakleigh with what they had – the doctor's aid was more immediately pressing. Night had long since fallen fully and they lit oil lamps at the front of the two gigs to illuminate their way along the dark road.

When they reached the manor grounds, they jumped down from the gigs, gathered up as many of the supplies as they could carry and rounded the corner to the new wing, where they found Bridget hovering restlessly by its side entrance. She brightened at the sight of Dr Lynch with his medical case.

'Oh, thank goodness,' she said. She pushed open the door a crack and called through, 'Bridie, go tell your mother that the doctor has arrived.'

Then she hurried up to Cormac and the others. The doctor's gaze landed upon her cheek with an air of professional curiosity but he didn't comment on it. He just pulled a cloth up over his nose and mouth and strode purposefully into the house. Cormac silently thanked God for the man's bravery – this was his vocation, true, and yet fulfilling it meant putting himself at risk of contracting the fever as well.

'Ellen wouldn't allow me inside,' Bridget said to Cormac. 'I told her to instruct the tenants to spread themselves out through the whole building, not just the west wing. How I wish they had done that already, considering that the rest of the manor isn't even occupied! But that was when I realised that there's no furniture or bedding in the main house. We need to acquire blankets and pallets for them as soon as possible.'

'I'll set out again right away,' he said, fighting off any thought of fatigue or concern about waking proprietors.

'I'll come with you,' John said. 'Let's see if we can find a farmer willing to lend us his cart—that way we'll be able to bring more back with us.'

It was mid-morning the next day before they returned again with a cart full of bedding and more food supplies. Cormac could feel exhaustion threatening to take him over as he brought the gig to a stop, but he was startled into sharp alertness when Bridget came running around the corner of the house, her expression so anguished that a wave of cold fear swept over him.

'What's happened?' he asked quickly, handing the reins to John and jumping down.

'It's Liam,' she choked out. 'Dr Lynch has examined him and—oh, I'm so sorry to tell you but he says he does not have very long left.'

Cormac's heart stuttered in his chest.

'Lord have mercy,' John said huskily.

Cormac swallowed back the sudden lump in his throat. 'What about Aidan?'

'The doctor is more hopeful for him. But he's certain that Liam's condition has deteriorated too far for him to recover.'

'I want to see him,' he said, wishing he had gone to Liam as soon as they had first arrived, wishing they had managed to reach Oakleigh sooner, wishing so many things that he didn't have the power to change.

'But the fever...' she said, her dark brown eyes anxious.

'I'll be as careful as I can,' he said. 'I have to see him.'

She nodded in understanding. 'I know you do.'

A short while later, Cormac stood outside a door on an upper floor in the new wing, a cloth wrapped around the lower half of his face, his shoulders slumped in misery. He straightened when Ellen came quietly out of the room, her own nose and mouth covered and her eyes swollen with tears.

'I'm glad you made it in time,' she said, her voice barely more than a croak. 'Go on in. I'm going to fetch Liam Óg and Bridie. I've tried to keep them away as much as possible but they need to be here when their da—'

She cut herself off, unable to say it out loud. Stooped with grief, she walked away down the corridor. Cormac turned apprehensively back to the door. Ellen had left it ajar and he pushed it wider as he stepped up to the threshold. A breeze wafted towards him from the open window and the sun streamed into the room across two narrow beds. Aidan was curled up in the one on the right; a sheen of sweat coated his forehead, although he appeared to be in reasonably peaceful slumber. Dr Lynch stood by the bed on the left, closing his medical case. Liam lay in the bed, his eyes closed and his arms resting limply above the bedcovers with his shirt sleeves rolled back. Cormac's breath snagged at the pitiful sight of his friend. The bones stood out on his haggard face but his arms were the greater shock to behold, swollen far beyond their usual lankiness.

Dr Lynch came over to join Cormac at the door. 'Dropsy,' he muttered behind the cloth over his mouth. 'Fluid has accumulated in his body as a result of extreme hunger. It has affected his legs too. They will swell until they burst.'

Cormac felt sick. Good God, what a terrible affliction. He wouldn't wish it upon his worst enemy, let alone his oldest friend.

'I wouldn't advise you to go any nearer,' Dr Lynch said. 'The open window helps to dissipate the miasma but some of the noxious air can still linger. Perhaps you would like to speak to him at a distance though? While the fever has confused his mind, some limited sense of your words might still sink in.'

Cormac managed to nod. The doctor gave him a sympathetic grimace and left the room. Cormac looked back at Liam. The sunshine fell across his skeletal features – his eyelids flickered and he mumbled something inaudible.

'Liam?' Cormac said hoarsely. 'Can you hear me? It's Cormac.'

Liam's eyes opened and he stared up at the ceiling. 'Will you help me?' he murmured, his words slurring together.

Agonised by the sound of Liam's frail voice, Cormac had to force himself not to step closer to the bed. 'Yes,' he said. 'I'll do anything you—'

But Liam had already carried on speaking. 'The lady needs her horse saddled,' he said faintly. 'Will you help me?'

With a twist of his heart, Cormac realised that Liam's mind was neither here in this room nor in this present time. He recalled the years they had spent side by side as stable hands – they had been hardly more than boys then, unaware yet of the impact two extraordinary women would have on their lives, unaware that they would each father three precious children, unaware that this was how they would part for the final time.

'I'll help you,' he said, knowing the question that Liam would ask if he were not in the throes of delirium. 'I'll help them, I swear. You can be at peace—they will be safe.'

Liam said nothing further. After a minute or two, his eyelids fluttered closed. Cormac couldn't tell whether Liam had even heard him, but he prayed that he had.

When he left the room, Ellen was standing outside it, clutching Liam Óg and Bridie to her. Liam might not have heard what he'd said but Ellen had, judging by the way her wet eyes fixed upon his with fervent gratitude. He dipped his head and stood back to let her and her children pass into the room to say their last goodbyes.

It felt as though a vice was clamped around his ribs, compressing so tightly that he could scarcely breathe. He stumbled away down the corridor and nearly walked into Dr Lynch coming out of another room with his medical case. He halted, grappling for his composure.

'Thank you very much for your efforts here, Dr Lynch,' he said thickly. 'I understand that you cannot save everybody, but I'm positive that your presence here will keep alive many who would otherwise have perished.'

The doctor winced. 'Though it's by no means sufficient, I'm glad to be of some service. But the numbers are even greater than I realised. I must return to my house as soon as possible to gather more supplies.'

It was like the doctor had thrown Cormac a lifeline to keep his grief at bay a little longer. 'May I do so on your behalf?' he said. 'My time is not half as valuable as yours. Your expertise is needed here.'

'Yes, very well. My maid will be able to direct you to the necessary items in my cabinets.'

And so, armed with another list, Cormac set off in the farmer's cart again, glad to have a purpose that would distract him. He desperately wanted to be alone with Bridget but she was supervising the distribution of the fresh bedding and food. Giving themselves over to their sorrow would have to wait.

It wasn't until late that evening that he and Bridget were finally able to seek a brief respite by themselves. As the moon rose, they retreated to the orchard to stand beneath their oak tree together for the first time in eleven years. They beheld their weathered initials on the tree trunk and wrapped their arms around one another, shaking as each accepted the weight of emotion that the other unloaded. Liam had died during the afternoon.

'*Ar dheis Dé go raibh a anam,*' Cormac said softly into Bridget's hair, certain that Liam's soul was already at God's right hand.

At length, Bridget drew back and wiped her eyes. 'I know you will continue to have responsibilities in England,' she said, 'but I want to make Oakleigh our primary home eventually, after this calamity has passed. What do you think?'

'I agree wholeheartedly,' he replied. 'I can travel back and forth to Bewley Hall as needed. This right here' – he touched his palm to the trunk of the oak – 'is our true home.'

'It is,' she said with a sigh, resting her hand next to his on the trunk.

He knew it in his bones. They were always meant to settle with Irish soil under their feet, and they would raise the next generation where the previous generation had lived and died, in honour of their memories.

After a long, surprisingly peaceful moment, she said, 'Let's go back. We still have a lot of work to do.'

CHAPTER 35

'Jack! Gus!' Emily called after her brothers as she reached the top of the stairs in the east wing and glimpsed them running along the corridor in the direction of their bedchambers.

'Can't stop!' Gus threw over his shoulder and dashed into his room.

Jack faltered and looked behind him. 'Do you want us?' he asked.

'Yes,' she said, exasperated by Gus's cheeky disappearance. 'Please go fetch your brother.'

Jack traipsed into Gus's bedchamber and the two of them returned momentarily, Gus clutching his tricorne.

'We don't have time,' he whined. 'Mr Comerford says he's got a job for us. He wants us outside right away.'

'A job?' Emily said, diverted. 'What sort of job?'

'He didn't say,' Jack replied. 'He just said we needed to be quick, but of course Gus had to go get his hat first.'

'I shan't delay you then,' she said, 'but I'll accompany you outside and we can talk along the way. I have a message—'

But Gus had already taken off, plunging down the stairs at top speed. 'Slow down!' she exclaimed but he was already halfway down the flight of steps and pretended not to hear her.

As he vanished from view, Jack said in a long-suffering tone, 'I'll pass your message on to him.'

Following Gus down the stairs with Jack at her side, Emily pulled a letter from her pocket. Another came out with it but she stuffed it back in; it was an answer to her enquiries about the prospects for the local lacemakers and the news had not been what she had hoped.

She showed Jack the first letter. 'I've heard again from Papa.'

His face lit up; he worshipped the ground their father walked on. 'Are we to join him and Ma in Ireland?' he said hopefully.

'I'm afraid not. He has written to say that we must not travel. The situation at Oakleigh is wretched. He and Mama do not want us exposed to it and, besides, the estate wouldn't be able to cope with even more mouths to feed. It's simply not fit to house a family in the present crisis. We are to stay here at Bewley Hall and they will return to England later in the summer.'

Jack's expression fell. 'Will they be back by Independence Day?'

'I don't know,' she replied. 'Let us hope that they will.'

They caught up with Gus below stairs in the kitchens. 'I knew he'd stop by here,' Jack said sagely to Emily.

'What about there being no time to delay?' she asked Gus.

'We can't work on empty stomachs,' he protested thickly, his mouth full of pastry. He grabbed another mince pie and ran out the back door of the kitchens. Thinking she ought to inform Mr Comerford of her parents' plans, she once again joined Jack in pursuing her boisterous younger brother.

They found him and Mr Comerford outside one of the sheds. To her surprise, Rory stood there too – Mr Comerford was handing him a small leather pouch.

'It's on this side of Gildham when you're coming from the Hall,' the agent was saying. 'Not too far from the village, at the edge of the road. There's a wall covered with moss at the front. You won't miss it.'

'I'll see 'tis done,' Rory said, tucking the leather pouch into his pocket.

Before Emily could ask about this exchange, Gus demanded, 'What work do you need me and Jack to do for you, Mr Comerford?'

Mr Comerford levelled a censorious eyebrow at him. 'Hmm, I figured if you two boys are going to keep getting under my feet, I might as well put you to some use. I'm going out to collect rents from the tenants and I need deputies who can assist me but not ask too many questions. Can you manage it, do you think?'

Gus looked nearly ready to burst with pride. 'We can!'

Jack beamed too.

'Very well then,' Mr Comerford said, starting to turn away. 'We've already fallen behind since you had to go get your hat, so hurry up and come with—' He cut himself off as he glanced upwards and, clutching at his chest, let out a most uncharacteristic gasp. 'What the—by Jove!'

He stared up at the house and they all whirled to look in the same direction. From where they were, they had a full view of the back of Bewley Hall. At the very top of the building was the narrow attic window...and in the window stood a figure veiled in white. Emily goggled, dumbstruck. Rory's jaw dropped. Jack and Gus both yelped. Gus's tricorne slid over his forehead and he hurriedly pushed it back up.

'It's Lady Dorothea!' he cried.

'As I live and breathe,' murmured Mr Comerford.

The figure slowly raised a hand as though in acknowledgement. Jack and Gus shared a look of awe and then, tentatively, they waved up at the attic window. The figure dipped its head and glided out of sight.

'She was saying thank you!' Gus exclaimed, ecstatic. 'She's at peace at last!'

He threw his tricorne up into the air and tried to catch it. It slipped through his hands and landed on the ground. Unfazed, he picked it up, dusted it off and jammed it back onto his head with a whoop. Emily caught Mr Comerford looking at Gus, an unmistakable expression of fondness on his usually uncommunicative face. She squinted at him appraisingly.

He noticed her attention upon him and cleared his throat. 'Well, now that the excitement is over, we'd best be off. Plenty of rents to collect before the day is done.'

He motioned at Jack and Gus, but Emily said, 'Might I have a word with you before you go, Mr Comerford?'

After an almost imperceptible pause, he grunted. 'If it's quick. Like I said, we've got places to be. We're behind schedule and there are shorter legs to take into account.'

'I won't delay you but a moment. Perhaps Jack and Gus can go on ahead to get a head start?'

He gave a reluctant nod. 'Make your way down the avenue, boys, and I'll catch up with you shortly.'

They took off, chattering excitedly about the ghost's appearance as they scurried around the side of the house. Emily gazed after them.

'My little brother is so endearing, isn't he?' she said lightly. 'I do believe no one can remain impervious to his lovable nature for long. Not even you, Mr Comerford.' She raised her eyebrows at him.

He reddened. 'I don't know what you mean,' he said gruffly.

Next to them, Rory chuckled. 'Arrah, of course, how did we not see it before? There's no way that ring and bone would have stayed buried at such a shallow depth for over a hundred years. Burrowing animals would've disturbed them at some point.'

'I also thought that the ring looked remarkably untarnished despite its age,' said Emily. 'And come to think of it, Mr Comerford, I seem to recollect my mother mentioning that you intended to pay a visit to the blacksmith the day she went to the postmaster's house.'

His mouth twitched. 'You don't think the boys have figured it out, do you?'

'Not at all,' she assured him. 'They are entirely convinced that they have rescued the ghost of Lady Dorothea from eternal torment.'

'Well then,' he said, his eyes twinkling, 'that's all that matters, isn't it?' He made a move to leave.

'Wait,' she said. 'Perhaps you could enlighten us before you go? Where did the bone come from? It certainly wasn't a finger.'

He cocked his head. 'It was a rib. Your father might not have great aim with a rifle, but I can still hit a rabbit cleanly at thirty yards.'

She gestured up to the attic window, which was now empty. 'And the "ghost"? Did you rope in one of the servants?'

'My sister,' he admitted. 'She's a widow but she's holding onto her bridal gown in the hope that Polly finds a decent young man to settle down with someday.' He shrugged. 'The servants helped in other ways though. David told the boys about the iron ring and Jennie said she spotted the lady's name on the back of the painting.'

'So is Lady Dorothea's story a total invention then?' Rory asked.

'No, no. She did exist and sadly she did die under tragic circumstances. But I may have...embellished some of her history to create a good mystery for our budding detective to solve.'

Emily laughed and bounced up on her tiptoes to plant a kiss on his cheek, his mutton chops tickling her. 'You are an absolute dear. Thank you for being so good to the boys.'

He coughed. 'I'd best be going now.' He glanced at Rory. 'Do you want a horse to go to Gildham?'

Rory shook his head. 'I'm not confident enough yet. I'll walk.'

Mr Comerford nodded and strode away around the corner of the house after the boys. Emily stared at his retreating back with great affection. 'Gus truly has the capacity to soften even the most guarded of hearts, doesn't he? I believe Mr Comerford had been giving serious consideration to leaving his post, but I do hope this now means that he'll stay. Papa needs people he can trust.'

'I hope he can rely on me too in the future,' Rory said. He patted his pocket where he had stowed the leather pouch. 'I asked Mr Comerford if there was anything I could do to help around the estate. I don't want to be idle and I want your da to know that I'm willing to commit to a life here, if this is where you want to be.'

She wasn't sure yet what her preference would be, but she smiled as she envisioned their possible future at Bewley Hall. 'So you might become his apprentice again, just as he had originally proposed? It has been quite the winding road to return to this point.'

He grimaced. 'There were a few mistakes made along the way. But seeing as we've ended up here anyway, maybe that means this was always meant to be.'

'I like to think so,' she breathed.

Almost of their own accord, her feet moved closer to him until their bodies were only inches apart. He gazed down at her with a blistering expression in his eyes and it made the air thrum between them. She recalled the first night he had come to her bedchamber and the five glorious nights since then, each one full of rapturous revelations as they discovered how to please one another. She had experienced some pain again on the second night but no more after that. Part of her wanted him to whisk her into the nearby shed right now and ravish her, but modesty prevailed. They were in full view of anyone looking out the back windows of the house. What if Mr Comerford's sister was still lingering up in the attic? She swallowed and grudgingly forced herself to take a step back from him.

'What business do you have in Gildham?' she asked.

The blaze in his eyes faded a little as he, too, regained control of himself. 'I'm to visit a couple called Harry and Jill Barnes. Your da told Mr Barnes that the estate would cover the cost of fixing his roof. I'm bringing the money to pay the thatcher.'

'May I accompany you? There is actually someone I wish to visit in the village too.'

He nodded eagerly, not even trying to conceal how pleased he was. She understood; all she wanted was to be in his presence every minute of every day. She had finally begun to comprehend the driving force behind her parents' actions when they had embarked on their love affair long ago. Who on earth could resist a power like this? How lucky that she and Rory were both free to be together and that she had not tied herself to another gentleman.

She went back into the house to retrieve her bonnet for their walk and they set off, leaving the grounds of Bewley Hall and following the road that led to the village of Gildham.

'I reckon I'll be confident enough to try riding the route after a few more lessons from the stable hands,' said Rory.

'I doubt whether I will ever have the courage to ride a horse this far,' she said. 'I wonder why I didn't inherit the skill from my parents?'

He nudged her with his elbow. 'You got all the artistic talent instead, and then some.'

She worried at her lower lip with her teeth. 'Rory, how would you feel if I tried to sell my art commercially, even though it is a male-dominated sphere?'

'Jesus, I'd be so proud of you I'd probably explode.'

She glowed with happiness. In the next instant, she heard a buzzing in her ears and he lunged at her, swiping at her bonnet and knocking it askew.

'What on earth—!' she yelped.

'There was a bumblebee,' he puffed, pointing.

She turned and discerned the furry creature drifting away blithely on the air. 'Oh,' she said with a laugh. 'I'm not scared of bees.'

'You're not?'

'No, are you?'

'No,' he replied quickly. 'But I'm...not fond of them.'

She twinkled at him. 'And yet you put your life in danger to save mine?'

Colour bloomed all the way from his neck to his ears.

'I'm teasing you,' she said. 'I think it was a very sweet thing to do.'

He shrugged but looked pleased nonetheless. He fixed her bonnet for her, taking the opportunity to linger where her curls gathered at her temples, and then they walked on.

It was nearly a week into June and the summer sun was hot on their shoulders as their feet kicked up dust on the road. The walk was longer than Emily had expected and her throat had become quite parched by the time Rory pointed ahead and said, 'I think that's the place.' A thatched cottage sat at the side of the road, its boundary marked by a low, moss-covered stone wall. The thatch on the roof appeared fresh and neat.

They approached and Rory knocked on the door. A baby's cry resounded from within. The door opened and a woman emerged with a tiny newborn cradled in the crook of her arm. Emily's heart leapt with instant adoration, even though the infant's face was screwed up with dissatisfaction.

'We're so sorry,' she said. 'Did we wake your baby?'

'Not to worry,' replied the woman. 'He's due for a feed soon enough anyway. Can I help you?'

'Are you Mrs Barnes, ma'am?' Rory asked, a little stilted.

She frowned. 'I am.'

'We're from the Hall. I'm here to bring the money to cover the thatching work done on your roof.' He pulled out the leather pouch and offered it to the woman. 'The land agent said your husband would be able to pass it on to the thatcher directly.'

The confusion in her features cleared to be replaced with gratitude. 'Oh, yes, thank you so much!' She kept a firm grip on her child as she took the pouch from Rory with her other hand. 'The thatcher finished the repairs yesterday and did such a fine job. I'll make sure Harry gets this to him as soon as he comes home.' She squinted at them. 'Did you walk here all the way from the Hall in this heat? Lord, you must be thirsty. Come inside for a little shade and some water.'

The invitation was too tempting to refuse. They entered the dim cottage, which was sparsely furnished with a table and bench in its centre and a cupboard to one side.

'The water pail is out the back,' said Mrs Barnes. 'We have a hollow in the ground that helps to keep it cool in this weather.'

Looking at the woman's full hands, Emily said, 'Shall I hold your baby while you get the pail?'

Mrs Barnes gave her a smile. 'Thank you,' she said before gently transferring the newborn into Emily's arms. Then she put the pouch on the table and went back outside.

Emily took a seat on the bench and stared down into the baby's face. He had quietened and was now opening and closing his tiny mouth. Overflowing with affection, she put the tip of her little finger against his lower lip and he sucked on it. She thought of her friend Louise with whom she had shared a berth on the *Integrity* and tried to picture her little cherub of a daughter, Philippa, who had to be nearly three years old now. Louise had travelled on to Yorkshire after they disembarked in Liverpool; now that Emily was in England, she ought to contrive a way to visit her. How wonderful it would be to see her friend and her enchanting little girl again.

'Oh, I can't wait to have a baby,' she said unthinkingly. Then she froze. When she gathered the courage to look up, Rory was just standing there, equally rigid. Before she could say anything further, Mrs Barnes came back in carrying a pail. She didn't notice the total silence between Emily and Rory as she retrieved two cups from the cupboard and dipped them into the pail.

'Here you go,' she said, handing one to Rory. He accepted it dumbly.

'Shall we swap?' she said to Emily and they carefully exchanged the baby for the cup of water. Emily drank hastily to hide her embarrassment.

Mrs Barnes rocked her baby. 'Are you both servants up at the Hall?'

Emily's discomfiture increased. 'I'm actually, um...my father is the landlord, Mr McGovern.'

Mrs Barnes's mouth went slack. 'I should've realised. Your clothes are too fine. Lord, I'm very sorry for my impertinence, Miss McGovern.'

'There was no impertinence at all,' Emily reassured her. 'Please call me Emily.'

Mrs Barnes furrowed her brows. 'You're just as down-to-earth as your father. He didn't hesitate to climb up on our roof even though he's the owner of the whole estate! And here you are, sitting in a tenant's cottage drinking plain water. It's baffling, to be honest.'

Emily baulked. Had she somehow harmed her family's reputation?

But it was Mrs Barnes's turn to reassure Emily. 'I like it. I reckon your father's going to do good things around here.'

Shortly after that, the baby grew fretful again and could not be calmed.

'We'll take our leave,' Emily said, wanting to give the woman privacy to feed her child. 'We must head on into the village.'

'Come by here on your way back,' Mrs Barnes urged them. 'If Harry's home by then, he'll take you in the cart back up to the Hall. It'll save you walking in this heat.'

'Oh, that is very kind,' Emily said, glancing at Rory who only nodded his mute thanks.

Mrs Barnes waved to them from the door of the cottage and they walked away up the road in the direction of Gildham.

The silence was heavy between them as they both stared straight ahead. Emily felt too tongue-tied to speak. She was sure she had unnerved Rory with her careless declaration.

But then he drew in a breath and turned his head to her. 'I like the idea too.'

He gave her a small grin. In a flash, her insides transformed from squirming mortification into bubbling exhilaration.

'That makes me so happy!' she said. 'Would you like a big family?'

He laughed at her eagerness. 'Well, I come from a big enough family myself, so I suppose I'd be fine with that.' In the next instant, his laughter died away.

Startled, she peered at him. 'What is it?'

'I was just thinking about the other ones,' he mumbled. 'In Liverpool.'

Maud Pratt's three children. Rory's half-brothers and half-sister.

'If we stay in England, do you think you will try to establish a connection with them?' she asked.

He shrugged noncommittally. 'Maybe they won't want me to.'

She let the matter rest for now but knew he would need to come to terms with the notion of his extended family at some future stage.

As they entered the outskirts of the village, the cottages began to increase in number and Emily scanned them. If she couldn't find the one she was searching for, she would knock on a random door and make an enquiry. But then she spotted a cottage with an open window and an elderly woman sitting inside it, her hands busily working over a lacemaking pillow. She pointed out the cottage to Rory.

'That's where I need to go. Will you give me a few minutes to conduct my business? It's sort of...private.'

He looked taken aback but said, 'All right so. I'll wait out here.'

She wished she could kiss his cheek, but she just smiled at him and approached the cottage. She knocked on the door and a girl around her own age opened it.

'I'd like to speak to Ethel Cobb,' said Emily.

'That's me,' the girl replied.

'Oh,' said Emily. 'Is there perhaps another Ethel under this roof? The lady I'm seeking is, um, more advanced in years.'

The girl gave her a mischievous wink. 'You must mean Nan. Come on in.'

She beckoned her inside and Emily stepped over the threshold. The cottage was larger than the one belonging to Harry and Jill Barnes, boasting a hallway and two separate rooms. The girl led Emily into the room where the elderly woman was still working tirelessly.

'Nan, you've got a visitor,' said the younger Ethel.

Mrs Cobb didn't stop working. She glanced up at Emily and back down at her busy hands. 'Who are you then?'

'My name is Emily McGovern. I believe you had a visit from my mother a couple of weeks ago. The Lady Courcey?'

Mrs Cobb looked up with a sharper glance this time. 'That's right.'

'She tasked me with making enquiries into the lacemaking industry and ascertaining its impact on the future of the lacemakers here in Gildham. She said you believed that the demand for handmade lace would decline with the advance of machinery that could do the same work much quicker.'

'That's right,' the elderly woman said again.

Emily gulped. 'I regret to say that my enquiries have established much the same attitude throughout the industry. However, neither my mother nor I want to see you lose your livelihoods. Therefore I mean to put arrangements in place to ensure that the lacemakers here are sufficiently well trained on the new machines, and Bewley Hall will cover all the costs. It will be a different lifestyle to the one you are accustomed to, but I hope it is an idea you are willing to entertain.'

The younger Ethel gave her grandmother a bright look. 'Sounds like they're doing all they can to help us, Nan.' She swung her gaze to Emily. 'Nan taught me everything she knows about making lace by hand, but we're resigned to the fact that the machines are here to stay. I'm willing to learn, and I know a few others around who ought to be too.'

'Well, I'm not,' her grandmother said flatly. 'You know I'm too long in the tooth to start from scratch, Ettie.'

'And that is entirely understandable, ma'am,' Emily was quick to interject. 'Which is why I have another path in mind for you, if you are amenable.'

'Go on,' Mrs Cobb said warily.

'Could I please commission you to make a handmade wedding veil?'

Mrs Cobb perked up. 'For you?'

Emily nodded, blushing. 'No expense need be spared. I should like it to be very special.'

The younger Ethel grinned. 'For the eyes of a very special fellow, is it?'

Through the open window, Emily glimpsed Rory ducking wildly as he swatted a bumblebee away from his ear.

'The most special,' she said, smiling.

CHAPTER 36

Cormac was astonished by the feeling that washed over him when he and Bridget finally returned to Bedfordshire and the edifice of Bewley Hall came into sight through the carriage window.

Seven weeks had passed since they had first arrived at Oakleigh and that period of time had been a gruelling one. They had made tireless efforts to ensure that the tenants inside the manor received essential supplies and doctor's visits, and had lived each day in fear that they would hear news of further victims to the fever. Apart from Cormac's visit to Liam's bedside, they had abided by Ellen's advice not to enter the house themselves and, out of a lack of options and not a little nostalgia, they had opted to sleep at the McGoverns' family cottage which Ellen and Liam had taken over when they had married. It had fallen into some disrepair after the Kirwans had fled to the manor for help, but Cormac had fixed the leak in the roof and chased out the family of mice that had taken up residence inside the dresser in anticipation of Ellen's eventual return with her children...although this time she would live there as a widow.

He and Bridget had travelled by rail to Dublin and stayed there for a few days to complete the final sale of Courcey House on Merrion Square. Once they had returned to Carlow with those crucial proceeds, they had felt it would be acceptable for them to go back to Bewley Hall for a time. It had been too long since they had seen their children. And of course Mr and Mrs Sandler still needed to be dealt with.

Cormac had engaged the services of two members of the local constabulary to escort the Sandlers on their journey back to England. While he had made certain that Bridget never saw them, he had paid them a brief visit himself during which they had implored him to show leniency. He had ignored their pleas. Feeling no inclination whatsoever to show them any pity, he had tasked the two constables with escorting them to Newgate Prison in London once they landed on English soil and had already written to Mr Carruthers to inform him of the duty that would fall to him in court. The lawyer had replied to say that he would see it done.

Once Polly's sprained ankle had healed, she and David had travelled down to Oakleigh and joined in Bridget and Cormac's endeavours to provide relief to the tenants, helping to wash bedding or fetch more provisions from Tullow. They had subsequently accompanied them back to England and Cormac now perceived a profound gladness emanating from both of them as the carriage rolled to a stop in front of Bewley Hall.

What astonished him was that he found himself experiencing a similar emotion. It wasn't a sense of homecoming as such – rather, it was a feeling of congruence. Bewley Hall was a place where he was meant to be and, quite startlingly, somewhere he might actually belong. This estate had fallen into his hands; whether that had been wisdom or folly on Lord Bewley's part, Cormac had chosen to welcome it, and he somehow felt as though it had welcomed him in return. For once, when he imagined his parents looking down on him from above, he hoped that Maggie and Jack – and Lord and Lady Bewley, too – could be proud of him.

He gestured for Polly and David to exit the carriage first. David had been exempted from his footman duties for the journey and appeared to have thoroughly enjoyed riding within the vehicle rather than at the back of it, judging by his broad smile as he helped Polly out. Cormac and Bridget had barely descended from the carriage after them when two figures came barrelling out of the house and down the front steps.

'Wait, wait!' Cormac exclaimed before Jack and Gus could throw themselves at them. 'You need to be gentle around your mother.'

They faltered, registering the bandage on Bridget's face. 'Ma, what happened?' Jack asked, distraught.

'Nothing, my lamb, I just had a little accident. Come here to me, and you too, my miracle.'

She reached out and they stepped carefully into her arms, wrapping their own around her waist. Cormac hoped they wouldn't notice how thin she had become; she had not regained much of the weight she had lost during her ordeal at the farm as they had both eaten quite frugally at Oakleigh while trying to save the bulk of the food for the needier tenants.

Her daughter, however, noticed in a heartbeat. As Emily came down the front steps after her brothers, Rory just behind her, her countenance went pale. She approached her parents, her fingertips pressed to her mouth.

'Oh, Mama,' she murmured.

Bridget released Jack and Gus and she and Emily embraced, holding each other in tender silence. When they parted, both of their faces were wet.

Fishing out a handkerchief, Bridget dabbed at her eyelashes before giving Rory a watery smile. 'It's so good to see you, Rory. Are you well?'

'Yes, ma'am, and I hope you are too,' he replied, his green eyes full of concern.

'I'll be quite fine, thank you. And thank you also for staying so long here at Bewley Hall—we are indebted to you.'

'It was no trouble,' he said, glancing furtively at Emily.

Mr Comerford appeared next, stamping down the steps as if he were in a bad mood, but his expression lifted as soon as he saw Polly. She ran towards him and he enfolded her in his arms, which struck Cormac as most incongruous with his gruff nature. What was also odd was the way Jack and Gus gravitated towards him, hovering by his side like eager puppies waiting for their master's attention.

After Mr Comerford let go of his niece, he said to Bridget, 'Welcome back, my lady. I am heartily sorry for what you have suffered and for the part I played in it by not voicing my concerns about that scoundrel.'

'Think no more on it, Mr Comerford. It is behind us now and I am very glad to be able to stand here and say that.'

He gave her a deferential nod and turned to Cormac. 'Sir, we have much to discuss about the estate.'

Thinking the man could have at least let him step inside the house before he mentioned business, Cormac said, 'I'm certain we do. Let's meet later in my study to talk about it.'

However, when he made his way to his study later that day, he found Emily and Rory waiting for him outside it instead. And they were holding hands.

He grinned. 'Well, I'm glad to see that you two have finally come to your senses.'

Emily went pink. He chucked her affectionately under her chin and clapped Rory on the shoulder.

'May I speak to you, sir, if 'tis convenient?' Rory asked. 'I've something I'd like to ask you.'

Cormac's heart squeezed at the adoring look on his daughter's face. Although it filled him with gladness to see her so joyful, at the same time he comprehended his own incontrovertible loss. Bottling it up, he waved a welcoming hand towards the door of his study. 'Come on in, then.'

He and Rory went inside and closed the door, leaving Emily hovering with anxious hopefulness beyond it.

There was a letter sitting on the desk bearing the Wyndham seal. Cormac's stomach flipped.

'Please wait a moment while I open this,' he said to Rory. 'I believe it's important.'

He broke the seal in a hurry and scanned the page. The message was brief: Garrett curtly notified him that Patrick had decided to resume his studies at Eton in order to complete his final two terms, and thus Garrett was preparing to deliver his speech about Irish aid to the House of Lords at their next session. He would write again in due course to relay the outcome, after which point it would be mercifully out of his control and he would consider his side of their bargain fulfilled.

Cormac clenched his fist triumphantly on both counts, disregarding the gentleman's blatant lack of gratitude or grace. What tremendous news – the future held hope for Ireland's people and for his nephew.

Pocketing the letter, he took a seat behind his desk and gestured for Rory to do the same opposite him. Rory did so, pressing his palms nervously into his knees.

'Sir,' he said, 'I'd like to ask you for Emily's hand in marriage.'

It was only at that moment that it occurred to Cormac that Emily and Rory had been residing under the same roof now for weeks without any parental supervision.

'Rory,' he said, focusing his gaze upwards at the ceiling, 'have you already deflowered my daughter?'

He heard Rory swallow audibly. After a long pause, he said, 'I have, sir.'

Cormac shut his eyes and privately lamented the loss of his little girl's innocence. When he opened them again and dropped his gaze back to Rory, the lad's features were grey with trepidation.

'I asked you to stay here to watch over her and the boys,' Cormac said, his voice hard. 'Would you agree that your actions betrayed the level of trust I placed in you?'

Rory managed a jerky nod, looking miserable.

'And what about Emmeline? Is this not a betrayal to her too?'

'No, sir,' Rory replied quickly. 'I was never with her. I invented our relationship to free Emily for a more advantageous match.'

Well, that certainly cast the events back in Boston in a clearer light. Considering Rory's conduct from this more selfless perspective, Cormac comprehended how much it must have pained him to relinquish his future with Emily.

'Do you truly love my daughter?' he asked.

'God, I do,' said Rory, his manner so earnest that Cormac was entirely convinced.

'I wish you had waited,' he said, his tone becoming resigned. 'I understand the longing you both must have felt, but also the dangers of surrendering to it before the union was made official. Still, I suppose I can't censure either of you for doing so when Bridget and I couldn't resist it ourselves. I can only tell you how much I wish I had whisked her off to Father Macken's doorstep first before bedding her.'

Rory's grey pallor had turned the colour of beetroot. Cormac concealed a smile at the lad's discomfort.

'What's done is done,' he said, 'but calling the banns for your nuptials would take another three weeks. It might be best to obtain a marriage licence instead to hasten the process along.'

'Thank you, sir, yes,' Rory managed to utter in a stifled voice.

Cormac laced his fingers together on top of the desk. 'Emily hid it well but I suspect you broke her heart in Boston.'

Rory looked so regretful at that. 'I didn't realise how much damage I did at the time, but I've mended it since.' His mouth tightened. 'I witnessed my da make my ma cry on that New Year's Day when Jack was born, and it resulted in two things: I lost all respect for my da and I vowed never to do that to any woman. But I broke that vow when I hurt Emily to push her away, thinking she'd be better off with a gentleman. I'm going to do my damnedest to outweigh that idiocy by trying to be the best husband I can to her, I swear.'

'I'm very glad to hear it,' said Cormac, and he sincerely meant it. He didn't know how Emily and Rory had resolved their differences but he felt in his bones that this was the right man for his daughter. He cleared his throat. 'Has it occurred to you that when you become her husband, you may be obliged to escort her to social events? If we ever manage to get a foothold in society, that is.'

Consternation crossed Rory's face, and maybe even a tinge of fear.

'Don't let it trouble you,' Cormac said reassuringly. 'I've walked that path myself and I'll do all I can to assist. You'll be fine.'

Rory winced. 'Thank you, sir. I wanted to ask you as well about the apprenticeship you previously offered me here. Is that still a possibility if Emily decides that this is where she wants to stay?'

'Certainly,' said Cormac. While he and Bridget had decided that Oakleigh would be their primary home, Emily and Rory were entitled to make their own choice in that regard. 'Should you opt to stay here, and should Mr Comerford choose to stay on in the role of land agent, perhaps you can acquire the competency to occupy the deputy role that he once had.'

'I'd really appreciate the opportunity, sir.'

'Then we're agreed.' Cormac spread his hands. 'All that remains for me to say is that I would welcome you to the family, except you're already a part of it.'

Rory flushed and mumbled his thanks again.

After Rory left the study, Cormac rose and went over to the bookcase where he had hidden Lord Bewley's cane. He took it down and, setting the tip on the floor, gripped the T-shaped handle firmly. It gave him pride to see how far he and his family had come and he finally, truly, believed he had made the right choice in accepting Lord Bewley's inheritance.

'You have my deepest gratitude, my lord,' he said aloud, 'for the immeasurable gift you have given us.'

***

Emily couldn't stand the stress of waiting outside the door of her father's study, so she had gone to her parlour and was now pacing back and forth. She knew her father would approve, she was quite positive he would give them his blessing...surely he would not say no?

The door opened and Rory came in, his countenance morose. Her heart plummeted.

'What did he say?' she choked out.

'Yes,' Rory said simply.

She flew across the room and he caught her in his arms.

'You looked so downcast!' she cried, happiness flooding her. 'I didn't know what to think!'

'Well, he did say something that worried me a lot.'

She frowned. 'What could he have possibly said to make you feel that way?'

350

Rory set her down and ran a hand through his shaggy hair. 'He said you might have to attend social events and that, as your husband, I'd be expected to accompany you.'

'Does that bother you?'

He grimaced. 'It's just...that's really not me, Emily. I haven't a clue how to socialise with the upper classes. And 'tis made me realise that you're still a level above me.'

She took his big hands in her smaller ones. 'Listen to me,' she said seriously. 'I never want you to think like that. I may have some more experience in these matters, but that only means that if the time comes when you're obliged to attend a society occasion with me, I can help you navigate those waters. It by no means makes me superior to you. I consider us to be equals in all respects.'

She kissed him and felt his acceptance in the softening of his lips. She put her arms around his waist and tried to deepen the kiss, but he drew back. 'What's wrong?' she asked.

He went red. 'Your folks are back in the house. And your da...well, he knows that we, ah...'

'You *told* him?' she yelped, mortified.

'He guessed. I just think maybe we should keep our distance a little bit more until the wedding.'

She reluctantly had to agree with him. He definitely could not pay any more clandestine night-time visits to her bedchamber. She sighed in frustration.

Rory brushed a knuckle against a stray curl at her neck. 'But the good news is that he said we could get a marriage licence. Which means we won't have to keep our distance for long.'

She brightened at that and decided she would go to Gildham that very day to find out how close Ethel Cobb was to finishing her wedding veil.

After revealing the news of her engagement and sharing more tears with her mother, this time joyful ones, she implored her to come to Gildham too, eager to show her the beautiful veil taking shape. However, her mother declined, claiming tiredness after the long journey. Emily took her at her word, but she feared that her mother might shun going out in future due to self-consciousness over her injury. How she detested the man who had dared to hurt her in such a violent way. Her father said he had been adequately punished, but Emily wondered whether any punishment could be sufficient. At least the engagement seemed to cheer her mother immensely.

Further good news arrived in the form of a letter two weeks later, only a day before Emily and Rory's wedding, which was to take place at the Chapel of St Paul's in Bedford. The letter had come all the way from Chicago and was signed by Orlaith, although it looked like she had dictated it to someone else. No doubt that was because she had her hands very full – to everyone's thrilled surprise, her letter revealed that she had given birth to twins at the end of May. Both babies were healthy girls and they had been named Daisy and Poppy. According to Orlaith, they had their da wrapped around their tiny fingers already.

'Not one but two new cousins for you!' Emily's mother said with delight to Jack and Gus, who feigned interest but were clearly disappointed that the babies were not boys.

As for Emily, she absorbed the news of Orlaith and Charlie's great fortune with a physical yearning deep inside her. She could not wait to carry Rory's child although, for propriety's sake, it was probably for the best that she had not fallen pregnant before they got married.

Her longing only increased, however, with the arrival of two very special guests: Louise Shelby and her daughter Philippa. They had travelled down from Yorkshire for the wedding, and Emily was elated to see her kind friend again and in raptures over three-year-old Philippa. The little girl was even more adorable than she had been as a newborn on the *Integrity*, full of questions and giggles, especially when Rory loosened up around her and gave her the tickles. Emily glowed as she watched them together and knew he would be a marvellous father when the time came.

But first, she was certain that he would be a devoted husband. As her father walked her up the aisle the next day at the Chapel of St Paul's, her heart nearly split apart with emotion when she saw Rory waiting for her at the top, nervous but plainly eager for her to reach him. In fact, he was so impatient to be married that he rushed through his vows and the priest had to get him to repeat them more slowly. She could scarcely contain her mirth or her affection as she gazed up into his beloved, bashful face.

Then he took her left hand and slipped a ring onto her finger. She looked down at it and her lips parted in astonishment. It was made of wood.

''Tis walnut,' he mumbled to her. 'Your da offered to give me money for a gold ring but I wanted to earn it first, so he helped me make this instead. I promise to buy you a better ring as soon as I can.'

She raised her hand to stare at the ring. The circle of walnut wood sat comfortably at the base of her finger, its rich dark brown colour so smooth and gleaming that it must have been polished a thousand times. It was magnificent in its simplicity.

'I don't want another ring,' she breathed. 'This one is perfect.'

He blushed. His knuckles grazed the edge of her exquisite lace veil as he cupped her cheek and kissed her. They kept the kiss chaste, mindful of the small group of family and friends watching them from the pews. When he pulled back, his green eyes were full of tenderness.

'You know I'm no good with words,' he murmured, 'but even if I was, I don't think they'd be enough to tell you how fiercely I love you.'

'I love you just as much,' she whispered in reply, never so sure about anything in her life.

They turned exultantly to face the rest of the chapel. As she beamed on her husband's arm, overflowing with happiness to be married at last, she looked at her parents standing in the front row smiling back at her, and she hoped with all her might that this joy lay in their future too.

What's Next

You've come to the end of the book, but how would you like to stay with these characters a little longer? If so, I have a special treat for you! I've written an extended scene of Chapter 33, where Emily and Rory spend their first night together. You can read this scene and also view some exclusive character artwork at **subscribepage.com/the-bedchamber**. I really hope you enjoy it all!

Please help other readers discover this series by leaving an honest review about A Class Inherited on Amazon and/or Goodreads. A short review will make a huge difference in spreading the word about A Matter of Class. Thank you so much!

The next book in the series will be A Class Divided. Visit **www.susiemurphywrites.com** for updates about its release.

Acknowledgements

When I decided to embark on my publishing journey, it was because I wanted to share my stories with readers and bring them joy. I never anticipated just how much joy I would receive in return. Becoming an author has helped me to connect with so many wonderful people around the globe and I want to thank each and every one of you. You have welcomed these characters into your hearts and it fills me with gratitude when you get in touch to tell me what they mean to you. I am in awe that this path I've chosen has produced special friendships with people I would never otherwise have had the opportunity to know (I'm looking at you in particular, Elle and Julia!). I repeat: it is a joy, and I do not take it for granted.

Thank you to the talented professionals who keep the cogs turning smoothly in my business: my editor, Averill Buchanan, my cover designer, Andrew Brown, my narrator, Gary Furlong, and my accountant, Oliver Clare. I'm very grateful to Thomas Conneely at Thebookshop.ie, John Butler and Sinéad at Bookworm Bookshop, and Bryan Canter at Successful Writer for helping my books reach more and more readers. Thanks so much also to Shannon Sweeney at the Tipperary Star and Fran Curry at Tipp FM.

The writing community are an incredibly generous bunch and I'd especially like to thank these authors who have been so kind to me: Elizabeth Bell, Lisa Boyle, Kelsey Gietl, James Conroyd Martin, Pam Lecky, and Joanna Penn. Thanks a million as well to these lovely book reviewers: Claire Bridle, Ashley O'Melia, Anne Mendez, Lisa Redmond, and Mandie Griffiths.

An extra special mention goes to my wonderful beta readers: Mam, Deirdre, Bob, Miriam, Noreen, Elizabeth, Elle and Julia. I was blown away by the time and thought you all put into this manuscript – it means more to me than words can say. I also deeply appreciate every member of my marvellous advance reader team who read the finalised version of A Class Inherited before it was released into the world.

I honestly can't describe how thankful I am for my family and friends who show their support for me in so many different ways. My dad hands out my business cards to everyone he meets. My mam and my sister-in-law are convinced that this series will make it to the screen someday. My mother-in-law and my aunt reply to every single one of my newsletters. My husband listens to me talking about plots and characters at all times of the day or night. My friends send me excited messages with lots of exclamation marks! I could go on and on, but I will finish with this: my nephew says I inspire him, and to hear that from the next generation is the most tremendous motivation I can imagine.

Get in Touch

www.susiemurphywrites.com
www.facebook.com/susiemurphywrites
www.twitter.com/susiemwrites
www.instagram.com/susiemurphywrites
www.tiktok.com/@susiemurphywrites